Table of Conten[illegible]

Cover photo credits:

Front cover: Tom and Patti Mount on the *Pilotfish* submarine in Bikini Atoll, Marshall Islands.

Back cover: Topside photo by Tom Mount of Patti Mount gearing up for a Trimix dive.
Akumal cave photo by Steve Gerrard of Aquatech/Villas de Rosa.
Riches of the wreck of the *Cazador*. Photo courtesy of Key West Divers, Inc.
Exumas Wall, Bahamas photo of Patti Mount by Tom Mount while diving with the liveaboard *Bottom Timer* of Ft. Lauderdale, FL.

About The Authors

Tom Mount is the CEO of IANTD. He has been diving for more than 40 years and has done military, commercial and recreational diving. He is an experienced saturation diver and sat supervisor. His first technical dives were in 1962 when he began cave diving. Tom was one of the four founders of the NACD in 1968, and he has also been the diving officer at the University of Miami Rosenstiel School of Marine and Atmospheric Sciences. Tom was a former President and Training Director for NACD, and was the training director for the YMCA in the late 1970's. He has been a photojournalist, the author of several diving textbooks and technical publications. He was instrumental in the development of the IANTD Standards and Procedures. Tom is one of the most experienced technical divers in the world having participated in virtually every form of technical diving and equipment testing.

John Zumrick, MD, Capt., MC, USN (ret.), is a former medical research officer and senior medical officer at the US Navy Experimental Diving Unit. While there he was responsible for major investigations on the use of closed circuit diving apparatus, diver thermal protection, and deep saturation diving experiments. He has been the subject of numerous diving physiological experiments and was a dive subject on numerous saturation dives, one lasting 37 days which reached 1,500 fsw (458.7 msw). When not establishing Navy Diving Procedure he could be found cave diving in the various springs in north Florida and Mexico. He started cave diving in 1971 and has been responsible for many of the initial exploration of these springs. He is a fellow of the National Speleological Society, and of the New York Explorers Club.

Dr. David Doolette (Ph.D.) is a Research Fellow in the Department of Anesthesia and Intensive care, University of Adelaide/Royal Adelaide Hospital, Australia. Trained in neurophysiology and neuropharmacology, he is also interested in diving physiology. His current research areas include: function of the nervous system; decompression procedures, decompression illness and health management in occupational divers; and basic mechanisms of inert gas exchange. He is an adviser for diving physiology to the recreational and occupational diving industry in Australia. David has been diving since 1979 and is now primarily involved with underwater cave exploration in Australia. In addition to exploration, he has been responsible for design of decompression protocols, design mixed gas diving procedures, and health management for extended duration caving.

Bruce Voss MD, is an anesthesiologist, he spent 13 years in doing oxygen studies combined with critical care management. Bruce is a hyperbaric physician and US Army reserve medical diving officer. He is a Trimix diver. Bruce has 20 years of diving experience.

Dr. Jolie Bookspan is a research scientist in environmental physiology – the effects on human physiology of heat, cold, altitude, pressure, exercise, immersion, high-G forces, and injury (sometimes all at once). Her father taught her to dive in the Hudson River in the 1960's. After serving in the Army, she became a research physiologist for the US Navy (even skilled scientists can make the same mistake twice). Jolie has lived and worked in laboratories underwater and at altitude, taught anatomy at a college in the mountains of Mexico, did a doctoral fellowship in cold immersion and did a post-doctoral in altitude decompression. She then when on to research oxygen toxicity at the University of Pennsylvania's School of Medicine involving hyperbaric hypoxic and hypercapnic response to rest and exercise, and other scientific thing-a-ma-bobs.

Kevin Gurr is the UK Licensee for IANTD and is an Instructor Trainer at all technical diving levels. He was the first to develop an EANx dive computer and is the developer of ProPlanner decompression software. As a leading wreck diver in the UK Kevin has been instrument in the development of technical diving training aids. He is an author and accomplished wreck explorer having dived the *Lusitania* and led an expedition to the *Brittanic.*

Lamar Hires is the President of Dive Rite manufacturing and is a leader in the development of safe technical diving equipment. He is the leader of the Dive Rite Dive team and a world renowned cave explorer. Lamar is past President of the NSS-CDS and a member of the NACD training committee. He is an IANTD EANx Cave Instructor Trainer and a member of the IANTD BOA.

JP Imbert worked 19 years as Safety and Diving Manager at Comex, one of the most respected commercial diving companies in the world. While there he ran research on deep diving and decompression procedures. From this work the French air and mixed gas commercial diving tables were published in 1992. JP is also currently the French Licensee for IANTD. In addition he is a cave diver and has supported the European cave diving community and designed the dive tables for Pascal Bernabe's 850 foot (250 meter) dive at Fountain de Vaucluse in 1997. JP is a Trimix Instructor trainer.

Jarrod Jablonski is an accomplished cave explorer, having dived throughout the world. JJ is an IANTD Trimix, and Cave Instructor Trainer. He is also an NSS-CDS and NACD Instructor and has been on the NSS-CDS Board of Directors and the NACD Board of Directors.

Martin (Animal) Shamilan, Ph.D. is a retired Army Special Forces officer and was an active diver and diving instructor while in the army. He has also been active as an instructor in recreational diving. Animal earned his nickname while in service and it continues to follow him. He has been active in hyperbaric research plus as a consultant as well as an instructor. Animal is an IANTD Instructor Trainer.

CHAPTER 1

The Leading Causes of Accidents in Technical Diving

Tom Mount

Accident-free diving doesn't just happen. It is the product of a comprehensive effort that includes awareness, training, ongoing practice and planning. There are any number of factors that contribute to diving accidents, and an equal number of behaviors and practices that can reduce the likelihood of these accidents. In this chapter, we will look at some of the most common causes of accidents, along with the most practical preventative measures and solutions to those causes.

Accident analysis is a process based on a continual review of the causes and potential prevention of accidents. The facts and opinions shared here are based on documentation gathered over more than 20 years of accident analysis by dive safety professionals, the experiences and insights gathered during the author's 40-plus-year diving career, and the collective experiences and opinions of numerous other technical diving veterans and experts.

Tom Mount preparing for a Cis-Lunar MK 5 dive.
Photo: Don Townsend

As you will discover in this chapter, the causes of most accidents can be linked to a lack of training, practice or education. In the following pages, we will look at **the ten most common causes of accidents in technical diving**, as well as ways to prevent these accidents.

1. Training

Ignorance is the root of most accidents. Ignorance is not stupidity. It is the behavior and reactions of someone who has not been properly informed, and is therefore unaware of critical facts and potential dangers.

In the realm of technical diving, the only effective path to informed safety is through a formal, credible training program. Lack of *supervised* training, or inadequate training, is the number one cause of accidents in technical diving - be it cave, wreck or deep diving.

How can you recognize a safe *and* effective training program? Proper training for technical diving not only provides theoretical classroom education, but also dry land, pool and in-water exercises designed to develop the performance of critical skills *to the point of reflex action.* It also provides the student with a comprehensive knowledge of the demands and dangers of the diving environment, builds safety awareness and emergency preparedness, and teaches the diver to control and overcome the effects of stress. The following general statements reflect the author's opinion regarding proper training:

- Training is a standardized method of informing an individual. Once the individual is informed, ignorance and its associated dangers can be overcome.
- Training will cause a change in behavior and in the reactive patterns of the diver.
- Training only takes place when the student is ready to accept the wisdom shared by the teacher. All the lectures and skill performance in the world do not constitute training until an open mind receives the lessons. There is an old adage, "*When the student is ready, the master will appear.*"
- Training should develop emergency response skills.

What to look for when seeking training for technical diving...

- Seek a program that has a proven history of safety, one developed by known and experienced technical diving educators. IANTD programs fulfill this requirement.

- Insure that the training program includes skills that are relevant to water safety. Stress management skills - those skills that develop discipline and self control - are absolutely essential for technical diving. These skills must duplicate realistic circumstances and develop self-discipline in the student. In addition, the simulated emergencies should duplicate problems the diver may encounter.
- A proper course must include a standard knowledge and skill base through the use of texts or reference materials combined with in-depth lectures and in-water skill performance. Student's knowledge should be evaluated by written exams.
- Penetrations and depth should be achieved in increments under direct supervision of the instructor.

Avoid training programs that...

- Do not provide intense skill development.
- Rush you to more extreme forms of diving without progressive education.
- Do not provide text or a required and standard knowledge base for all students.
- Simply provide guided tours.

For training to be effective, learning must take place. The only way knowledge can be transferred is through communication to a mind that is open and accepting. The wise diver thirsts for **and** digests all the information that can be garnered from the instructor.

2. Disorientation and/or Failure to Follow a Continuous Guideline

This is a major concern in overhead environments, but also important on open water dives involving decompression stops on a down line or anchor line, or cases where a diver might become lost at sea. In open water environments, the diver must develop navigational skills, and become competent at using visual references. While diving, the diver should continually refer to check points and other visual indicators to keep themselves oriented.

In cave and wreck diving, the lack of a continuous guideline is a serious safety violation. Accident analysis has shown it to be the second greatest contributor to fatalities within an overhead environment. Guidelines should be used on any dive involving penetrations into an overhead environment. Penetration begins at any point where a diver enters an area where he cannot make a direct ascent to the surface. It also begins at areas where visibility may be reduced to a point that surface light cannot be discerned.

Correct use of a reel and guideline requires training. Improper use of reels and lines can lead to entanglement. Always seek out training prior to use.

3. Gas Management

Far too many divers have experienced gas sharing emergencies - even fatalities - simply because they failed to properly manage their gas supply. The mere fact that you have an ample gas supply for a given dive does not necessarily guarantee the safe management of that supply. Even some highly experienced divers are guilty of poor gas management practices, while many more don't understand what the term gas management involves.

Gas management is not simply a matter of carrying enough gas to complete the dive and return to the surface. To insure adequate gas supplies for unforeseen delays and emergency situations, divers must incorporate a set of rules that dictate how the gas supply will be used. On no-stop dives and dives in open water no deeper than 130 feet (39 meters), the half-plus-200 psig (13.6 bar) rule is adequate. Once the diver exceeds these parameters, however, the Rule of Thirds applies.

> **All dives made in an overhead environment, deeper than 130 feet (39 meters), or with decompression stops must use the Rule of Thirds. The Rule of Thirds states that dives should be planned to allow the diver to surface with 1/3 of the gas supply remaining.**

Using "The Rule of Thirds"

Plan your dives based on the premise that you will begin your return to the entry point with two thirds of the gas supply remaining. The reasoning behind this practice is to use a third of the gas supply during the progression of the dive, and one third more for the return to the entry point. This will allow one third of the gas supply to remain in reserve for emergencies and/or gas sharing.

Note: If the primary gas supply is to be used for decompression, the gas needed for decompression must be included in the two-thirds used during the dive, and should not come from the third held in reserve.

The reserve third buys needed extra time in cases where the diver may become entangled, disoriented, delayed during ascent, or experience any other mishap during the dive. In addition, failure to reserve a third prevents safe and predictable gas sharing with ***a dive buddy.***

In open water some argue that one can always escape to the surface. However, if the dive involves staged decompression stops, those stops represent an overhead environment every bit as real as the metal casing of a wreck or the limestone of a cave. Divers who escape to the surface during a staged decompression dive may in this case solve the out-of-gas problem but face a high probability of injury or death caused by explosive decompression sickness, combined with the very real possibility of being lost at sea.

If a diver is forced to make an escape to the surface, he/she can reduce the risk of becoming lost at sea by carrying and deploying lift bags. In areas such as south Florida where drift decompressions are common, and where dive operators are on watch for lift bags and surfacing drift divers, this may be a safe alternative procedure.

But in many parts of the world where dive boats remain anchored or moored, dive operators do not post lift bag watches. A free-drifting diver is at great risk of being lost at sea. Therefore, it is certainly safer to observe gas management rules that will allow you to surface at the point where the surface crew expects you to be.

Remember...

- **No one** has died from too much gas; but the combined effects of too little gas and failure to manage gas are among the greatest contributors of accidents.
- If someone recommends that you take a bare minimum gas supply, avoid this person; they are a threat to your safety!

4. Exceeding Physiological Limits

This is one of the most dangerous practices in diving. Physiological limits that are of concern to the diver include oxygen exposure, narcosis limits and decompression risks.

Oxygen limits are a prime concern when divers plan to breathe elevated oxygen mixtures for extended periods during decompression, during long Nitrox dives and on air dives deeper than 180 feet (52 meters). Oxygen limits must also be calculated and respected when planning for a Trimix dive.

Oxygen exposure is not the only physiological limit for which divers must be made aware. Based on oxygen exposure limits alone, dives of up to 180

Patti Mount hand feeding the sharks of Cay Sal Banks.
Photo: Tom Mount

feet (52 meters) may be performed on air, while still allowing a sufficient oxygen window for decompression on accelerated (high oxygen content) mixes.

In many cases, however, the effects of narcosis, combined with possible CO_2 retention, has led industry professionals to recommended that Trimix be used on dives deeper than 170 feet (50 meters). In addition, most research - and the personal experiences of divers exploring deep water - reflect a noticeable increase in productivity when Trimix is used on dives in excess of 160 feet (48 meters).

One other area that has been the source of some controversy in recent years is that of decompression limits. With software programs now on the market that allow a diver to create custom decompression models, some within the dive community have created "accelerated" decompression profiles that leave very narrow safety margins.

Because decompression is not an exact science, and because a diver's physiological reactions may vary greatly from dive to dive, the use of extremely "fast" decompression models may place the user at significantly greater risk of DCI. To lower the risk, divers should understand all the factors influencing decompression, and should be appropriately conservative when planning decompression schedules.

"Take calculated risks. That is quite different than being rash." - George S. Patton

5. Exceeding Risk/Benefit Limits

All divers should be governed by personal limits based on their individual level of training and experience. These limits should also take into account such factors as depth, workload, diver fitness and the overall degree of risk, difficulty and discomfort the diver feels willing to encounter.

Establishing these limits often involves the process of risk-to-benefit analysis. When weighing risk against the overall benefit derived from a particular dive, the diver must be certain that what is gained is worth the potential price. Explorers, for example, may often accept a level of risk far greater than that which a recreational or less serious diver would feel comfortable accepting.

A diver preparing for a high-risk dive must weigh the possibility of death against the gratification of accomplishment if that price is acceptable then the dive can proceed. But if the risk level is not acceptable, then the dive should not be attempted.

Most divers are not willing to accept extreme risk, and have no desire to "push the envelope" in hopes of establishing a record-breaking dive. However, there will always be those who will boldly venture where no one else has survived. Without explorers and others who are willing to push the limits in life, we would have no new scientific knowledge or progress as a society.

We should point out, however, the difference between risk taking for the sake of discovery, and merely increasing risk by knowingly ignoring established safety practices, or by exceeding physiological limits.

When performing a risk/benefit analysis, divers must not only identify all potential risks, but also be able to honestly assess their tolerance for operating outside their normal comfort zone, including the degrees of physical discomfort and mental stress they can endure. When risk/benefit analysis is employed, and all potential risks are identified, the majority of divers will opt for lower risk profiles. It must be understood, however, that risks can not be eliminated from diving, but merely identified and minimized. All forms of diving encompass risk to one degree or another.

Only a fool assumes diving is free of risk!

Risks and Benefits

- The aware individual realizes that the more extreme the dive, the greater the price in the form of risk exposure.
- When creating a risk management profile, divers must identify all variables and potential, "What ifs?"
- List all potential problem areas, then provide a proposed solution and outcome for each.
- Once the list is complete, ask yourself if these risks are acceptable to you.
- When exploring new areas, reduce risk by working up to the ultimate goal progressively.
- Visualization may help solve problems before they happen.

Regardless of your personal risk tolerance, there is no acceptable reason to push air depth limits. Deep air dives expose the diver to the combined effects of oxygen, nitrogen narcosis and carbon dioxide retention. When these physiologically debilitating factors are combined with strenuous work, a dive that is normally within acceptable risk limits may become life threatening. Statistics show that while deep air records may continue to move deeper, the path to these accomplishments is paved with those who did not succeed.

6. Quitting

Such a simple word, yet so critical to survival – or to failure. Dive literature is filled with accounts of trapped or lost divers who spent their last moments of life composing letters to their loved ones. The press and many within the diving community tend to glorify these emotionally charged actions, and the deceased is glorified for the love and concern shown for those left behind.

Yet, in many cases, upon recovery, it was determined that had the same energy and gas supply been spent attempting to survive rather than stopping to compose a last message, the diver could have reached the surface alive and safe. *The impassioned letter is in fact an epitaph to the true cause of death:* ***QUITTING.*** A true hero is the one who does not quit! This person does survive the seemingly impossible.

In Tom Mount's *Save Cave Diving* and *Practical Diving*, Bob Smith contributed chapters on stress that best describes in-water survival:

> **"When faced with dying or achieving the impossible, some choose to live by accomplishing the impossible."**

Unfortunately, that "some" remain a minority, while the majority do not choose overcoming the impossible. While it is not logical that some individuals give up before the end, it is explainable. Many people do not have the training background, experience, confidence, self-discipline, or belief in themselves needed to confront what seems to be impossible. These persons' deaths are not due to the circumstance but rather to the perception of both the event and their own fragility.

A good training program can help by developing the skill level, discipline and survival attitude that can reduce the probability of quitting. However, it is the individual who must refine his own abilities, develop a strong belief system, continually seek knowledge and fine tune his own skill level in order to face all of life's challenges.

A positive survival attitude and response comes from within and is produced by belief, confidence, on-going personal training, and learning from the experiences of oneself and others.

Thoughts on Survival

- **Survival** frequently comes down to the ability to focus the mind. A focused mind cancels out worries about the current situation and concentrates on problem solving.
- A wise diver will design a custom survival-training program. This can be accomplished without placing safety in jeopardy.
- Survival training programs employ exercises demanding mental and physical demands beyond one's comfort level and maintaining the correct and consistent respiratory rate.
- A survivor, when asked, **"Don't you know when to quit?"** responds with an emphatic ... **"NO!"**
- Quitting in an adverse situation leaves no alternative except death.
- Success comes from thinking out how to continue onward and upward, and how to react accordingly regardless of the odds.
- Continuing regardless of the odds provides the option of survival.
- The discipline to avoid quitting is developed by mental and physical exercise producing mind/body control.
- A focused mind allows us to gain control over our behavior and physical reactions.

> ***To quit is to admit failure:*** Answer ***"YES"*** to survival, say ***"No"*** to failure.

7. Improper Equipment/Equipment Configuration

You won't have a good dive if you start with "bad" equipment. Sounds obvious, but the record shows that improper, inadequate and poorly maintained equipment have factored into far too many diving accidents. For the technical diver, scuba gear is life support equipment, and should be treated as such.

- **Top quality equipment is your insurance to successful exploration.**
- **Use equipment you will bet your life on, because you are.**
- **Remain open-minded and modify your equipment and its configuration as better solutions are presented.**
- **Do not be fixed and immovable; instead seek perfection.**

Different dive scenarios require different equipment choices - a fact some divers fail to realize when they fall into a "more is better" mind set. Before each dive, select those specific pieces of gear essential to the chosen environment and diving mission. Use redundancy on personal life support items, but avoid unneeded items.

The way in which you configure your selected equipment will also affect the safety of the dive. Hanging gauges, dangling regulators and poorly secured backup lights produce potential entanglement problems, and are more vulnerable to damage. A backup regulator can't provide redundancy if it's clogged with mud, and a back-up light that's been banged against a shipwreck and flooded won't be of much use.

Protect yourself from gear failure by protecting your gear. Secure all your equipment in a fashion that will allow for maximum protection, combined with a streamlined profile. Specific mounting techniques are the subject of any quality technical diving course, and remain a topic of study and conversation even among veteran divers.

A course that neither offers you guidance nor presents you with more than one form of configuration is restricting your growth and possibly inhibiting your performance and overall safety. Configuration is to fall within guidelines that present low drag, comfort, a streamlined profile with ease of touch identification, and self rescue. Due to variations in flexibility, physical characteristics, etc. **each of us will evolve to a personal best configuration.**

Failure to select proper equipment or to customize the configuration of that equipment to the diver's specific needs has led to accidents. Do not let something this simple turn you into a statistic.

8. Dive Team Selection

Although technical diving training programs stress self-reliance and self-sufficiency, these abilities are no substitute for safe, competent diving partners. A good dive team is stronger than it's individual members, and can solve problems and prevent accidents. On the other hand, poorly qualified diving partners, or an improperly matched dive team, have been the cause of circumstances that lead to accidents. A safe dive team requires not only that each team member be competent and responsible, but also that team members are compatible in terms of skills, experience, goals and attitude.

In some cases, accidents have resulted when highly qualified advanced divers unknowingly created peer pressure that caused their less-qualified dive partners to exceed their personal limits. On other occasions, divers have been known to push a partner beyond the partner's comfort zone and, more importantly, beyond his capability for self-control.

Accidents have also been provoked by direct ego challenges from one diver to another. This scenario can take place between friends and couples, often without their conscious knowledge. To prevent such occurrences, experienced, highly competent divers must be aware of the fact that not all divers share their capabilities and skills. Similarly, less experienced divers should recognize their personal limits, and should not allow their ego or the influence of another to put them in a situation that is beyond their ability level.

Do not goad or be goaded into a dive beyond your self-confidence level or your partner's.

9. Stress Management

Accidents occur when stress is not managed. Conversely, a diver adept at stress management can solve most problems encountered underwater.

The ability to manage stress is influenced by training, practice and overall mental toughness. A credible, professional training program will include numerous drills and lectures that enable divers to develop the ability to recognize and cope with stress.

A thinking diver is more resistant to stress-induced hazards. Pre-planning and determining answers to the "What ifs?" that can occur on a dive can pay off with major benefits in stress prevention. It is this combination of practice and planning that form the foundation for stress management.

10. Personal Training and Skill Maintenance

As stated in the beginning of this chapter, survival behavior is an ongoing cycle that begins with training, and continues with repetitive practice and skills maintenance. A large number of diving accidents are caused by the divers' failure to maintain or update their skill levels. The maintenance and updating of diving skills is perhaps the single greatest thing that a diver can do to reduce the probability of an accident. Yet, divers who sink into complacency and laziness too often overlook it.

As a diver progresses in technical diving, emphasis must be given to continuing education. Once a formal education at a given level is completed, it is just the beginning. At this point, the diver has an adequate baseline to begin his ongoing personal quest for additional knowledge and training.

If you review the cause of accidents, it becomes evident that positive actions will overcome almost any circumstance. **Knowledge, training, attitude, belief in oneself, and skill are the key to personal power.** These are all fundamental elements, easily within the grasp of each of us. The application of personal power allows us to keep going, even when the going gets tough. When you apply the concepts discussed in this chapter, **you will be among those who choose to live.**

Personal training must be based on a foundation of formal course work, but it goes well beyond the classroom. A prudent diver will always practice and expand upon the basic concepts and tools of the technical diver. Become an expert in the use of these tools.

- The key to safety is practice, practice and more practice, just like making love, **and performance improves with frequent repetition.**
- Be creative and improve upon the technology you have developed.
- Continually review your equipment, its configuration and your diving techniques to determine a better, more efficient and safer way to dive.
- Be open minded yet do not compromise your own ideals on performance.
- You are responsible for your actions, skill, knowledge and fulfillment.
- Share information and incorporate the knowledge of fellow divers.

CHAPTER 2
Equipment Configuration

Tom Mount

Developing a smooth, streamlined underwater swimming style takes practice and an understanding of proper technique. Equally important, however, is the way in which your dive equipment is configured and carried. Improper gear configurations cause excess drag, are more likely to cause entanglement problems, and can make it difficult or even impossible for the diver to access needed backup equipment. Proper configuration, on the other hand, allows the diver to minimize underwater drag, protects the equipment and allows for immediate access to all primary life support gear and important backup items.

Beyond these universal factors, there are endless variations on the specifics of proper gear configuration, and there is no single "best" way that dive gear should be worn. Differences in the diving environments and in diving styles place widely varying demands on equipment, and a rig that might be perfect for deep Trimix diving could be totally wrong for confined sump dives.

20 Essential Aspects of Equipment Configuration
(Listed in order of importance.)

1. It is safe and dependable.
2. It is comfortable for the diver.
3. It provides adequate rather than excessive redundancy.
4. It provides for self-sufficiency and self-rescue.
5. It is simple and user friendly (the KISS principle).
6. The valves and accessories are easily reached.
7. It provides buddy rescue/assist capability.
8. It is customized to the diver's needs and the objectives of the dive.
9. The diver has confidence in the configuration.
10. It presents a low drag profile.
11. The equipment is balanced.
12. The equipment is identifiable by touch.
13. It incorporates standard gear placement.
14. It is versatile.
15. It is streamlined and clean
16. When updates to the rig are made, they are done at a rate that is comfortable for the diver.
17. Decompression stage cylinders feature visual, touch and placement identification.
18. Cylinders are labeled for intended use.
19. On team dives it is compatible with the team concept.
20. The user continues to look for ways to improve the configuration.

Safety is the first consideration that must be addressed when planning an equipment configuration. The diving mission often dictates the gear to be carried - and it may have some influence of how that gear is worn. As the diver selects gear to match the dive's requirements, he should analyze each specific piece of hardware, and should select only items that will contribute to the overall safety and performance of the dive. Without a safe system, all other effort is wasted. Before designing a personal system, listen to the experiences of other divers and review accident case studies. By identifying potential problem areas, you can then create a rig that is not only personalized to your needs and habits, but is also created with maximum safety in mind.

Universal Considerations of the Technical Diving Rig

Comfort and fit are key to the enjoyment of any dive, but become increasingly important to diver safety within the context of the longer, more demanding scenarios of technical diving. An uncomfortable diver is more susceptible to stress, will tire sooner and may experience perceptual narrowing caused by the discomfort of the equipment. By contrast, a comfortable diver is more likely to remain alert, relaxed and aware of his surroundings, all of which contribute to dive performance and emergency preparedness.

In addition to providing a comfortable fit, the rig must be stable, even when all the accessories are added. Also keep in mind that your chosen rig should not only be comfortable in the water, but also on land. This is particularly important in cases where you are required to wait before entering the water, or to walk some distance to the dive site. If you are currently using a system that causes discomfort or pain, make an immediate change.

Redundancy is unquestionably technical diving's single greatest safety margin. The philosophy of redundancy dictates that any element of the diving rig that is essential to life support should be backed up by a working spare. Problems arise when divers carry the philosophy of redundancy too far, however. There is seldom any need for multiple backup systems, and excessive redundancy not only creates configuration problems, but also may actually decrease the overall safety of the diver.

Items that must be backed up include regulators on the primary gas supply and lights in cave and wreck diving. It is also desirable to back up the buoyancy control system.

Patti Mount prior to a Trimix dive on the *Nagata* in Bikini Atoll.
Photo: Tom Mount

This may incorporate either a dry suit with one BCD or a wetsuit with two BCD's. Recently, some manufacturers have developed back flotation systems that feature two sets of wings within one cover. These systems do have advantages, as they produce less drag than two independent sets of wings. The disadvantage of the enclosed double-wing systems is that they do not allow the diver the versatility of switching from two to one wing configurations. Another item worthy of backup is the cutting tool. This may be a small knife, surgical scissors or other form of cutters. For wreck diving the cutting tools must be able to cut wiring and fishing line.

Self-sufficiency combined with the ability to perform **self-rescue** is the primary requirement of any technical diving rig. The design must allow the diver quick access to any items needed for self-rescue, and should provide the diver with a realistic degree of self-sufficiency. Again, there is no advantage to carrying surplus safety items, and there may be disadvantages. There is a point where too much of a "good thing" may result in decreased performance instead of enhanced capabilities. Treat each dive as if you were diving solo. In other words, do not be dependent upon others for your safety. A self-sufficient diver is a survivor.

Keep it simple, and it will serve you better. Elaborate and complex gear placement leads to confusion. If the configuration is simple and easy to use, then it is ideal. If the complexity causes one to stop and think in order to determine where a needed piece of hardware is located, it will not suffice in a fast-moving, stressful situation. Tank valves must be reachable with a minimum of difficulty, and accessory equipment must be rigged in a fashion and a position to be readily available.

The ability to perform **buddy rescue** or a buddy assist is a mandatory component of any technical diving rig. One universal feature that allows for this capability is the use of a longer second stage hose attached to either the primary or secondary first stage regulator. This hose should be 5 feet or longer, with 7 feet being the more common length. The hose must also be easy to deploy and hand off to a distressed diver. Before a dive, buddies should familiarize themselves with the location of each other's safety and backup equipment, and should also check each item to make sure it is functional. Dive teams that work together on a regular basis might wish to go one step further and work towards a common, mutually agreeable means of configuration and positioning of the life support systems involved in buddy rescue.

Out-of-the-box diving equipment seldom meets all the specialized needs of technical diving. As a result, most technical divers have learned to **customize** their equipment to fit the specific needs of the mission. Before you can effectively customize your equipment for the best possible fit and function, you need to build a basic understanding of each piece of equipment that will make up the rig, and also gain some understanding of how these parts come together as a whole. Therefore, you should be willing to set aside a reasonable amount of time to analyze the components of the system and then determine how you want them to blend into a usable whole.

The backbone of your technical diving rig is the backplate harness - or one of the new technical soft backpacks. For this reason, special care should be given to adjusting the harness of the backplate /backpack for optimum fit. Too often, divers are either uninformed or unwilling to take the time needed to adjust this most basic piece of equipment for optimum fit. Improper adjustment creates discomfort and a loss of diver performance that could lead to errors in judgment or degraded diver performance.

Billy Deans doing final equipment check before entering the water.
Photo: Dan Burton

Many instructors devote one to three hours of a course assisting students in arranging equipment. This is a good starting point, but it should not be the end point. As a diver, you should always be on the lookout for a better way. If an item or technique looks to be more streamlined, easier to use or simply more comfortable to wear, then try it. As stated prior, there should be an ongoing search for the perfect rig.

Good technical diving rigs don't just happen; they evolve over time. Don't allow rigid thinking to lock you into a mindset in which you cease to evolve. If you do only one style of technical diving, you may develop an extremely specialized rig matched to that specific environment. If, on the other hand, you find yourself involved in more than one style of diving, you might wish to create a more versatile rig that is easily modified. For example, some of the aforementioned soft backpacks can accommodate single, double or side-mounted tanks with minor adjustments.

Regardless of your customizing efforts, the end result should inspire confidence in your rig, and should allow you to operate with minimal effort and maximum comfort. A **streamlined** diver creates less drag in the water. By streamlining, you lower the work of swimming and, in turn, increase your gas supply duration. A streamlined configuration also assists in avoiding entanglement and the possibility of becoming stuck in restricted areas.

Once you have selected and assembled your rig, you must look for ways to streamline and clean up the loose ends. Begin with careful scrutiny of each piece of equipment, looking for ways to streamline it to the point of least possible drag and bulk.

A streamlined rig will have few or no hoses protruding beyond the tank valve handles. Hoses must be stored neatly and gauges must be secured snug to the body. Accessory items should also be attached to minimize drag and the chance of entanglement. In general, you will want to avoid all dangling objects and items attached to the harness by a single clip or strap that allows for excessive movement.

One additional factor to consider when constructing an equipment configuration is the need to create a **balanced swim posture**. A rig that does not allow the diver to maintain a comfortable horizontal swim position is not suitable for the majority of technical diving applications. Any rig that is inherently unstable or which requires excessive effort to maintain a swimming position should be reconfigured or modified to alleviate the problem.

In summary, an effective technical diving rig should be balanced, comfortable and streamlined. It should provide for a standardized method of gear placement, but must also allow room for improvement or innovation. Each item of equipment should be easily identified by touch and visual identification. In addition, the system should be versatile, allowing you to transition smoothly from one diving environment to another with ease and comfort.

All cylinders used on a dive must be **properly labeled**. A number of fatalities, including those involving highly trained technical divers, can be directly attributed to a failure to identify and label breathing gasses. When using any gas other than air, you must analyze, identify and label the mixture.

It is obvious that we are all human, and human error is the greatest threat to all of us. Mr. Murphy will capitalize on all events that may lead to a human error. To prevent such accidents, you should take as many precautionary steps as possible. In addition to proper cylinder identification and gas content labeling that includes oxygen content and maximum operating depth, IANTD recommends - in Open Water training - that gases containing different mixtures and MODs be placed on opposite sides of the diver. The mouthpiece of the highest EANx or Oxygen should either be covered or have rubber tubing wrapped around it. This prevents accidental switches to the wrong regulators. The diver cannot breath from it until the cover or tubing is removed from the mouthpiece. This serves as an additional step to avoid confusion of gas cylinders. Do not allow something so simple as a cylinder mix-up to cause an accident.

Avoid getting stuck in the illusion that only one method of configuration will work. Adopt methods that are applicable to your dive style.

- *Always remain an individual and use your freedom of choice.*
- *It is YOUR safety, YOUR, life, YOUR comfort.*
- *Develop a configuration based on logical analysis of your needs.*
- *List the logic for each segment of your configuration.*
- *Be able to explain why and how you configure your equipment.*
- *Remember that the final word on configuration must be YOURS.*

Be prudent, Be responsible, Be open-minded, Be safe, and

TAKE THE TIME TO DO IT RIGHT.

Note: The use of any breathing gas other than air will require specialized training on the part of the diver. If you are using gasses other than air without such training, you are acting irresponsibly, and may be courting disaster.

Label your cylinders and always have a gas content identification. Your life may depend on it!

The Background of Technical Equipment

The more you know about the history, attributes, advantages and shortcomings of various pieces of technical diving equipment, the better you will be at selecting the items you incorporate in your personal life support system.

To understand the state of technical diving gear today, and where it might be going tomorrow, let's look into the history and evolution of some of our present day components and systems. In the 60s, the standard deep diving rig was a US Navy harness with a standard single-outlet, double cylinder manifold. Submersible lights were homemade by any number of jerry-rigged methods that might use motorcycle batteries for power and a plumber's helper for a bulb holder. These and may other off-the-wall ideas were tried, and many worked reasonably well. Around 1966, Frank Martz introduced lights that used a waterproof cylinder as a battery case. These lights proved to be highly reliable, and functioned consistently at depths of up to 300 feet (91 meters). Martz also came up with the first dependable safety reels, and the first auto-inflate system. These advances not only increased the diving community's safety, but also stimulated others to design new and improved systems.

Joe Citelli in the engine room of the *Hydro Atlantic* wreck in Boca Raton, Florida.
Photo: Tom Mount

In 1970 while doing exploration diving and filming with George Benjamin, a dive group consisting of this author, Frank Martz, Jim Lockwood, Ike Ikehara and Dr. Dick Williams became concerned with George's use of independent tanks. This concern was prompted by previous body recoveries involving divers using these systems.

The author suggested the tanks be mated together, and Ike Ikehara designed a system to do this. George took this drawing to Tom McCullam who built the Benjamin conversion valves. These were the first dual outlet valves used in technical diving. Shortly thereafter, several others begin to convert standard manifolds into dual valve systems. From this early beginning, the equipment has evolved to the selection of valves we take for granted today.

Not long after the horse collar BC was developed, technical divers began customizing these designs to make them more appropriate for their style of diving. The stabilizing (stab) jacket was developed next, and numerous divers elected to use them. The author's first recollection of the use of a back mounted BC for technical diving was by Patti-Ann Schaeffer (now Patti Mount) in a cave diving class in June of 1978. The wings had to be taped onto a Cressi-Sub harness, but they performed so well that within a week, the author and Bob Ledbetter had converted some "surplus" street signs into backplates, and used "diving wings" on all dives from that point forward. It is quite possible that someone else may have evolved wings before this time, but that was *my* first introduction to them.

Today, the back-mounted flotation system has evolved and matured, giving divers a number of styles to select from. This technology has yielded hard backplates of ABS, aluminum and stainless steel. The hard packs reigned supreme until the mid 90's. Today Zeagle, ScubaPro, Dive Rite and other manufacturers either have, or are in process of introducing, soft packs that may very well be the gateway to the future for technical diving applications. To complement this development, single-bag dual-bladder wings evolved through the efforts of OMS and Dive Rite. This evolution of dual wings was the result of numerous reports of BC failure and the need for redundant flotation aimed at divers wearing wetsuits.

Technical diving today has entered a new era and those wishing to continue maximizing their potential must maintain an open mind, remaining abreast of the new technologies. Failure to stay current will in many cases produce obsolete equipment and diminished exploration potential.

Regulator development has also kept pace with the needs of the technical and extended-range diver. In comparison to the equipment of a decade ago, many regulators now on the market offer substantially lower breathing resistance, greater rates of air delivery, higher overall performance and increased reliability.

In recent years, the dive industry has introduced tanks of much greater volume. The ability to carry significantly more gas in such high-volume tanks allows divers to increase safety margins, expand the limits of underwater exploration and open underwater frontiers not considered attainable a few years ago. The introduction of rebreathers to the recreational/technical community in the mid-90's will expand these capabilities to even greater depths.

Selecting the Components

Backplates

In your ongoing evolution towards an optimum personal equipment configuration, you must remember to select only those components that will provide safety and fulfill the needs of your dive objective. The best way to begin this selection process is by working outward from the foundation.

On a technical diving rig, the foundation of the system is the mounting platform - the backplate. For the purpose of this discussion, a backplate can mean either a hard pack or a soft pack. To decide which is best for a particular purpose, one should scrutinize the pros and cons of each.

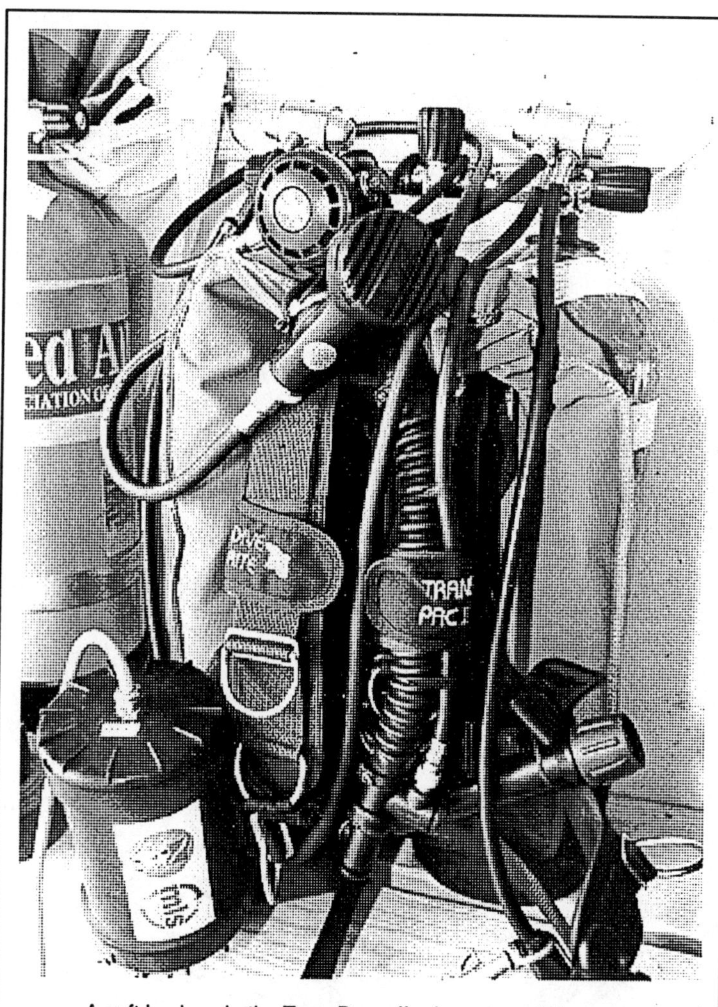

A soft backpack, the TransPac, affords a convertible setup for different diving styles.

Photo Tom Mount

The traditional hard backplate has been reliable and is available in ABS, aluminum or stainless steel. The plate can be easily configured and customized to fit all our mounting needs. It has a small profile, and thus creates little drag, and has proven to be very dependable. Due to its simplicity and ruggedness, the hard backplate is, and will continue to be, the foundation of preference for many divers.

The chief limitation of the hard backplate is its lack of versatility for multi-purpose use. The adaptive hardware needed to convert a hard backplate for use with a single tank is awkward at best. Granted, it does work, and is arguably superior to switching from one style BC to another. In addition, the backplate is not convenient for use with side-mount diving, nor is it as comfortable to wear on land as a soft pack. Additionally, hard backplates are a "one size fits all" proposition, and divers who are relatively short or tall will find it to be more uncomfortable than the multi-sized soft pack technology currently on the market.

Divers have experimented with soft packs for a number of years. In general, the early prototypes did not provide the stability needed to support doubles and stage tanks. For this reason they never gained popularity in the technical diving community. In 1995, two manufacturers, Zeagle and DiveRite, made dramatic advances in soft pack technology. Zeagle introduced an updated technical pack, and Dive Rite introduced the TransPac. Initially both of these systems had some inherent problems. The Zeagle unit lacked stability with doubles and stages, and the DiveRite was too cumbersome to set up. Both have made improvements that resulted in a usable and suitable system. As a result, there are now several "technical" soft packs on the market.

Whether you opt for a hard backplate or soft backpack, your first action should be to adjust and modify the unit for personal comfort and compatibility. Be sure to streamline this unit to the maximum practical point. No lose ends, no dangling material, and a snug fit are prerequisites.

When rigging a new gear system - either hard or soft - the author typically spends about two initial hours analyzing the pack with regards to personal needs. This includes several trips to a mirror to look at the effect each modification of the system creates. An additional 2 to 3 hours are then spent assembling and re-evaluating the completed configuration. Once the life-support system is optimized, it does not require anything except maintenance and an occasional tweak when a better way is observed or invented.

Regulators

If the backpack is considered the foundation of the technical diving rig, the regulators are the heart of that system. This heart has two parts - the primary and the backup regulator - and each is of equal importance to the life support system.

One mistake some technical dives make is to settle for a lower performance backup regulator. Remember, in the event of a problem, that backup regulator is for you, and you wouldn't want to go from a high-performer to a "hog" in a stressful situation.

Notice how all the hoses point straight down to keep a clean configuration.

Photo: Tom Mount

Likewise, you don't want to hand a hard breathing, low volume regulator to a stressed diver. Unfortunately, many divers select a ideal primary and then dig out their oldest and lowest performing regulator for the secondary. This is like waving a red flag at Mr. Murphy. The combination of stress and a low performance regulator may lead to an otherwise avoidable incident.

The diver may decide to breathe from the long hose or the short hose. Both techniques have outstanding safety records, and it becomes a matter of personal choice for the diver. The way in which the long hose is stored varies depending

When using different designs of regulators it is still possible to keep a clean hose configuration.

Photo: Tom Mount

on whether the diver breathes from it or not. Again, from a safety standpoint, both options have proven to be quite effective in gas sharing emergencies. Thus, deciding which method you should use requires a look at the primary advantages of both.

The primary advantages of breathing from the long hose are:

- It provides a simple hand-off to a distressed diver.
- It ensures the out of air diver receives a functioning regulator.
- In theory, a distressed diver will most likely go for the regulator in the mouth.

The primary advantages of breathing from the short hose are:

- It ensures the diver always has a functioning regulator even in an out-of-air emergency with another diver.
- It takes into account the fact that many divers no longer have the reflex to go for the regulator in the mouth.
- By connecting the short hose to the left post of the manifold, the diver will know immediately if the valve has been accidentally bumped shut due to contact in an overhead environment. (The valve shuts off clockwise on forward movement.)

While in training, a diver should practice with both methods, along with a variety of hose storage techniques. Generally speaking, there are two recommended ways to store a long hose. One is to drop the hose back along the back of the wings and then across the body around the left side of the neck with a ¼ turn around the neck.

The second storage method involves drilling holes in a backplate. One should be drilled at the upper right hand side and the other four inches below. A snug loop of surgical tubing should be threaded through these holes so they fit snugly around a double loop of the long hose. Both of these methods are equally easy to deploy, present low entanglement probability and provide clean drag profiles.

Other means of long hose storage include placing surgical tubing around the cylinder and running the hose through it and up under the diver's arm. While this method does take up the slack in the long hose it produces a much greater potential for hose entanglement and chaffing of the hose.

Storage of the long hose in a surgical loop behind the divers neck is another system favored by some divers. This causes the area around the valves to become quite busy and may lead to confusion when doing a valve shut down.

Underwater Lighting

Lights should be evaluated with regards to depth ratings, ease of storage and performance. When diving in overhead environments beyond the point of surface light, the diver must carry a primary light and two smaller secondary lights. If diving within a zone of surface light, a primary and one backup will suffice.

The physical positioning of the primary light varies widely among divers, but the three most popular methods are either waist mounted, backplate mounted, or butt mounted. Regardless of which method you choose, you should be aware of the advantages and disadvantages of both systems. Additionally, you should be aware of how to use the alternate method, since some situations may be better served by one than another. Safety lights should be carried in manner that minimizes drag while allowing for quick, easy access.

Buoyancy Compensation

The buoyancy compensation devices of almost universal choice among technical divers are the back-mounted flotation systems typically known as wings. Wing systems conform to the profile of double tanks, while leaving the diver's front free for the attachment of lights, accessories and stage tanks.

When selecting a buoyancy compensation system, make sure it has adequate lift capacity to support you and all the equipment you plan to carry, not only on the surface, but at depth, where compression will reduce the inherent buoyancy of a wetsuit or neoprene dry suit. Generally, technical divers tend to be negatively buoyant because of the double tanks and extra equipment that are part of the technical diving rig. For this reason, most experienced divers feel that some type of redundancy is needed within the buoyancy compensation system.

For the diver wearing a wetsuit, this may mean wearing a second set of wings, or a system, such as those marketed by DiveRite and OMS, that provides two bladders within one shell. When diving in a drysuit, the suit itself can fill the need for backup flotation. In this event, only one set of wings may be needed.

Diver error or faulty maintenance causes the majority of buoyancy compensator failures. Common causes of failure include pulling too hard on dump valves, snagging or abrading the air bladder on an environmental feature and allowing sand or debris to clog a dump valve seal. But even if you take exemplary care of your BC system, there is always some chance that an air bladder failure will cause you to lose buoyancy. A second set of wings or a dual bladder system is a small price to pay for the safety they provide.

Lift bags, while not strictly a buoyancy compensation device, are also a needed part of open water technical diving rigs. Bags should have at least 50 pounds of lift, with 100 pounds preferred by many divers, and the un-inflated bag should be stored in a manner that minimizes drag and the chance of entanglement.

Cutting Tools

Technical divers carry cutting tools not for the purpose of dismantling artifacts or the environment, but to extricate themselves from entanglements. The cutting tool should be appropriate for the diving environment. For example, a light-weight parachute cutter would suffice in a cave, where the only entanglement potential comes from nylon guidelines, while heavy wire cutters might be needed on wrecks draped in dangling cables, wires and discarded fishing nets. Surgical scissors typically work well in any environment and will cut either wire or line.

Reels

You must carry a safety reel on all technical dives, as it is a primary tool of self-rescue. If you become lost, disoriented or separated from a guideline in an overhead environment, the safety reel can be attached to a reference point, allowing you to perform search sweeps without straying further from the point of the initial problem. In open water, the safety reel can be used to deploy a lift bag.

In caves, and on wrecks of major magnitude, you or some member of the dive team should also carry a larger, primary reel, which will be used to form a continuous guideline to open water, either by deploying line throughout the dive, or tying into an existing guideline. Cave dives that call for jumps from one existing guideline to another will require additional small reels known as gap reels. Your dive team should carry one gap reel for every expected line jump, but there is no advantage to carrying more reels than the dive plan calls for.

Pressure Gauges

The large gauge consoles common in open water recreational diving do not find favor with technical divers. Instead, pressure gauges are typically fitted with a minimal cover boot, and are attached to a harness D-ring or stowed close to the diver's body to prevent entanglement. To eliminate the drag and clutter of a dangling high pressure hose, many divers order shorter hoses that end at waist level or above.

Exposure Suits

Because technical dives typically last much longer than recreational dives, heat loss becomes a concern much sooner. A reduced body temperature is a predisposing factor to DCS, so exposure protection is not only a matter of comfort, but also a safety concern.

In warm or temperate waters, many divers opt for the relative simplicity of a wetsuit, and may include a hood or hooded vest for longer duration dives. As in-water times increase and water temperatures decrease, most veteran technical divers will opt for a drysuit. Before diving a drysuit, you should seek additional specialized training in its use and maintenance.

Accessories

Items such as masks and fins should be selected on the basis of personal comfort, fit and durability. Because your underwater mass and profile are increased by the additional gear you carry on a technical dive, your fins should be large and stiff enough to move you without causing excessive leg fatigue.

Stage Tanks

In technical diving, additional gas supplies are often needed to either extend the range of exploration or to supply custom decompression mixes. To accommodate these gas needs, divers may carry permanent, semi-permanent or removable stage tanks.

Removable stage tanks are the most common option used by technical divers. But before discussing the particulars of removable stage bottles, we should review the other two options.

Three different methods of rigging stage cylinders.
Photo: Tom Mount

Wreck divers commonly use pony bottles, either for back up gas or for decompression gas. Pony bottles are generally smaller volume tanks, often of 30 cubic feet or less. In IANTD recreational courses, pony bottles are used as a combined safety gas and as an increased EANx mixture (in advanced EANx up to EAN 50) for safety or required decompression stops. On some occasions, pony bottles are also used on technical dives to hold decompression gas.

If a pony bottle is to be used as a safety tank, it is recommended that the pony contain a minimum of 1/3 of the original gas volume. In other words, if the gas supply is 100 cubic feet (2831 free liters), then the pony bottle must contain at least 33 cubic feet (934 free liters) of gas.

In cases where the pony bottle is used as a decompression gas, it must contain the desired amount of required stop gas plus a reserve of 25 percent to ensure adequate safety reserve for decompression multiply the actual gas needed by 1.2 - in the pony bottle as a safety margin.

Three and four tank systems allow the diver to carry reserve or decompression gasses in a permanently mounted configuration. In the early days of extended range exploration, similar systems were used to extend the range and duration of the dive, with the same gas mixtures being used in the auxiliary tanks as in the primary tanks.

In the past few years, a new type of triple or quad tank system has been developed to carry multiple gas mixtures. Such systems allow a diver to carry all the gasses needed for a dive in a unified rig. The disadvantage of this system is that the diver must isolate the various gas mixture regulators to prevent switching to the wrong mix.

Both pony bottle and permanent tank systems, although functional, have several drawbacks, including the increase in underwater drag, a higher probability of entanglement when diving in overhead environments, and a possibility of confusion with the various gas mixtures. The use of detachable stage tanks eliminates many of the disadvantages of both pony bottles and other semi or permanently attached add-on gas supplies. Stage tanks allow the diver access to removable, interchangeable gas supplies - a feature that provides a number of advantages. The term stage implies the use of a specific tank of gas for a specific portion of a dive. Because such tanks are removable, the diver need not carry those tanks not required for a particular stage of the dive.

In exploration diving, this is especially important. Cave exploration entered a new dimension when the concept of stage diving evolved. The practice was initiated by Sheck Exley and named by this author. By using the stage tank on the initial phase of the dive, explorers could extend their diving range. Then, by dropping the stage tank off at a predetermined point - or a point based on gas turn-points of the stage cylinder - the divers could reduce drag and increase their overall swimming efficiency.

During wreck penetration dives, the ability to drop stage tanks in open water reduces the risk of entanglement. In addition, the diver may then be able to fit into more confined areas of the wreck. In IANTD technical diving courses, standardized training requirements call for the use of stage tanks. Pony bottles in the typical permanent or semi-permanent mountings are limited to training purposes for advanced recreational programs.

While stage diving, the size and number of stages may vary depending upon the dive objectives, the abilities of the divers and the presence of support divers. On extensive cave explorations, literally dozens of stage bottles may be used to extend the lead divers' range and to provide bailout capabilities. Conversely, staging done for decompression purposes is usually limited to no more than three tanks.

Diver above is wearing two stages on left side, while the Diver left uses a stage on each side for easier gas identification.
Photos: Miria Denlay

There are several considerations that should be taken into account when rigging and using stage tanks:

- The stage tank must be easy to put on and remove.
- The stage must be rigged and worn in a manner that minimizes drag.
- The stage bottles must be placed on the diver in a manner that maintains good dive posture.
- The diver must be trained in management of stage tanks.

Proper rigging is the key to the easy handling and removal of stage tanks. A typical stage tank will have a snap hook near the neck of the bottle and at a position even to the diver's waist level when the tank is attached.

One of the simplest and most effective means of rigging stage cylinders is by using a piece of nylon line or parachute cord. With this method, the line/chord is pre-cut to length and then secured around the neck of the cylinder. Next, a snap hook is slipped up to near the neck and tied (a fisherman's knot or half hitch works well). The line is then run under a hose clamp tank band at the middle to lower portion of the tank, and the second snap hook is installed at the end of the line.

Several manufacturers are now offering large snap bolts welded onto neck rings. In addition, the bottom snap may be attached directly to a tank band or hose clamp to provide additional stability. For ease of handling, a strap that enables the tank to be carried like a suitcase when it is transported on land can connect the attachment hooks.

If divers are wearing gloves, larger attachment hooks must be used. Many divers avoid the use of boat snap hooks as they tend to attach themselves to wiring and loose lines, and may also allow for accidental disengagement. On the Eastern Seaboard, boat snap hooks are often referred to as suicide clips due to this tendency. Large snap hooks typically allow for faster and easier tank removable and replacement - a factor that can save extra minutes of bottom time spent struggling with a difficult stage attachment.

Patti Mount heads up to her decompression stop past the bridge on the giant aircraft carrier USS Saratoga, Bikini Atoll.

Photo: Kevin Denlay

Decompression stages must be configured in a way that allows for identification by touch and by visual reference. Shallow water mixes such as EAN 80 and oxygen should have the mouthpieces of the regulators either covered or wrapped by surgical tubing to prevent breathing from them without at least a conscious move to access the regulator. Surgical tubing, inner tube rings, or commercially available keepers should be placed along the side of a stage tank to secure the regulator hose when not in use.

In addition, the second stage should be attached to the stage tank by either a hook or secured by surgical tubing. This attachment must be easy to reach, to attach, and to remove while swimming. The physical placement of the stage bottle on the diver can have dramatic effects on his swim posture and drag profile. The majority of divers attach stage bottles on a D-ring high up on the shoulder and a waist D-ring on the harness. The snaps and support attachments are close to the bottle to reduce drag, and are positioned to keep the tank close to the diver's body. Each diver must arrive at a personal balance between a snug, streamlined and flexible configuration that allows for easy access, attachment and removal.

If the addition of stage tanks leads to marked head-down body trim, the bottom snap on the stage tanks can be moved from the waist band and shifted to D-rings around the primary tanks. This will tend to reduce the head down trim. When making such changes, however, be certain that the tanks don't create a swim posture that brings the feet below the divers midline in normal swim attitude. This type of head-up trim can cause the diver to stir up silt when swimming near the bottom. Note that in most cases, attaching stage tanks to D-rings on the main tanks will create additional drag, as the tanks tend to hang more loosely in this manner than when attached to the waist strap.

Before using stage tanks, divers should seek formal training in their use. Most respected technical diving courses devote considerable time to stage tank management. Divers should practice removal, staging and retrieval of the tanks until the operation can be performed flawlessly without a change of swim pace. Moreover, the diver must be able to place the proper tank at the correct location even without visibility. This is accomplished by practicing with closed eyes and by ensuring each stage bottle can be identified by the difference in its support attachments or by the difference in regulator design.

In some ways, staging tanks is similar to flying an airplane; one must think ahead of their present position, and anticipate upcoming actions. As a diver approaches the point at which a stage is to be dropped, the tank should already be removed from the harness and held ready to deploy.

Stage bottles should always be rigged and worn in a manner that allows them to be retrieved with ease. As the diver picks up a stage tank, he should be prepared to make buoyancy changes and to attach the bottle with a minimum of delay. The ability to retrieve stages efficiently prevents silting on wrecks and in caves and also reduces additional bottom time. In too many cases, divers who lacked the necessary stage handling skills have either totally silted out the environment or added significant decompression time to their dive due solely to slow stage retrieval.

Differences of Opinion

If you are new to the sport of technical diving, you can expect to encounter heated debates and widely differing opinions concerning every item and aspect of equipment configuration. Your best course of action is to observe, to examine various rigs with regards to the 20 points made previously, and to determine which is the most comfortable for you and your needs.

Once you make your decision, ask for assistance setting up the components you have selected. On the following pages, you will be able to look over a variety of configurations preferred by respected members of the technical diving community. Read these with an open mind. Then decide on either the system or the portions of the system you wish to take advantage of. Ultimately, it is your safety, your diving style and your preference for what works for you that counts!

The Alternative Configuration

The 'alternative configuration' cannot be attributed to any one diver, and in fact incorporates the thinking and refinements of a number of technical divers. This system is described first because it is a proven and widely used system that can serve as a starting point for later modifications or refinements. If, after evaluating this system, you wish to adopt it, remember to do so with an open mind and to continue to seek methods of improving and personalizing the rig to your particular diving needs.

Hose Configuration

- Double tanks joined by a dual-valve manifold with an isolator valve. When using this system, the primary regulator is placed on the left post. The purpose of placing the primary regulator on the left post is to warn the diver of accidental valve closures.
- Both regulators are configured so that all hoses leaving the first stage point straight down. This provides the cleanest possible configuration.
- No hose tees or swivels are used, as they may introduce additional problems.
- The long hose is stored through loops in the back plate or loops attached to a softpack. This places the long hose under the arm and outside of an area that will produce drag. It also prevents hose chafing that is characteristic of some configurations.
- The diver may choose to breathe from either the long or short hose, and will often test both during a dive to insure the system is 100 percent. This method of hose configuration will work regardless of the hose the diver uses.
- A retainer around the neck secures the alternate regulator's second stage. In an air sharing emergency, a diver breathing the long hose would simply donate the regulator from his mouth and reach to his neck to secure the alternate short hose regulator. A diver breathing the short hose would reach for his neck, twist the second stage free and hand it to the distressed diver.

Backplate Configuration

The back plate or TransPac is configured in the following manner:

- Backplate - It has surgical tubing at the base of the pack to install a lift bag when diving in open water or on wrecks. To install, drill a hole in either side of the plate, place surgical tubing through it and adjust for a snug fit around the lift bag. (Some stainless steel backplates feature pre-drilled holes.) Surgical tubing is installed on the right side of the backplate to accommodate the long hose. Again, this is done by drilling two holes in the backplate; the first at the level of the shoulder strap about 3/4 inch from the edge of the plate; the second 5 inches below the first. Surgical tubing is placed through the hole and adjusted for a snug fit around the long hose. On the opposite side, you can do likewise for storage of a small argon cylinder.
- TransPac - The surgical tubing is attached to the two small rings that are affixed to the soft pack on the right side. This is an ideal location and does not require additional modifications. For lift bag storage on the TransPac, use the grommets at the base of the backpack and run surgical tubing through them and

slide the bag into this area. The two rings on the left side are equally suitable for argon storage. In this manner, all components are near the diver's side to create a streamlined dive profile. Once the TransPac has been personally configured to fit both a wet and dry suit, all adjustable straps should be trimmed of excess material. This eliminates loose, hanging strap ends, and produces a cleaner configuration.

Submersible Pressure Gauge

The SPG is fitted to a custom hose 24 inches (57.6 cm) long, which is run under the arm and snaps into the D-ring on the left shoulder harness. With this arrangement, a quick downward glance allows you to read the SPG without ever handling it. This particular hook-up will not work with consoles. If you use a console, a chest-mounted configuration is preferred.

BC Inflation Hose

The BC inflation hose is cut to a 22-inch (52.8 cm) length, and runs through surgical tubing loops attached around the inflation hose. This combined unit is fitted through a surgical tubing loop on the upper shoulder of a backplate. On a TransPac, the hose runs through the Velcro-release retainer provided on the upper left-hand side of the shoulder harness. When diving wet, a backup BC inflation hose is attached to the side of the wings or to the back portion of the backplate/TransPac to reduce drag. On dry suit dives backup wings are not needed.

Reels

Reels are attached to the waist strap by means of a fixed D-ring. In open water, a single reel is needed for a lift bag. If you are wreck diving, you may take a second reel for penetration. In cave diving, you must always have a safety reel in the event you become lost. If you are running the primary reel or a gap reel you need the applicable additional reel. If you are not the diver running the primary or gap reel then you only need a safety reel.

Lights

For cave or wreck dives into an overhead environment, the primary light should have a minimum burn time of 1½ times the dive duration. The light may be butt mounted to produce less drag and to fit into more restricted areas of wrecks and caves, or it can be worn on the waist or backpack when diving in larger areas.

Safety lights are worn in one of three configurations:

- When using a backplate they are worn on the lower portion of the shoulder harness. They attach to the D-ring on the harness and then are placed through a surgical tubing loop (one light on each side).
- On either a TransPac or a backplate, they may be carried in a pouch worn on the waist harness.
- On a TransPac, the safety lights may be attached to the lower waist D-ring and then secured within loops of surgical tubing. This locates the safety lights near the tank and behind the waist D-rings. One light is carried on each side.

Cutting Tools

Such devices may be carried in a waist-mounted utility pocket, or in a custom-fitted pouch on a dry or wet suit. Small cutting devices may also be attached to the diver's wrist.

Stage Bottles

Stages are rigged with neck rings and a second lower ring held by a hose clamp. A tote strap is run from the neck ring to the hose clamp. The stage bottles are then hooked onto the waist and shoulder D-rings by way of bolt snaps. Decompressions stage bottles should be carried with the highest EANx mixture (usually EAN 80) on the right side and the other gas on the left side. The highest EANx mixture has either a bungee around the mouthpiece or a second stage cover. This configuration provides a balanced swim load and aids in avoiding confusion between decompression stage bottles. The stage bottles have a short 6 inch (14.4 cm) hose for a SPG and the regulators are secured to the tank with surgical tubing. A penetration stage bottle is carried on the left side. If multiple stages are used on a swim dive, they are carried on opposite sides; if used on a tow-behind DPV, they are carried on the left side.

Tom Mount's Configuration

The author has arrived at this configuration to meet the demands of varied diving environments. It has proven effective in many areas of the world and on a variety of dive missions. It may be used with either hardpacks or softpack technology.

- The doubles are manifolded together. If available, an isolator valve is used.
- The regulators are placed so that all hoses extend vertically downward from the valves. The long hose is on the right post and is the primary regulator. This hose is wrapped under the wings and, when using my normal waist light placement, underneath it, the hose is simply routed behind the wings, across the body and a ¼ turn around the neck. When diving without a light, the excess hose is tucked into the waist strap. The short hose is the backup regulator. A permanently attached surgical loop is attached to the backup regulator; this goes around the neck of the diver. This second stage should be right at the base of the neck just below the chin.

> When using this system, it is prudent to periodically check the left post to insure the valve has not been closed off. When breathing from stages, the long hose second stage is clipped to the D-ring at the shoulder.

- The SPG has a custom length of 24 inches (57.6 cm) and runs down from the regulator on the left post. It is attached to the left shoulder D-ring.
- The BC inflator hose coming out of the BC (wings) is a custom 9 inch (21.6 cm) hose. The power inflator hose is 15 inches (36 cm) long. This short hose arrangement is ideal for fine tuning buoyancy without a need to raise the hose or to use the lower pulldumps on the wings. The power inflator hose is attached to the left.
- When diving a wet suit use a backup BC. On dry suit dives, one set of wings can be used. The dry suit serving as a backup BC.
- The primary light for use in cave or wreck diving is normally waist mounted. When diving in areas that are narrow, such as some sections of wrecks or constricted caves, butt mounting is a logical choice. Waist mounting is a simpler configuration for use in less constricted areas and is ideal for long hose configuration.

Tom Mount's equipment configuration.

Photo: Bill Dooley

- The safety lights are mounted on the shoulder straps with one being placed on each shoulder strap. This allows ease of access to the lights while keeping them removed from busy areas and reducing drag.

- Reels as needed (use only what you need) are carried on the waist D-rings or on a ring attached to the backplate or back D-ring on the crotch strap. The lift bag is carried by two surgical tubing loops attached to the base of the backplate.

- Stage tank rigging is by having a line around the neck of the cylinder and to the point on the cylinder that will align the bottom snap with the waist D-ring. The line is covered with tubing. This can also be with stage straps.

- Backplate: I use a stainless steel backplate with a QD on the lower left shoulder strap. I have a back injury that flares up from time to time and the TransPac is friendlier on the back on those occasions. I also use a TransPac when traveling due to its lighter weight and ease of changing from singles to doubles. Attached to the backplate or TransPac is a continuos crotch strap that has a loop that goes around the waist strap. The crotch strap has a DPV ring at the front and a tow ring at the back of the strap. At the base of the backplate or TransPac a surgical tubing loop is at either side to allow storage of a lift bag when diving in open water.

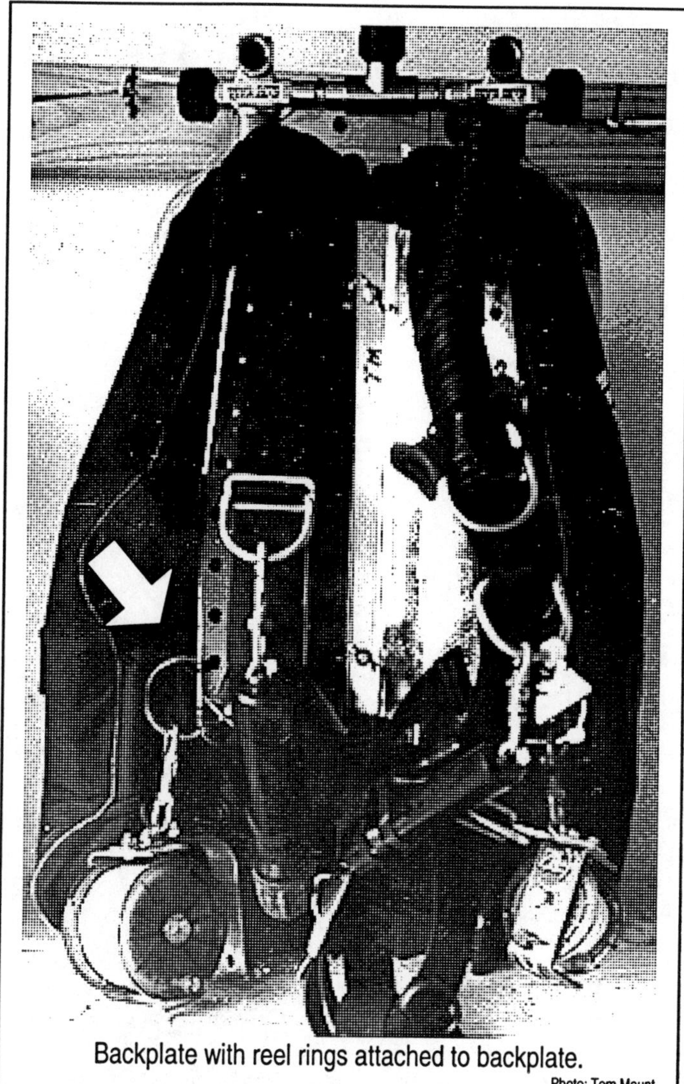

Backplate with reel rings attached to backplate.
Photo: Tom Mount

- Cutting tools are carried on all dives. A pair of surgical scissors is in a holster on the waist strap. A small knife is placed on the back of my light handle for immediate access.

- The cylinders normally used are double 112's (17L) for cave diving and double 85's (13 L) for deep open water and wreck dives. On dives not requiring larger cylinders, I use either double 45's (7L) or single cylinders with dual valve outlets that provide sufficient volume of gas for the planned dive.

The Hogarthian Gear Configuration

Jarrod Jablonski

Cave diving has undergone some significant changes in the past three decades. One thing that never seems to change, however, is the ongoing debate over the optimum gear configuration. Over the years, dozens of styles have marched to center stage and purported to be the most effective, the safest, the easiest, the cheapest, or lately, even the most "technical".

Some divers are able to maintain a causal tolerance for configurations other than their own, while others adamantly insist that their chosen rig is the only correct choice. How can one sport support such a variety of opinions and, perhaps more importantly, how is a diver to dim the clamor of opinions in order to make a sound and reasonable decision?

The most sensible way to make an educated decision is to gather information and evaluate which of the available options best satisfies your particular needs. Nearly all styles of gear configuration allow the average diver to perform a technical dive - be it cave, wreck or deep diving.

Jarrod Jablonski demonstrates the Hogarthian configuration.

Even many an open water diver has returned unscathed from an ill-advised venture into the depths, the belly of a wreck or the dark passages of a cave system. Yet despite such fortunate outcomes, the consensus of opinion within the industry holds that a certain minimum of equipment is necessary to safely penetrate these overhead environments.

It is the specific points of exactly how one should configure that equipment and what equipment to use that garnishes the lion's share of the sometimes bitter debate over equipment configuration.

Long Hose Styles

Technical equipment configurations come in a number of different styles, and there are endless variations on the finer points of each of these styles. One major dividing point that can be applied to most all rigs, however, involves the manner in which the long hose is worn and used. While many differences may exist within each of the two groups that will be detailed below, the common element that unites all other variations within the group - and which separates them from the other group - is the diver's belief in whether the regulator donated to an out of air diver should come from one's mouth or from one's retaining device.

The Bungie Style - Donating From One's Retaining Device

The most common style places the long hose in some type of surgical tubing or restrictive band. This band may be placed on the side of the tanks, near the manifold, on the back plate or nearly anywhere that suits one's fancy.

Proponents of this style vary in their degree of dedication to the refinement of their equipment placement, with some divers seeming to discount the need to streamline and reduce the overall clutter of the rig. However, a few divers practicing this style do begin to approach the minimalism concept so obvious in the Hogarthian style.

The Hogarthian Style - Donating Your Own Regulator

The Hogarthian Style has many minor variations, yet its general tenets call for a policy of gear minimalism. In other words, if it is not needed, it is a potential liability. The Hogarthian style strives to eliminate the unnecessary while configuring the necessary in the most streamlined manner possible. Named for its founding father, William Hogarth Main, the Hogarthian style is constantly being improved and refined. Bill Main himself, despite nearly 25 years of cave diving, is invariably showing up at local dive sites with modifications. Much can be learned from his dedication. Despite the minor variations that exist within the Hogarthian diving community, one will find the strictest of its practitioners to be remarkable similar in their configuration.

While the trademark of a Hogarthian diver is that they breathe the long hose and donate this hose to an out of air diver, the style is really about much more. Regardless of an individual's preference for which hose to donate, much can be learned from the adherence to minimalism so central to the Hogarthian configuration.

Many divers appreciate that certain extraordinary dives may require a degree of refinement simply unnecessary for the average diver. Yet, in much the same way space travel is merely a distant dream for the majority, the advances gained from this pursuit are abundant. How much of this refinement is reasonable or, more importantly, helpful?

One's attention to detail should at least be proportional to the severity of dives being done. If all your dives focus on the main line and penetrations are modest, your equipment requirements might seem less stringent in terms of refinement and streamlining through minimalism. Yet, if your dives begin to incorporate stage diving and longer penetrations, then you should pay a correspondingly greater degree of attention to the finer points of your rig.

In general, you should always evaluate your rig on the basis of how well the package functions as a whole. Equipment should be seen as a cohesive unit that facilitates safe diving, and is not a haphazard collection of available items.

Breathing the Long Hose

Despite its growing popularity, many divers remain opposed to donating the regular from their mouth. The following discussion addresses the most common objections concerning donation of the long hose from the mouth.

1. **"The last thing I want to do in an out of air situation is give up my primary regulator."**

   This does not really seem to be a rational argument. It is likely that a diver incapable of removing the regulator from his or her mouth for five to 10 seconds is not skilled or practiced enough to be in an overhead environment.

> **Editor's note:** Many divers who advocate breathing the short hose have exceptional skill. They elect to breathe the short hose based on the belief that the diver donating air should insure that their control is complete. This is based on the assumption that the out of air diver will be shaken and possibly on the verge of panic. In fact, many of the most disciplined and competent divers I know breathe the short hose. I personally advocate breathing from the long hose.

One may question this diver's ability to handle an out of air situation in which the out of air diver chooses the regulator in their mouth. A diver with this degree of concern over the regulator in their mouth may find it quite a challenge to even deal with the very real possibility of an accidentally dislodged regulator.

By donating the long hose regulator from the mouth in an out of air situation, one guarantees that the person most in need of a clean, fully functioning regulator is going to get one. If you pass any other regulator to an out of air diver, it is quite possible that the regulator received may contain contaminant that will be impossible for the stressed diver to manage. In essence, what you will have done is to place the last straw on the camel's back, creating the last problem your dive buddy can manage.

The advantage of donating your long hose primary is that you are always ready for this very real possibility. You are, in essence, always prepared for any eventuality rather than simply maintaining a fixed picture of how things should operate. Emergencies have an annoying habit of not going as planned, and the Hogarthian diver is prepared to manage a variety of out of air scenarios.

2. ***"I don't want to breathe my long hose. I want to have the best performance regulator in my mouth, and the long hose decreases this performance."***

With literally thousands of deep exploration dives accomplished by divers breathing the long hose, the performance argument seems rather a moot point. Yet, if one were to insist that the reduction of performance is unmanageable, it seems like a poor solution to leave the stressed, out of air diver gasping for air on this lower performance regulator so you can have a more relaxed dive.

Your best performance regulator *must* be on your long hose. If it's performance is unacceptable in a relaxed diving situation, it is certainly inappropriate to suggest that your stressed dive buddy is better prepared for this increased resistance in a time of stress.

3. ***"I just don't want to deal with that hose around my neck."***

Any skill worth learning usually takes refinement. The long hose may, at times, seem uncomfortable to some people, but, regardless of your storage location, you have to deal with that hose. When you tuck a long hose into some surgical tubing, you feel that it is forgotten. Indeed, for some people, it is forgotten. But what happens when that hose pulls free, or it is not set right?

If one relies on his or her buddy to arrange that hose, what guarantee is there that it will be to your personal liking? In a sport that preaches self-sufficiency, it does not seem logical to configure your equipment in a way that forces dependence on a dive buddy.

4. ***"You can't stage dive and breathe the long hose."***

I would never have imagined that people thought this to be true, yet exposure to cave instructors whose abilities I otherwise respect has proved me wrong. Stage diving Hogarthian style is in no way more difficult than for any other style. In fact, the majority of cave exploration currently being conducted is by divers breathing the long hose, despite the fact that they are a minority in the cave community.

The System Approach

No review of the Hogarthian style is complete without a discussion of the system itself. It is not merely the streamlined nature of their equipment nor the use of the long hose that sets the Hogarthian diver apart, it is the way the pieces are carefully arranged to create a harmonious system.

In the Hogarthian style, your equipment must function cohesively and be configured to provide you with the greatest support. It is, after all, life-supporting equipment.

For example, let's assume that you have made the commitment to breathing the long hose. That decision must not be the end to your deliberation. In fact, it is really only the beginning. Where and how you store the balance of this length of hose and, indeed, how long it is are at least as crucial as your decision to use it as a primary regulator.

Most divers following this style have opted for the 7 foot (2.1 m) length and run the extra hose under a hip-mounted light canister, across the chest and finish with one-half loop around the neck and into the mouth. This system has proved to be ideal because it allows nearly 5 feet (1.5 m) of hose to instantly be available, and the remaining two can be deployed with a quick flick of the hand. A 9 foot (2.8 m) is ridiculous and dangerous in most situations, and 5 foot (1.5 m) is precariously short in restrictive passages. Do not try and wrap this hose around your neck multiple times as its deployment will be time consuming, awkward and potentially dangerous.

Why a hip mounted light canister? The hip mounted canister allows for easy removal in the event of entanglement, visual verification (I prefer clear housings) to assure it has not become a "water-cooled" version, a shorter cord to deal with, and assurance of general stability. In addition, the lack of a light swinging from the bottom of your tanks provides ample room to store reels and extra scooters, and even provides an ideal place to tow a stranded diver during an aborted scooter dive. Finally, the hip mounted canister is much easier to remove and replace, and there is much less danger or setting 100-plus pound tanks on top of it.

Reduce, Reduce, and Reduce

Too many divers today seem to be under the impression that more is always better. In technical diving, what is needed is *better* equipment, not more. Whatever equipment is not needed is simply a detriment.

Equipment choice should be made as a result of a cost versus benefit analysis in which one must weigh the potential risk against the perceived benefit. The difficult part and, in fact the thing that really defines a safe and effective diver, is his/her ability to accurately evaluate the benefit while candidly weighing the acceptable risk.

Lights are an essential portion of your equipment; yet, again, more is not always better. One primary and two backup lights are all that is required in most situations. Unless one intentionally dives with faulty equipment or ignores common maintenance, the likelihood of a triple light failure is statistically insignificant.

If one carries six lights, he or she is likely to encounter many other unnecessary problems. Not only is one less likely to care for these lights, but they will cause him/her numerous entanglement hazards that will far outweigh the perceived benefit.

"Hogarthian Configuration" stern view.
(Arrow indicates long hose.)

Three good lights-one strong dependable primary with two small backup lights-is more than sufficient for most dives. If light failures are common on your dives, you should re-evaluate your equipment and/or your technique.

I have discussed the placement of the primary light canister and the advantages of hip mounted operation, but how about one's reserve lights? These lights can be stored in several places. Many people prefer to mount the backup lights on the tanks. This system can appear fairly clean, depending on the user's dedication, but the lights may pull free in smaller caves and passageways in wrecks plus they tend to get tangled in the line. When lights are instead placed on the harness below the arms, they tuck neatly out of the way and are essentially snag-free.

The primary light is an integral part of any diver's equipment. Your light must provide ample illumination, be reliable, and allow flexible use. The test tube style light satisfies all these requirements and more. The light beam has excellent illumination properties, is simple to operate, has tremendous flexibility, and, when connected to a canister style light, will provide stalwart reliability.

The Goodman style handle that rests atop your hand allows for further flexibility, as it provides the unencumbered use of both hands. A Goodman style handle allows just as much flexibility as the helmet mounted light, yet does not blind your dive buddies. It also allows the diver to be more aware of his/her surroundings as the light is easily directed around the cave or wreck.

Cages tend to be somewhat controversial topics. First, let me say that I dislike valve cages. I am not against the objective they purport to accomplish - protecting the valves and manifold from impacts - but I am against their apparent success.

First, let us look at the supposed problem: contacting the ceiling. If a diver hits the ceiling on a regular basis and concludes that a cage is the correct solution, I would argue that they are using flawed, or at least questionable, logic. If a diver hits the ceiling a lot, they should not look for mechanical substitutions to becoming a better diver. A diver should just work on their technique. Okay, so everyone hits the ceiling on occasion, but how hard? If the diver is swimming, I think a diver is being a bit reactionary and the wearer should really reconsider the risk and need for a cage.

If the diver is scootering, then they have a somewhat legitimate concern. They may choose one of the large dome style cages that appear to be solid protection but also have an annoying habit of wedging their owner in small places. Given the likelihood of a manifold failure, I would much rather go cageless and remain flexible in small areas.

If one uses the smaller, more streamlined version of the cage which substitutes curved metal guards above the regulators, then I think one is fooling himself/herself. I have witnessed two people break their DIN regulators off at the manifold despite the presence of these protective devices. If, in fact, these devices are limited in their ability to accomplish what they were designed for, then their large line catching profile is far more a risk than a benefit.

Manifolds are, in general, the best method to manage your air supply. The only exceptions, in my opinion, are when a diver is solo diving or using a side mount configuration. If a diver is not pursuing either of these two options, then they should not configure as if they are. I caution you to be wary both of using independent valves and of diving with those who use independent valves.

It requires great care and superior gas management capabilities to effectively monitor independent cylinders. Experience has shown that most people are not capable of proper management. Given the likelihood of manifold failure, I will remain an ardent supporter of manifolds in nearly all diving environments.

Isolators are nifty little inventions that responded to our desire for the cake after it was eaten. They are, in theory, excellent ideas and, in practice, probably fairly decent. As long as one maintains an awareness of his/her strengths and weaknesses, isolators remain effective pieces of equipment. They are, however, not necessarily the saving grace some may have you believe.

First, while they may provide a redundant option to isolate your cylinders, they are also another valve and just as likely to fail, as is the valve you are circumventing. Be aware that due to the nature of their construction, failure of an isolator will allow only one cylinder to be isolated, thus protecting only half of the gas supply. Furthermore, one must always guard against the common occurrence of valves that are inadvertently turned off during filling or during safety drills.

Valve knobs should be given some degree of attention. Rubber knobs are my personal favorite. They are durable, shock absorbent, shatter proof, and easy to turn. Their only down side is a tendency to shut the left post down upon contact with the ceiling or sides of an overhead environment. Personally, were I diving a manifold where this was a problem, I would probably still use rubber knobs but be more cautious.

Plastic knobs are dangerous because they can shatter, leaving you with nothing to turn on or off. The metal knobs attempt to solve this and the auto-shut-off problem, yet fall a little short because they can bend upon impact and be rendered useless.

Tanks come is a variety of flavors, and I will spend very little time on them. My preference is for the larger volume, lower pressure steel cylinders. Tank size should be based on your size, your needs, and your available funds. Do the cave and yourself a favor and really evaluate your needs. Don't just buy the largest, most expensive tanks your wallet can handle. Steel 95's (15 L) seems to be the best overall buy, but you must evaluate your personal needs.

Gauges are necessary pieces of equipment, but people often succumb to the more-is-better philosophy. Two timing devices should be more than sufficient for anyone's needs. The gauges should be wrist mounted to avoid bulky consoles and the resulting dredging effect they can create.

The pressure gauge should be free from a bulky console and mounted is a clean area. A pressure gauge that is clipped to the belt keeps the chest free from clutter and limits the items you will potentially drag in the mud. The advent of hoseless gauges promises to solve all these problems, yet, like most cure-alls, I remain patiently optimistic but, as yet, remain unwilling to bestow all my air management faith in their reliability.

The body is the central component to any effective diving locker, and no discussion of equipment would be complete without giving it a mention. Many debates have revolved around the necessity of fitness in diving, and there is no doubt that these debates will continue for years to come.

It seems that the most reasonable course would be to evaluate the type of diving to be done and adjust one's level of fitness accordingly. The average diver should be seeking good cardiovascular fitness with aerobic activity at least three days a week for a minimum of 20 minutes. Good fitness can serve you in life as well as diving, and a thorough fitness routine will leave you more prepared for the rigors that diving can produce.

A person winded by a flight of stairs can certainly dive, but their ability to manage stressful, air critical situations is limited by their physical response to elevated exertion. This may seem inconsequential in a leisurely dive but in an emergency, it can make all the difference. Certainly, excessive exercise could be a potential liability as scar tissue accumulation at the joints could reduce circulation, but this is a rare case.

Conclusion

The next decade of diving will undoubtedly be full of excitement and prodigious change. Undoubtedly, equipment advancements will continue and many exciting advancements are bound to grace the diving world. Yet, regardless of the level of change beyond the year 2000, two things will undoubtedly remain constant: there will always be new equipment for people to obsess over, and there will always be people arguing over how that equipment should be configured. Your response to these arguments should be based on your actual needs, and on the requirements of your diving environment.

Equipment Configuration International Style

Lamar Hires

My diving background is primarily cave diving. I know that many areas of equipment configuration cross over between cave and wreck diving and I have had no problem adapting in my limited wreck diving experience. I would then say, "The fundamentals of configuration are the same," but don't ask me where I put my lift bag, I haven't needed one in a cave yet.

In the course of my teaching career, I have had many students emulate my equipment configuration and diving style, then pass it along to friends who also came to me for training. I had to disappoint some of these new divers by telling them their equipment needed to be modified and adjusted (two very popular buzzwords of technical divers). This new student then says to me, "Lamar, Joe said this is how you configured your equipment when he took his class from you eight years ago."

Equipment configurations evolve as technology advances, and we seek out more demanding environments to challenge ourselves. So as I write this section on how I presently configure my equipment, remember I am constantly looking for a better way to master the environment.

I use the Dive Rite TransPac for singles, doubles, staging and side mount diving. In the past I used one setup for singles, doubles and staging and another setup for side mount. I wanted one setup for all my diving needs for many reasons.

Lamar Hires, President, Dive Rite Manufacturing
Photo: Bill Dooley

The TransPac was designed to do this, and offers the following advantages:

1. Travel - One setup means I take less equipment on trips. That means I forget fewer items when I travel. The more you take the more likely something will be forgotten.
2. Comfort and Fit - As diving environments change, warm water to cold water, strap adjustments had to be made for changes in suit thickness. This became bothersome with my previous rigs, as it often took two or three dives to make the adjustments needed to get the fit just right.
3. Consistency - I wanted all back up equipment to reside at the same location regardless of my configuration. This way, learning to access a given item could become second nature.

My Equipment Positioning for Doubles is as Follows:

Regulators

Two Poseidon first stages with all hoses positioned straight down for streamlining. The short hose second stage is on a right angle low pressure swivel to bring it from the left-hand post behind my head over the right shoulder. Some will argue the swivel is one more failure point. I have weighed out the pros and cons and will take my chances on the percentages that three more O-rings I have added do not outweigh the comfort gained by proper hose positioning (this is the only swivel on my doubles configuration).

The long hose regulator second stage is a classic design (Sherwood style), easy to maintain since its use is in emergencies. The long hose is stowed via two small loops of shock cord attached to the 1" D-rings directly below the regulator on the TransPac. The hose rests just off the side to the point of not even being seen and deploys very nicely I store the long hose regulator second stage in a loop attached to the chest strap.

Lights

I butt mount my primary light or when using the smaller MLS light waist mount it. I like getting it out of the way of the harness for more room and streamlining. Under the cylinders is the best place to position the bulky battery canister. My backup lights are very small lights with adequate burn time. These consist of two Princeton Tec 40's carried in a quick release pocket on my right and a UK mini Q 40 on the mask. I use the Q 40 for reading gauges while scootering and as a reading light for survey work.

Backup Mask and Cutters

This is carried in a quick release pocket on my left side. I carry two line cutters. A Z-knife (razor knife) on the strap of my wrist-mounted dive computer and a small knife attached to the left front hip pad so I can reach it easily with my right hand. Slate and dive tables are in a two zippered pocket on my left side.

Reels

I always carry two reels on any cave dive. My safety reel is a primary reel with approximately 250 ft. (76.5 m) of knotted line on it, carried on a D-ring on my cylinders. This gives me a lot of extra spool to decrease the change of line back lashing or reel jams. Most divers never deploy the safety reel except in training. Remember the reason for a safety reel: to search for a buddy, to search for the line or do line repairs. Usually, when either one of the first two occur, they will be accompanied by low visibility. I have had to look for recovery victims in low/zero visibility, and in those conditions, a full reel only adds to the problems – especially when trying to deploy or retrieve it in the absence of visibility. The other reel is a small reel for the occasional change in dive plan when new passage is seen on a dive. This reel is carried on the waist on my harness.

Tank Mounting

With double tanks, I use an isolation DIN manifold. The cylinders are put together with stainless steel bands with bolts spaced for a backplate. The TransPac assembles just like a backplate, Wings slide over the bolts, then the harness and finally the stabilizing plates go on and are secured with wing nuts.

Single Tank Adaptation

The only changes I make for singles is the addition of cam straps to secure the cylinder. My light is positioned on the right side, attached to the top and bottom 1" D-rings on the harness back. All backup equipment stays in the same place.

The Side Mount System

Side mounting refers to the practice of positioning of the primary scuba cylinders on the diver's side rather than on the back. Side mounting may appear to be more streamlined than conventional back mounted cylinders, but this is not the case, it actually presents more drag and increased task loading of equipment management.

This style of cylinder positioning is not new, but has evolved over the years when applied to caves in different areas of the world. I will try to give credit where credit is due, but divers, especially cave divers, are secretive so someone may have used side mount before the time or place mentioned so please do not get offended.

The British cave divers and some Europeans have been using side mount for years. The first need for side mount was established as sumps halted dry cave exploration - underground pools of water in a dry cave possibly leading to a drier cave. Equipment had to be transported by cavers for the cave diver to explore the sump. The distance and terrain traveled inside the dry cave made taking two cylinders configured as twins almost impossible to transport, so singles were preferred for transport. Assembling the singles as independent back mounted doubles required additional hardware, and as sump divers soon learned, the less hardware required, the more likely they were to get dry caves to assist on more than one trip.

Lamar 's side mount configuration.

Photo: Bill Dooley

The British use a wide belt with tank cam straps sewn to it to attach the cylinders at one point on the hip. This is functional, but as the cylinders drop in pressure they get buoyant and start to turn perpendicular to the body, increasing drag.

Kiting up was not a one-man job with this style. The diver would assemble the belt, then lay down while an assistant cinched the waist belt. Cylinders could not be removed and put back on by the diver. This style was acceptable for low to zero visibility diving where trim and body positioning were secondary to the objective of swimming. In some cases, divers would simply walk along the sump in these conditions.

In the United States, most of the easily accessible caves were explored by the early eighties. New techniques were needed to push into deeper, longer and smaller caves. Exploration of the longer, deeper caves is now possible because of new high-powered DPV's, new high-volume cylinders and mixed gasses. Meanwhile, side mounting has opened the door to many low profile caves.

Side mounting gained recognition in North Florida in the late seventies. Woody Jasper started side mounting to explore small caves inaccessible with conventional gear. In the beginning side mount was adapting whatever equipment was handy. This soon proved futile when long range exploration was part of the equation. Today, side mounting is no longer simply a matter of throwing a couple on cylinders on a backplate stage style while leaving the doubles off the back plate. It is a very involved, specialized process, both in terms of equipment and mindset.

The Side Mount Mindset

Whatever the reason for using the side mount configuration, the reality of the potential hazards should be understood. By removing cylinders from the back, the diver is more exposed. While riding a DPV, the cylinders are not a bumper, so to speak (divers should not think this way, but it's reality). A collision with the ceiling or wall puts the diver at great risk of injury, and in an overhead environment this could be fatal.

Any diver prone to claustrophobia could experience elevated tendencies in tight areas, since he can feel his body being pressed in both the back and the chest area. In small areas, low visibility is likely to be an unavoidable reality of the dive, and the diver must be able to deal with this reality.

Divers may apply side mount for it's convenience of transport down pits, over rough terrain or for in order to manage the weight of one cylinder at a time rather than two. But regardless of the reason, the potential to get into small areas is there, whether planned or not.

Task loading is increased by the need to manage two independent gas supplies, and the position of the cylinders forces all hoses to be run on the diver's chest. Lighting, reels and all back up equipment has to be thought out carefully, as it must be accessible when the diver is in a confined position.

As I stated earlier, side mount diving has evolved into a specialty. The days of 'This is what I have to work with, so how can I make it work' are over.

Side Mount Equipment

Cylinder Connection

One of the most critical points of any side mount system is the primary connection of the cylinders to the harness. Some divers use a bolt snap on a short leash attached mid way down a cylinder. Another alternative is a D-ring on the cylinder and a clip on the harness. A new method is a pin on the cylinder and a receiver tube on the harness. All three methods require the neck of the cylinder to be attached to the chest area by means of a bicycle innertube run across the back and attached to D-rings on the chest. The innertube also helps hold down the air cell.

Air Cell

Jacket style buoyancy compensators can be modified by taking the hard plate out and adding the bottle attachments to the waist belt. Wing style buoyancy compensators must have tie downs added to keep them from butterflying on the divers back. Wings need to be combined with a harness to provide a platform.

Backup Equipment

Wearing cylinders on the side interfere with the most logical places to store lights, reels and pockets for dive tables. Side mount divers typically clip off these items anywhere they can. If worn on the harness in the chest area, access is limited and difficult. Reels often end up clipped off behind the cylinders on the waist area.

Hoses and Valves

Regulators should be as streamlined as possible with short (preferably 6 inch (15.2 cm) high-pressure hoses) and 28 inch (71.1 cm) second stage hoses. Since the hoses are on the chest area, this becomes a very busy area, and air management is more intense. Selecting a regulator that allows three hoses to come off one side makes it easy to manage hoses and reduce task loading. Standard 'K' valves with left and right hand on/off knobs prove easier to work with. The innertube goes over the on/off knobs to pull the valves into the body and act as the secondary tie in point.

A Unified System Approach

I have tried a number of different side mount configurations over the years. One of the major concerns I addressed with my current rig is the ability to changing from side mount to doubles to singles - or any combination of these. Most divers approach these scenarios individually, and therefore end up with three different rigs. Transitioning between rigs often creates a level of task loading that distracts the diver to some degree from the real focus of the mission.

I got tired of this learning curve, so I set out to combine all the needed tools to decrease the task loading of changing rigs. The end result was one harness with interchangeable air cells (Wings). With this system, all back up equipment stays in the same location, regardless of cylinder placement. The harness can carry up to six cylinders and still be comfortable. One of the greatest advantages of this system is for travel. When traveling to a remote area where the requirements of the diving environment are unknown, a diver has to remain as versatile as possible and must travel light. My new system allows for this versatility, and is far more compact and lightweight than the three separate systems that would otherwise be needed to cover all configuration possibilities.

Equipment Configuration in the UK One Man's Preference

Kevin Gurr

Equipment configurations should be governed not only by the tenets of redundancy, streamlining, reliability and functionality for the task in hand, but also by the environment in which the dive takes place. By environment, however, I do not mean the physical characteristics of a wreck or cave, but rather the overall diving environment, which includes such variables as tides, water temperature, turbidity and currents.

The following description is offered as a Northern European opinion on equipment configuration. It is not intended to represent some universal standard, but is instead the configuration I currently use to meet the specific needs of my diving environment.

The majority of my diving is done on wrecks, of which there is an abundance of in Northern European waters. Local conditions often include strong tides, low visibility and cold seas. These factors, coupled with the presence of major shipping traffic, smallish dive boats and frequently long runs to the site, have governed the evolution of this particular rig. To describe my gear configuration system, I will start at the top, deal with each item on an individual basis, then attempt to justify its' place in my configuration.

Regulator Guard

Despite its' name, guarding the regulators from impact during the dive is not this unit's prime function. In my opinion, if a diver lacks the buoyancy control needed to avoid contact with the ceiling, he should not go into an overhead environment.

I use the regulator guard to protect the manifold while on the surface. On numerous occasions, I have found that fill stations and boat operators tend to grab the rig by its' manifold. This has lead to the displacement of O-rings. The addition of a regulator guard prevents this tendency, and thus the prime function of my guard is to transport the rig. Additionally, on our smaller dive boats, with 8 mixed-gas divers on board, things tend to be a little cluttered and things do get dropped on other things. Again, the guard offers protection.

A third function of the guard is for assistance with gas shutdowns. In winter, our water temperature is often less than 3 degrees Centigrade (37.4 F), and the diver's primary task is avoiding hypothermia. Hence more underwear must be worn. This reduces maneuverability, especially for those over-the-head valve closing routines. When wearing more underwear, I use a looser harness, which cause more play in the tank set. To overcome this problem, I will grab the guard to position and secure the tank set while I do the shutdown.

On some occasions (especially when scootering), I have used the guard for its' intended purpose as a regulator protector. I have also had structure fall on my rig while wreck diving, and the guard has helped there as well. As a final point, I would never consider inverting my set and relying on the guard being strong enough to protect the regulators during kiting and de-kiting. Although inversion does make certain elements of gas shutdowns simpler, the benefits are easily offset by longer more cumbersome hose runs.

The Isolator Manifold

The argument of isolators versus non-isolators is ultimately a matter of personal choice. I have had instances (often just after a hydrostatic test) where a tank's neck O-ring dislodged, resulting in a complete loss of gas. An isolator at least reduces the loss by ½.

Also, until recently it has not been common practice in the UK to use steel banding kits for twin sets. The cylinders were simply locked together with a double plastic boot and cam banded to the backplate. This practice has lead to twisted manifolds and subsequent manifold failure. My current view is that even a non-isolator has at least two extra O-rings, and if one of them goes you have a massive problem so why not protect against it with an isolator.

If the isolator itself does fail, it is unlikely to fail on both sides, so you still end up with half of the gas left. In any event, if the set is properly put together using steel bands a manifold failure is unlikely (especially if you don't carry the rig by it!).

A final point about isolators. During filling, the isolator is left wide open. Prior to diving, I almost shut the valve. I leave it open just enough to allow the cylinders to equalize during the dive. In a shutdown situation I can quickly isolate it with a single turn of the writs. I see many people dive with fully open isolators.

Regulators

I use Poseidon's throughout my rig. Why? Because, as yet, I have not had a failure. The new first stages are simple enough to service and the parts are interchangeable between the Jetstream, Cyklon and Triton, the only set up difference being a slightly higher innerstage pressure on the Cyklon. I use Jetstreams for my primary and backup regulators. The argument against this practice is that if I have to hand off a Jetstream to a panicking diver, they probably would not have the peace of mind to clear it properly in a stressful situation (the tilt your head towards the diaphragm maneuver), and this would exacerbate the problem. My own reasoning for sticking to this setup is that the backup regulator is there for my use, and I want it to be as good as the one that just failed. If someone really needs gas out of my Jetstream they will get it, eventually. Also as both my primary and secondary are touch identical, I know either one is OK to go for in a lost regulator scenario.

Which brings me to the subject of positioning. One Jetstream comes over my right shoulder (the long hose from which I breathe) and the other one to my left side. I have a philosophy of, "Everything *Primary* is on the right." I know if my long hose fails I reach over my right shoulder and isolate the right hand pillar valve. The same reasoning applies to the secondary systems run from the left. The left-hand second stage is fixed round my neck on a piece of surgical tubing so that I always know where it is. This also allows me to perform regular breathing checks throughout the dive with minimal effort.

Hose stowage of the long hose is a hot issue. Due to the way I rig lights and stages, I have opted to stow the hose under the bungees of my wing. The hose comes out of the regulator, goes under two or three of the bungees behind my head to my left shoulder and then back in a loop under the bungees to the right. The hose then comes free and around the right hand side of my head to the second stage.

I do not feel that I am increasing drag by stowing the hose in this position, and deployment is an easy, one- handed action. In addition, with this configuration, there is less risk of the hose snagging or getting in the way of stages. If I need to deploy and then re-stow the hose, I do a simple Hogarthian loop. Using the wing-mounted bungees does not seem to inhibit inflation of the wing.

The primary regulator has a high pressure gauge attached in a small console, along with a backup depth gage/timer and compass. This hose comes under my right arm and clips into place on a harness ring. Because of the layout of the new Poseidons, the HP has to come out on a right-angled adapter to allow all the hoses to flow down the set. I should stress this is not a swivel connection, and I tie-wrap it to the other hoses to prevent it from moving.

From this same regulator, I also take a feed to one wing. The other wing does not have a low pressure connected (just another failure point). If I really need it, I will cross patch (remember this is my third level of buoyancy as we always use drysuits). The spare wing inflator does have an audible surface alert attached. Again if I need it on the surface I just cross patch it.

The secondary regulator normally has only a suit inflator as an additional hose. Whenever possible, I like to use identical or compatible connectors on all low-pressure fittings. In some instances, I run a hoseless computer link (Aladdin Nitrox), which means I put a HP sensor and another right-angled adapter on this reg. I use the computer as a primary timer and datalogger (as it normally gets "bent" on mixed gas dives). I find the features useful, and I hate writing up logbooks.

Wings

As mentioned above, I currently favor a back mount wing - specifically, the OMS dual bladder set. It offers an acceptably low drag profile coupled with adequate lift. One cautionary note: Be careful of tying the bungees so tight that the wing cannot completely inflate (pre-stretch the bungee before tying). The primary wing inflator has a neoprene sleeve in which I run both its low-pressure inflator hose and the inflator for my dry suit. Both come under my left shoulder.

The suit inflator then plugs in and the aural inflate for the wing is looped to a piece of surgical rubber on the right hand shoulder D-ring. This allows me to have one-handed buoyancy control, with the suit inflator, wing inflator and wing dump being in one place and accessible by either hand. I have also shortened all of the dump pull strings to prevent them from snapping. Other than that, I have made no special modifications.

Harness

My harness consists of webbing and a Stainless steel backplate. I use this because I hate wearing lead, due to a back injury. I find that when I am suited for winter diving with a single stage and my primary light (a lot of my diving is teaching technical programs) I need no lead.

The harness itself has a quick release on the right shoulder, primarily because some sea states require that the rig is dropped in the water and the diver exits without any kit on. The release buckle allows for removal to be done quickly and safely.

I use neoprene shoulder pads, but not as a matter of comfort. One pad houses a dual-function backup light and strobe, the other a seat belt cutter. Both of these items are tied in with a small length of surgical rubber to prevent accidental loss. The light is primarily used for reading gauges in low vis (in total darkness, a primary light will often 'white out' a timer screen).

On my right hand waistband, I have one more neoprene sleeve where I keep a small mirror used for surface signaling. I have also had to use it in solo diving situations to decide whether a leaking gas noise was actually coming from a critical part of my system. Being able to check you own first stages is a useful feature.

The left hand waistband carries and EPIRB and a utility pocket. There is a scooter ring under the center buckle. The EPIRB is a small (100 x 100 x 50mm) device which in its' case is water-proof to 330 ft (100 m). (When out of its' case it works to 33 ft (10 m). The aerial simply loops around your neck. I change the single 9v battery once a year. A lot of our diving takes place 40 miles (48 kilometers) off shore in a major shipping lane. Having the EPIRB makes me feel better having been "lost at sea" several times in the past due to boat failures.

The utility pocket is divided into two zipped compartments. Each zipper has a small - 30 cm (12 inch) diameter - fishing net attached floats (a practice golf ball is also good) to allow easy access when wearing dry gloves or with extremely cold hands.

The front of the pocket is for every day use items. In here I keep a slate for communication, a spare double-eye bolt and a small piece of string (old boy scouts die hard) which could double as a Jon line. Jon lines are not particularly applicable for our waters, but you never know when you need a piece of string!

The rear pocket houses my emergency kit, backup decompression tables, surgical scissors and two sausage surface marker buoys, one yellow and one red. Our diving style often involves the use of decompression stations. The purpose of the buoys is to inform the boat skipper and standby divers of an impending problem. If a diver becomes separated from the station and sends up an orange buoy, this means, "I am on my own but OK." A yellow buoy means "HELP". For a full explanation of this system and the resultant emergency procedures, see the section on decompression stations.

The chest strap of the harness houses my primary knife, which is a Wenoka Laser. It has a replaceable razor blade one side and a wire cutter the other. This is the only knife I have found that is compact enough and does not rust. It is always sharp. I use a crutch strap, which I keep relatively loose to cater for varying underwear and any scootering I do. Any spare webbing ends are taped and stowed.

At the base of the back plate I have drilled holes to take surgical tubing for lifting bags (2). In the UK, these are not used as deco bags, they are purely for artifact recovery. Europe has been using the specific deco SMB's for some time, and most skippers know the difference. The bags are stowed in this position to reduce drag.

I keep my primary light under my right arm. This is basically a stainless steel tube housing the battery, with an over-shoulder cable to a hand mount head worn on the back of the hand. I use a maximum of a 35-watt bulb for UK conditions. The beam is relatively focused, if the visibility is bad I do not get too much backscatter.

The steel tube has two stainless jubilee bands around it which locate two small D-rings with retainers. On the backplate, there are holes drilled in the right hand edge where I have two shackles that mate with the D-rings. The light lead simply comes up over my shoulder and twists down my arm. I invert the battery housing to protect the cable exit gland. I have made a few small modifications to improve the integrity of the electrical connections and have eliminated the screw-on aluminum hand mount in favor of a surgical tubing affair. The screwed-together handle kept coming loose.

This side mounted torch arrangement might sound like it creates an imbalance but it is quite close to my center of gravity, and with a stage the other side, it is perfectly balanced and out of the drag zone.

In winter, I fit a small Argon cylinder on the other side of the backplate, using the same clip arrangement.

Reels

I generally carry two reels. One of about 250 ft. (75 m) line length, and one of about 115 ft. (35 m). The larger of the two is a clutch reel and has fluorescent pink line for easy identification in low visibility. If I have to shoot a bag and do a solo decompression, this is the reel I would use. Once at a stable stop the reel can be locked off (not a friction lock).

The real reason for carrying two is that in a solo decompression situation, if one jams on deployment, I can use the other. Or, if the jam occurs in mid deployment, I can then grab the second reel (which is a smaller friction reel with the lock off), clip it to the first reel, and let it go. Each of these reels are stowed on a D-ring on the base of each stage cylinder. This is the same D-ring that links the stage to the harness (via a double eyebolt). Again the primary reel is on the right.

Primary Cylinders

For most diving down to about 262 ft. (80 meters) I use twin 80 cubic foot cylinders (12 L cylinders). Past that, I would use twin 95 cubic foot cylinders (15 L cylinders). These cylinders are manifolded with an isolator and have steel bands and a bolt kit to link them to the backplate. On the lower bands, I mount a D-ring to which I attach the stage cylinder.

I do not like staging D-rings on the waistband of the harness. This is primarily because, with the heavy underwear I wear, my feet tend to float. To offset this tendency, I move the rear stage mount back to the main tanks. In extreme situations, I may use small ankle weights to alleviate the problem. I would rather be able to put a lot of Argon in the suit at the expense of carrying a little extra weight.

Stage Cylinders

I use two 70 cubic foot (10 L) steel stage cylinders. Each has a unique use, the one being used for an initial deco/travel gas, and the other containing a high O_2 (normally 80%) decompression gas. These are never mixed up. Each has a steel band and D-ring near the base and a brass ring with a snap hook on webbing for the neck clip. As a general rule I never use snap hooks, as they become line traps. My one exception to this rule is on the stage cylinder neck, as mentioned.

The reasons for this are that it is a visible shackle (clipping to the shoulder D-ring on my harness), and with dry or thick neoprene gloves it is easy to detach it quickly if needed in a pitching sea. I still use a double eye (piston clip) for the rear mount. This is not a problem, as I normally detach this clip during the last few minutes of stops on station, which is a lot simpler to do than in a heaving sea at the surface. I then swing this end up to the stage retrieval line attached to the boat and quickly snap off the shoulder snap.

One stage uses a Poseidon Triton (high oxygen) the other a Cyclone (travel/deco gas). These regulators are very different when placed in the mouth. The pillar valves are also different for ID purposes. Both second stages are attached to the neck of the cylinder with a rubber loop and mouth guard. The high-oxygen first stage has an Oceanic high pressure gauge which just screws into the first stage). It does not give a finite indication of pressure, just in 1500 psig (100 bar) increments, but this is sufficient. As there is no HP hose to fail or tangle, this configuration improves reliability and safety.

The travel gas/deco regulator has the same high pressure gauge and a suit inflation whip for Trimix diving. The innerstage hoses of these regulators are retained under surgical tubing bands. I tend not to use inner tube rubber as it lays too flat and cannot be operated easily with large gloves.

I line the base D-ring of the stage cylinder up with the DIN valve outlet on the side mount, this makes the regulator head face into my body when the cylinder is attached to the harness, thus providing protection. All hoses flow down the cylinder.

Drysuit

I think most divers have suffered the quest for the perfect dry suit. Does such an creature exist? It is certainly not a stock item.

After years as a neoprene diver, I went back to a membrane suit for the following reasons:

- No buoyancy loss with depth. This must be balanced against the fact that in shallow water, the neoprene expands and provides some thermal benefit.

- With the right material (not heavy tri-laminate) there is less restriction of movement.
- Extremely durable.

I modified my dry suit in the following ways:

- A small wrist pocket is added on the right arm to take tables.
- One thigh pocket is added, using a zip instead of Velcro. It lays flat when not in use.
- Extra gussetting under the arms and across the back to assist with general maneuverability.
- Integral hood (with neck water drains) for warmth. I always wear the mask strap inside the hood to avoid accidental dislodging during a gas-sharing emergency.
- Internal braces (suspenders).

All seals are heavy-duty latex with the ability to take a dry glove interface. Body fluid removal is via nappies (diapers) rather than puncturing the suit with a catheter system. Gas dumping is via an adjustable shoulder valve (left hand shoulder). Other than that, the suit is a clean, low-drag affair.

Underwear

Basically, I use a 150g thinsulate with a 2oz "Milair" breathable nylon outer and an inner fleece made from "K2 Karisma". This underwear is a 90% wool Scandinavian two piece design. Being green, it isn't too sexy *but* it does the job. On particularly cold dives, I add another thinsulate.

Summary

As I stated at the beginning, this isn't necessarily the "best" rig, it is simply the one that works the best for me. My whole gear ethic is governed by the fact that I do a range of diving from teaching recreational Nitrox to Trimix diving for fun (and a bit of caving when I can). I try not to change my configuration other than dropping off those items I really do not need to take for the task in hand.

CHAPTER 3
Dive Planning

Tom Mount

Dive planning is the process by which divers determine and clarify the objectives of a proposed dive, rehearse the specifics of the dive plan, and review their proposed actions in order to eliminate or minimize the associated risks. To accomplish these goals, there are four important processes that must be undertaken: information gathering, group planning, personal planning, and contingency planning to allow for personal and environmental unknowns. Once a dive plan is developed, it should be followed according to the guidelines that will be explained in this chapter.

Lee Wardwell on a South Florida Wreck.

Photo: Tom Mount

Information gathering, the first step in the planning process, should include all the facts necessary to prepare a safe plan of action on the dive, and should recognize the variables and unexpected contingencies that might occur. In technical diving, detailed information gathering is paramount to the safety and survival of the diver and/or dive team.

The basic elements of information gathering include:

- Gathering pertinent data on the dive environment
- Determining the history and qualifications of the participants
- Determining what equipment may be required
- Identifying mitigating or complicating factors

When gathering information on a given location, you should refer to all available resources to ensure that both an adequate amount of information is obtained, and that the information is accurate and current. The basic references should include visits to the site, conversations with those who have dove the site and printed reference materials such as cave maps or ship's blueprints.

Once this preliminary information is gathered, a basic dive plan can be formulated. If there are charts or maps of the location carefully review them and ensure that each person on the dive team is familiar with the specifics of the location. While in the process of planing the route, duration and proposed actions of the dive, you should also discuss the impact your dive plan will have on the underwater environment.

Next, your dive team should determine what equipment would be needed to perform the dive safely, along with any additional specialty equipment that will enhance dive performance. Then follows the process of determining the correct gas mixtures to make the dive and to efficiently decompress

When beach diving, for example, divers should determine the wave patterns, the probability of rip currents, the underwater topography and the location safe areas of entrance and exit points. On cave dives, teams should anticipate the entrance and underwater conditions, including surface hazards, current, silting, passage size, expected depth, and so forth. If there are reversing currents, the team should establish an optimum dive window.

When boat diving, investigate the particulars of water entries and exits from the craft. If the dive will be a fixed anchor dive, be certain you make visual reference and know where the anchor (upline) is located. If using decompression stages, do not affix them to the anchor line as the line may break free.

If the stops are to be done as a drift dive, become aware of the procedure used on this diving operation. There are numerous methods of securing drift decompression and ascent lines, so insist on having the system explained anytime you are diving a new boat, location or under different circumstances than those you are familiar with. When doing drift dives, be responsible enough to become informed of the procedures used at this location and by the operator with those who are diving. Do not assume anything. Be informed and be safe. Be certain all divers in the group on open water dives have a lift bag so that if they should become separated, they will have a stable up-line and an indicator to the diving vessel of their location.

Ensure that each diver in the group has the adequate type of equipment and the appropriate amount of redundancy for a safe team dive. Prior to entering the water a safety drill (known as an S drill) should be performed. During this process, each diver will check their buddy's equipment for functionality and possible leaks. This includes breathing from the long hose, checking lights and seeing if there are any gas leaks in the tanks, valves, and regulators. In cave and shore based diving, the s drill is to be performed in the water. Even when boat diving, a leak check should be made upon entry into the water if conditions allow.

Gas mix planning is a major concern for technical divers. The factors to be determined during this portion of the planning process include oxygen management, narcosis planning, gas density considerations and decompression planning. In general, the longer the dive or the deeper the dive, the more detailed the dive plan must be. In addition, when making repetitive dives, allowances must be made for tracking residual oxygen in the system.

One of the greatest hazards in technical diving is the risk of central nervous system oxygen toxicity (CNS). Due to this risk, one must carefully plan out the combined risk of bottom mix gases and decompression gas. In most technical diving situations, an oxygen partial pressure (PO_2) of 1.4ata is the maximum target operating depth (TOD). The maximum operating depth (MOD) is a PO_2 of 1.5ata. For decompression, the maximum PO_2 is 1.6ata with 1.55ata being the recommended limit. In addition, on long decompressions following lengthy bottom exposures, it is often necessary to reduce the PO_2 to 1.5ata at decompression stops with bottom mix exposures well under the 1.4ata TOD limit. Environmental and dive performance factors also affect gas planning. In dives involving cold water and/or increased work loads, the bottom mix PO_2 should be reduced by 0.05ata per variable and decompression PO_2 is reduced by 0.025ata for each variable.

In addition to CNS exposure, a diver will need to track the accumulation of oxygen tolerance units (OTU) which effect whole body/pulmonary exposure. The OTUs are primarily a concern in saturation diving or when a need for treatment presents itself. As a rule of thumb, if a diver remains within a CNS exposure not exceeding 100% of the allotted dosage, OTUs remain within safe limits. On extended dive programs involving six or more continuous days of diving, the OTU limits may become the controlling factor in oxygen management.

When planning oxygen exposures the first determination is the PO_2. To do this, refer back to the "T" formula and solve for the best mix. For example assume the dive is to 140 feet (43 meters) and will be a combination of hard work, cold water and a bottom time of 50 minutes. To maximize safety a PO_2 of 1.35ata will be used for the bottom mix.

$$Pg = Fg \times P$$

$$Fg = \frac{Pg}{P} \qquad P = \frac{Pg}{Fg}$$

$$\textbf{Best Mix } FO_2 = \frac{PO_2}{P}$$

Imperial -US: $\frac{1.35}{(140 \div 33)+1} = \textbf{25.7 \% or 26\%}$

Metric: $\frac{1.35}{(43 \div 10)+1} = \textbf{25.5 or 26\%}$

In the above example, if once the gas has been mixed and the true analysis was EAN 28 the PO_2 at 140 feet (42 meters) can be found by using the PO_2 equation.

$PO_2 = FO_2 \times P$

Imperial-US: $PO_2 = 0.28 \times (140/33 + 1) = 1.46$

Metric: $PO_2 = 0.28 \times (42/10 + 1) = 1.456$

As shown, this is too high of a partial pressure of oxygen to be used on the dive, thus, the mix would need to be adjusted or the depth limit should be set shallower. To determine the maximum depth with this mix and our desired PO_2, use the MOD formula. The same equation is used for determining the target operational depth (TOD). The TOD is the actual planned depth of the dive whereas the MOD is the deepest possible depth available on the dive. Dive plans should consist of both a MOD and TOD for a given mix.

Target Operating Depth

TOD = $\frac{1.35}{.28} - 1 x 33 = 126 feet$ (For metric, substitute 1 x 10 for 1 x 33 & the answer is 38.2 m.)

Maximum Operating Depth

MOD = $\frac{1.5}{.28} - 1 x 33 = 143.7 feet$ (For metric, substitute 1 x 10 for 1 x 33 = 43.57 m.)

In the selection of tables, the IANTD EAN 28 Tables would be used incorporating the accelerated schedule at 20 and 15 feet (6 and 4.5 meters) using EAN 75.

To avoid mistakes in calculating PO_2, use the IANTD PO_2 Table 1. You may also use the IANTD EAD Table 8 to determine EAD, CNS%, OTU, and MOD/TOD values in a known mix. Each of the proceeding examples may be determined through use of these tables.

EANx Example:

Part One:

A dive is planned to a depth of 140 feet (42 meters). The dive is on a wreck that has a maximum depth of 170 feet (52 meters). The TOD will feature a PO_2 that cannot exceed 1.40ata. The MOD must remain at or below 1.50ata. Referring to Table 1 the best mix to allow the diver to meet both the TOD and MOD needs is EAN 24 in this case, although the TOD desired is 1.4ata PO_2. For safety in event of egress to the bottom, the MOD at 170 feet (51 meters) of 1.5ata or less restricts the TOD PO_2 to 1.26ata. If the MOD requirement had been ignored, the diver could have used EAN 26.

Joe Citelli on a deep wreck in South Florida.
Photo: Tom Mount

Part Two:

For decompression, a gas mix is going to be used that will be no greater than 1.45ata PO_2 with a gas switch at 20 feet (6 meters). Referring to Table 1 or Table 2, we will find that EAN 90 provides a PO_2 of 1.45ata at 20 feet (6 meters)

To provide an accurate CNS% and OTU calculations the data is based on the following parameters. Table 3 is valuable on longer dives where exact CNS% values must be computed to insure a safe exposure. In the following text, you will be presented with a table that is expressed in 0.05ata increments and is easier on which to calculate dives. For the majority of technical dives, and for all examples in the remainder of this text, Table 5 will be used. The additional advantage of Table 5 is that it combines information from both Table 3 and Table 4. To compensate for the oxygen clock during ascent employ the 2 + 2 rule. That is add 2% to the CNS clock and 2 OTU's. This is simple and conservative and more than covers the oxygen clock additions on ascent.

To read the CNS repetitive CNS% chart, Chart 1, begin at the top left column with 100%. Read to the right and after 30 minutes Surface Interval, you will read down the column to see that the diver still has 83% of the CNS O_2 clock loaded, while after 6 hrs. S.I., only 7% of the CNS O_2 clock will remain. All dives should be planned to avoid exceeding 100% of the CNS clock and within the daily OTU units.

Now, let's put all these tables plus the IANTD dive tables to use by planning an actual dive. On this dive, the desired TOD PO_2 is 1.4ata. The dive is on a wreck with a maximum depth at the sand of 160 feet (48 meters) and the planned dive depth on deck is to 140 feet (42 meters). The MOD must be considered as one of the operational parameters even though the diver does not plan to dive to 160 feet (48 meters). Thus, we must first determine a mix that does not exceed 1.5ata PO_2 at 160 feet (48 meters). The second consideration is that the TOD PO_2 is to be no greater than the planned 1.40ata. By referring to the PO_2 Table 1, or EAD Table 8, we discover that at 160 feet (48 meters) a mix of EAN 26 presents a PO_2 of 1.52ata, and we decide to accept the slight excess oxygen risk.

~~The MOD must be considered as one of the operational parameters even though the diver does not plan to dive to 160 feet (48 meters). Thus, we must first determine a mix that does not exceed 1.5ata PO_2 at 160 feet (48 meters). The second consideration is that the TOD PO_2 is to be no greater than the planned 1.40ata. By referring to the PO_2 Table 1, we discover that at 160 feet (48 meters) a mix of EAN 26 presents a PO_2 of 1.52ata, and we decide to accept the slight excess oxygen risk.~~

The second step is to insure that EAN 26 will not exceed a PO_2 of 1.40ata at the TOD. Again, by going to a depth of 140 feet (42 meters) with EAN 26, the PO_2 is found to be 1.36ata. As this is slightly lower than the planned TOD value, it is acceptable. It should be noted in this example that while we elected to accept the slight (0.02ata) excess as a MOD or "What ifs" value, the same acceptance would not apply to a TOD value. The bottom time on this dive is to be 50 minutes. In addition to Table 1 the IANTD EAD Table, Table 8 can be referenced to determine TOD and MOD values at PO_2's of 1.3, 1.4, 1.5, and 1.6 as well as the equivalent air depth. This Table also has the CNS % per minute and OTU s per minute registered on it.

For the sake of example, we will work this dive in three different methods using the IANTD Dive Tables, to reflect the differences in decompression time. The first dive will be on the Accelerated Tables using EAN 26 throughout the decompression. The second will use the same Table but follow the EAN 75 schedule at both 20 and 15 feet (6 and 4.5 meters). The third method will be using the IANTD EAN 25 Runtime Tables using EAN 78. The Runtime Tables do not feature EAN 26; thus, the EAN 25 Tables will be used. If the correct mix is used, the CNS% is given on the Runtime Tables. However, as our mix is EAN 26, we must manually calculate the CNS and OTU values. Once analyzed, our decompression gas is EAN 80.

Note! Both the Accelerated Decompression Tables using EAN 75 at 20 and 15 feet (6 and 4.5 meters) and the Runtime Tables are available in waterproof versions from your local IANTD Facility.

Plan the gas actually needed on the dive by assuming the diver breathes 0.6 ft^3 (17 L) while swimming on the bottom and 0.5 ft^3 (14 L) at rest during decompression. Use Table 11 to determine the diver's gas consumption at depth. For gas planning, plan the time to the first stop as part of the bottom mix requirements. For example if the ascent takes three minutes for gas planning then plan that ascent as if it were spent on the bottom. This provides a little more safety in the gas management plan. Once the actual gas needed has been determined then plan for the total gas to be carried. Remember that the dive must be made on bottom mix within the rules of thirds. Record the total gas needs under totals at the base of the worksheet or IANTD technical diving logbook along with the CNS and OTU totals.

To find the bottom mix needed, multiply the gas needed by 1.5. Decompression planning is not quite as conservative so, multiply the gas needed on decompression by 1.2.

Note! When planning the CNS and OTU exposure do not be surprised if your answers vary slightly from those in the example. It is possible to have a minimum amount of variation depending on if the per minute values of CNS% and OTU's are used or if the set bottom time numbers are added. Calculators will also produce some minor variations based on where they round off at.

Following the first dive, a second dive is planned to 110 feet (33 meters) 3 hours later for 40 minutes using a bottom mix of EAN 29 with EAN 80 as a decompression gas. The dive will be made on the IANTD EAN 29 Runtime Tables. Please read the following and work through the repetitive dive as you go through the dive worksheets. It is important that you understand these procedures.

When planning repetitive dives using Runtime Tables the procedure is:

1. Go to the next lower EANx Accelerated Tables and get the beginning SIT group from that table.
2. Go to the next lower EANx Table from the Table the next dive is to be made on for the RNT.

In the examples we are working on this series of dives, do the following:

- First Dive to 140 feet (42 meters) on the EAN 26 tables for 50 minutes. See the work sheets for decompression schedules, oxygen tracking and gas used. It is recommended that you work these to insure you understand this phase of dive planning.
- Go to the EAN 26 Accelerated Tables to get the beginning SIT group. In this case, "**K**".
- After three hours a dive to 110 feet (33 meters) will be made for 40 minutes on the EAN 29 Runtime Tables.
- Go to the EAN 28 Accelerated Tables to get the end of SIT group. In this case, "**G**".
- RNT: 40 minutes + 40 minutes actual BT = 80 minutes equivalent nitrogen time / bottom time.

> **Note!** On the repetitive dive on Runtime Tables as the schedule will be a 80 minute schedule, then to convert to the real time runtimes subtract the 40 minutes residual from all the indicate runtime stops and this will correct the schedule for the actual bottom time. (See "IANTD/IAND, Inc. Technical Dive Planners" that follow for corrected runtimes.)

When diving Runtime Tables, switch to decompression gas at a point that you are actually breathing on it upon arrival at the stop requiring the gas switch. Do not wait until arrival to switch the regulator as this may take a minute or so to do. On the IANTD Runtime Tables you are to leave the stop at the designated time at that stop depth. For instance if a schedule read BT 50 minutes it means leave at 50 minutes. If a stop states 56 minutes you must ascent to the next stop as soon as you reach 56 minutes.

On a runtime table if you are using a 50 minute schedule but leave the bottom at 48 minutes, it is safe to subtract 2 minutes from each of the runtime depths. In other words if your first stop says 56 minutes, leave at 54 minutes. This keeps the actual stop duration the same, as it would be on the 50 minutes schedule.

If you leave the bottom late then you must go to the next greater schedule and subtract the time differences, just as you did in the above example. If the ascent rate is faster than the schedule, stop 10 feet. (3 meters) below the first scheduled stop for the time difference. If the ascent is slow but within 2 minutes of schedule then add the time to the runtimes at the stops. If the ascent is delayed more than 2 minutes switch to the next greater schedule.

Refer to Table 8 and determine the EAD for this dive.

Go to EAN 26 then to the actual depth of 140 feet (42 meters) and down the page to the EAD depth. The EAD is 129 feet (38.7 meters) for this dive.

This same problem could be worked using the EAD formula.

$$\text{EAD} = \left[\frac{Fn2(.74)\ x\ depth + 10(42+10}{.79}\right] - 10 = 38.7 meters$$

(If using Imperial (US), substitute 140 feet for 42 meters and add 33 instead of 10 and then subtract the results by 33. The answer is 129 feet.)

In planning Nitrox dives an important consideration is preparing the gas mixture. Detailed procedures for mixing gases is included in the IANTD Blending Courses. However for a better understanding of this process, a review of Chart 5 will be presented in this discussion. Please understand this presentation is solely for developing an understanding and for those with a need to blend gas, a blending course with more in-depth theory and practice is mandated.

Using Chart 2, four examples will be presented as methods of producing an EANx mixture.

Example 1:

The first example is developing an EANx mixture beginning with an empty cylinder. Bear in mind that all cylinders used with partial pressure blending must be prepared to oxygen service compatibility levels. In this example EAN 30 will be blended at a pressure of 3,000 psig (200 bar).

- Go down the left side of the chart to EAN 30, then go across the page to a point that is below the pressure of 3,000 psig (200 bar), and record the number 342 psig (23 bar). This represents the amount of oxygen that must be added to the cylinder beyond the amount included in air to yield EAN 30 at the specified pressure.
- Thus 342 psig (23 bar) will be placed in the cylinder and then it will be topped with air to the target pressure.

Example 2:

The second example allows for a partially filled cylinder at a given EANx mixture to be upgraded to an increased EANx mixture. In this example we will convert an EAN 30 mixture in a partially filled cylinder at 1,000 psig (68 bar), to EAN 34 at 3,000 psig (200 bar).

- First align EAN 30 to the left of the chart and 1,000 psig (68 bar) at the top of the chart. Next record this value which is the amount of oxygen in the cylinder greater than what would be in air alone. This will be 114 psig (8 bar).
- The next step is to-do the same procedure with EAN 34 and 3,000 psig (200 bar). Again record this amount of oxygen. This is 394 psig (33 bar).
- To determine how much oxygen to add to the mix to convert the EAN 30 to EAN 34, subtract the amount of oxygen in the cylinder from the total amount needed to yield EAN 34. This 280 psig (19 bar) of oxygen to add.

Example 3:

The third example consists of determining the new EANx when a partially filled EANx cylinder is topped off with oxygen compatible air. In this example start with a cylinder containing EAN 34 at 1,000 psig (68 bar). The cylinder will be topped off to 3,000 psig (200 bar).

- First go across the page from EAN 34 until it intersects with 1,000 psig (68 bar). This represents the amount of oxygen in the cylinder more than what would be in air. That value is 165 psig (12 bar).
- Go across the top of the page to 3,000 psig (200 bar). Then go down the page until you find the approximate value of excess oxygen in the cylinder from step A.
- To find the new mix go across the page and record the EANx listed. If it is between values round up if it is greater than 0.5 of the listed mixture and down if less. In this case select EAN between 25 and 26, but since it is closer to 25, let's round down to EAN 25.

Example 4:

The fourth example deals with decreasing an EANx mixture to a desired mixture when topping it with air. In this instance we will have an EAN 32 in a cylinder with 1,200 psig (80 bar) in it, and will decrease it to a mix of EAN 24 at 3,000 psig (200 bar).

- At the top of the page go down the column under 1,200 psig (80 bar) to where it is at EAN 32 and discover how much oxygen is in the mix greater than what air alone would contain. This is 167 psig (12 bar).
- Next locate 3,000 psig (200 bar) and go down the page until the correct amount of oxygen is found that produces EAN 24. If the oxygen remaining in the cylinder is greater than the desired amount bleed the cylinder to a pressure that will provide the correct amount. In this event bleed the cylinder down to 800 psig (55 bar). A second way to achieve EAN 24 is to increase the fill pressure provided it remains in a safe range of the cylinders rating. If the cylinder contains too little oxygen then just pressurize it to a final pressure that will yield a mix of EAN 24.

Dive 1 Using IANTD/IAND, Inc. EAN 26 Accelerated Dive Tables – Imperial-US

FSW MSW	MIX	ATA	END	TIME	PO_2	%CNS	OTU	NEEDED
200 60		7.06						
190 57		6.76						
180 54		6.45						
170 51		6.15						
160 48		5.85						
150 45		5.55						
140 42	26%	5.24	129	50	1.36	33.33	81.44	155.00 3.1 x 50
130 39		4.94						
120 36		4.64						
110 33		4.33						
100 30		4.03						
90 27		3.73						
80 24		3.42						
70 21		3.12						
60 18		2.82						
50 15	26%	2.52	45	2	.65	.32 .16 x 2	.74 .37 x 2	2.60 1.3 x 2
40 12	26%	2.21	35	6	.58	.83 .69 + .14	1.57 1.31 + .26	6.60 1.1 x 6
30 9	26%	1.91	26	11	.50	0	0	11.00 1.0 x 11
20 6	80%	1.61		5	1.28	2.78	7.39	4.00 0.8 x 5
15 4.5	80%	1.45		26	1.16	12.38 9.52 + 2.38 + .48	34.37 26.44 + 6.61 + 1.32	18.2 0.7 x 26
	26%			3		2	2	9.30 3.1 x 3

**Add travel time to first deco stop into bottom time and use 2 + 2 Rule for CNS and OTU calculations.

TOTALS (include residual values): CNS%: 47.64 OTU 117.13 Run Time 103 Gas Needed:
Bottom Mix (155+2.6+6.6+11+9.3) x 1.5 = 276.75 Deco (4 + 18.2) x 1.2 = 26.64

Dive 1 Using IANTD/IAND, Inc. EAN 26 Accelerated Dive Tables - Metric Version

FSW MSW	MIX	ATA	END	TIME	PO_2	%CNS	OTU	NEEDED
200 60		7.0						
190 57		6.7						
180 54		6.4						
170 51		6.1						
160 48		5.8						
150 45		5.5						
140 42	**26%**	5.2	**38.7**	**50**	**1.35**	**30.30**	**77.67**	**4400.0** 88 x 50
130 39		4.9						
120 36		4.6						
110 33		4.3						
100 30		4.0						
90 27		3.7						
80 24		3.4						
70 21		3.1						
60 18		2.8						
50 15	**26%**	2.5	**13.4**	**2**	**.65**	**.32** .16 x 2	**.74** .37 x 2	**70.0** 35 x 2
40 12	**26%**	2.2	**10.6**	**6**	**.57**	**.83** .69 + .14	**1.57** 1.31 + .26	**186.0** 31 x 6
30 9	**26%**	1.9	**7.8**	**11**	**.49**	**0**	**0**	**297.0** 27 x 11
20 6	**80%**	1.6		**5**	**1.28**	**2.78**	**7.39**	**110.0** 22 x 5
15 4.5	**80%**	1.45		**26**	**1.16**	**12.38** 9.52 + 2.38 + .48	**34.37** 26.44 + 6.61 + 1.32	**527.8** 20.3 x 26
	26%			**3**		**2**	**2**	**264.0** 88 x 3

**Add travel time to first deco stop into bottom time and use 2 + 2 Rule for CNS and OTU calculations.

TOTALS (include residual values): CNS%: 48.61 OTU 117.13 Run Time 103

Gas Needed: Bottom Mix 5217.93 x 1.5 = 7825.5 Deco 637.8 x 1.2 = 765.36

Dive 1 Using IANTD/IAND, Inc. EAN 25 Runtime Accelerated Dive Tables – Imperial -US

FSW MSW	MIX	ATA	END	TIME	PO_2	%CNS	OTU	NEEDED
200 60		7.06						
190 57		6.76						
180 54		6.45						
170 51		6.15						
160 48		5.85						
150 45		5.55						
140 42	**26%**	5.24	**129**	**50**	**1.36**	**33.33**	**81.44**	**155.00** 3.1 x 50
130 39		4.94						
120 36		4.64						
110 33		4.33						
100 30		4.03						
90 27		3.73						
80 24		3.42						
70 21		3.12						
60 18		2.82						
50 15	**26%**	2.52	**45**	**1**	**.65**	**.16**	**.37**	**1.30** 1.3 x 1
40 12	**26%**	2.21	**35**	**8**	**.58**	**1.11** .69 + (.14 x 3)	**2.09** 1.31 + (.26 x 3)	**8.80** 1.1 x 8
30 9	**80%**	1.91		**6**	**1.53**	**6.67** 5.56 + 1.11	**11.11** 9.26 + 1.85	**6.00** 1.0 x 6
20 6	**80%**	1.61		**4**	**1.28**	**2.24** .56 x 4	**5.92** 1.48 x 4	**3.20** 0.8 x 4
15 4.5	**80%**	1.45		**25**	**1.16**	**11.90** 9.52 + 2.38	**33.05** 26.44 + 6.61	**17.5** 0.7 x 25
	26%			**3**		**2**	**2**	**9.30** 3.1 x 3

Add travel time to first deco stop into bottom time and use 2 + 2 Rule for CNS and OTU calculations.

TOTALS (include residual values): CNS%: 57.41 OTU 135.98

Run Time 97 Gas Needed: Bottom Mix (155 + 1.3 + 8.8 + 9.3) x 1.5 = 261.60

Deco (6.00 + 3.20 + 17.5) x 1.2 = 32.04

Dive 1 Using IANTD/IAND, Inc. EAN 25 Runtime Accelerated Dive Tables – Metric Version

FSW MSW	MIX	ATA	END	TIME	PO_2	%CNS	OTU	NEEDED
200 60		7.0						
190 57		6.7						
180 54		6.4						
170 51		6.1						
160 48		5.8						
150 45		5.5						
140 42	**26%**	5.2	**38.7**	**50**	**1.36**	**30.30**	**77.67**	**4400.0** 87.79 x 50
130 39		4.9						
120 36		4.6						
110 33		4.3						
100 30		4.0						
90 27		3.7						
80 24		3.4						
70 21		3.1						
60 18		2.8						
50 15	**26%**	2.5	**13.4**	**1**	**.65**	**.16**	**.37**	**35.0** 35 x 1
40 12	**26%**	2.2	**10.6**	**8**	**.57**	**1.11** .69 + (.14 x 3)	**2.09** 1.31 + (.26 x 3)	**248.0** 31 x 8
30 9	**80%**	1.9		**6**	**1.52**	**6.67** 5.56 + 1.11	**11.11** 9.26 + 1.85	**162.0** 27 x 6
20 6	**80%**	1.6		**4**	**1.28**	**2.24** .56 x 4	**5.92** 1.48 x 4	**88.0** 22 x 4
15 4.5	**80%**	1.45		**25**	**1.16**	**11.90** 9.52 + 2.38	**33.05** 26.44 + 6.61	**507.5** 20.3 x 25
	26%			**3**		**2**	**2**	**264.0** 88 x 3

Add travel time to first deco stop into bottom time and use 2 + 2 Rule for CNS and OTU calculations.

TOTALS (include residual values): CNS%: 54.38 OTU 132.21

Run Time 97 Gas Needed: Bottom Mix 4947 x 1.5 = 7420.5

Deco 757.5 x 1.2 = 909.0

Dive 1 Using IANTD/IAND, Inc. EAN 26 Accelerated Dive Tables EAN 26 used for deco – Imperial-US Version

FSW MSW	MIX	ATA	END	TIME	PO_2	%CNS	OTU	NEEDED
200 60		7.06						
190 57		6.76						
180 54		6.45						
170 51		6.15						
160 48		5.85						
150 45		5.55						
140 42	**26%**	5.24	**129**	**50**	**1.36**	**33.33**	**81.44**	**155.00** 3.1 x 50
130 39		4.94						
120 36		4.64						
110 33		4.33						
100 30		4.03						
90 27		3.73						
80 24		3.42						
70 21		3.12						
60 18		2.82						
50 15	**26%**	2.52		**2**	**.65**	**.32** .16 x 2	**.74** .37 x 2	**2.60** 1.3 x 2
40 12	**26%**	2.21		**6**	**.58**	**.83** .69 + .14	**1.57** 1.31 + .26	**6.60** 1.1 x 6
30 9	**26%**	1.91		**11**	**.50**	**0**	**0**	**11.00** 1.0 x 11
20 6	**26%**	1.61		**7**	**.42**	**0**	**0**	**5.60** 0.8 x 7
15 4.5	**26%**	1.45		**57**	**.34**	**0**	**0**	**39.9** 0.7 x 57
	26%			**3**		**2**	**2**	**9.30** 3.1 x 3

Add travel time to first deco stop into bottom time and use 2 + 2 Rule for CNS and OTU calculations.

TOTALS (include residual values): CNS% 36.48 OTU 85.75 Run Time 136

Gas Needed: Bottom Mix (155+2.6+6.6+11+5.6 + 39.9 + 9.3) x 1.5 = 345.0 Deco gas needed ______

Dive 1 Using IANTD/IAND, Inc. EAN 26 Accelerated Dive Tables EAN 26 used for deco - Metric Version

FSW MSW	MIX	ATA	END	TIME	PO_2	%CNS	OTU	NEEDED
200 60		7.0						
190 57		6.7						
180 54		6.4						
170 51		6.1						
160 48		5.8						
150 45		5.5						
140 42	**26%**	5.2	**38.7**	**50**	**1.35**	**30.30**	**77.67**	**4400.0** 88 x 50
130 39		4.9						
120 36		4.6						
110 33		4.3						
100 30		4.0						
90 27		3.7						
80 24		3.4						
70 21		3.1						
60 18		2.8						
50 15	**26%**	2.5		**2**	**.65**	**.32** .16 x 2	**.74** .37 x 2	**70.0** 35 x 2
40 12	**26%**	2.2		**6**	**.58**	**.83** .69 + .14	**1.57** 1.31 + .26	**186.0** 31 x 6
30 9	**26%**	1.9		**11**	**.50**	**0**	**0**	**297.0** 27 x 11
20 6	**26%**	1.6		**7**	**.42**	**0**	**0**	**154.0** 22 x 7
15 4.5	**26%**	1.45		**57**	**.34**	**0**	**0**	**1157.1** 20.3 x 57
	26%			**3**		**2**	**2**	**264.0** 88 x 3

Add travel time to first deco stop into bottom time and use 2 + 2 Rule for CNS and OTU calculations.

TOTALS (include residual values): CNS% 33.45 OTU 81.98 Run Time 136

Gas Needed: Bottom Mix 6528.1 x 1.5 = 9792.15 Deco gas needed ______

Dive 2 (repetitive dive) Using IANTD/IAND, Inc. EAN 29 Runtime Accelerated Dive Tables – Imperial-US Version

FSW MSW	MIX	ATA	END	TIME	PO_2	%CNS	OTU	NEEDED
200 60		7.06						
190 57		6.76						
180 54		6.45						
170 51		6.15						
160 48		5.85						
150 45		5.55						
140 42		5.24						
130 39		4.94						
120 36		4.64						
110 33	**29%**	4.33	**96**	**40 actual**	**1.26**	**22.22**	**59.09**	**104** 2.6 x 40
100 30		4.03						
90 27		3.73						
80 24		3.42						
70 21		3.12						
60 18		2.82						
50 15		2.52						
40 12		2.21						
30 9	**80%**	1.91		**7 (50)**	**1.53**	**7.78** 5.56 + (1.11 x 2)	**12.96** 9.26 + (2 x 1.85)	**7.00** 1.0 x 7
20 6	**80%**	1.61		**5 (55)**	**1.28**	**2.78**	**7.39**	**4.00** 0.8 x 5
15 4.5	**80%**	1.45		**27 (82)**	**1.16**	**12.86** 9.52 + 2.38 + (.48 x 2)	**35.69** 26.44 +6.61+(1.32x2)	**18.9** 0.7 x 27
	29%			**3**		**2**	**2**	**7.8** 2.6 x 3

**Add travel time to first deco stop into bottom time and use 2 + 2 Rule for CNS and OTU calculations.

TOTALS (include residual values): CNS%: 47.64 + 12 residual = 59.64 OTU 117.13 + 85.75 = 202.88

Run Time 82 RNT 40 (80 minute schedule)

Gas Needed: Bottom Mix 111.8 x 1.5 = 167.7 Deco 29.9 x 1.2 = 35.88

Dive 2 (repetitive dive) Using IANTD/IAND, Inc. EAN 29 Runtime Accelerated Dive Tables - Metric Version

FSW MSW	MIX	ATA	END	TIME	PO_2	%CNS	OTU	NEEDED
200 60		7.0						
190 57		6.7						
180 54		6.4						
170 51		6.1						
160 48		5.8						
150 45		5.5						
140 42		5.2						
130 39		4.9						
120 36		4.6						
110 33	**29%**	4.3	**28.7**	**40 actual**	**1.25**	**20.51**	**56.00**	**2920.0** 73 x 40
100 30		4.0						
90 27		3.7						
80 24		3.4						
70 21		3.1						
60 18		2.8						
50 15		2.5						
40 12		2.2						
30 9	**80%**	1.9		**7 (50)**	**1.52**	**7.78** 5.56 + (1.11 x 2)	**12.96** 9.26 + (2 x 1.85)	**189.0** 27 x 7
20 6	**80%**	1.6		**5 (55)**	**1.28**	**2.78**	**7.39**	**110.0** 22 x 5
15 4.5	**80%**	1.45		**27 (82)**	**1.16**	**12.86** 9.52 + 2.38 + (.48 x 2)	**35.69** 26.44 +6.61+(1.32x2)	**548.1** 20.3 x 27
	29%			**3**		**2**	**2**	**219.0** 73 x 3

**Add travel time to first deco stop into bottom time and use 2 + 2 Rule for CNS and OTU calculations.

TOTALS (include residual values): CNS%: 45.93 + 12 residual = 57.93 OTU 114.04 + 81.98 = 196.02

Run Time 82 RNT 40 (80 minute schedule)

Gas Needed: Bottom Mix 3139.0 x 1.5 = 4708.5 Deco 847.1 x 1.2 = 1016.52

Note: When using Trimix, the starting PO_2 may be a hypoxic mix at the surface. Table 2 may be used for determining the safe depth to breathe the mix as well determining the MOD and TOD values for a given dive.

Trimix Example

Part One:

A dive is planned on Trimix. The target operating depth (TOD) of the dive is 280 feet (84 meters). The maximum depth obtainable is 320 feet (96 meters), thus the MOD value PO_2 of 1.5ata is to be at 320 feet (96 meters). A PO_2 of 1.35ata is selected for the TOD, with the MOD not exceeding 1.5ata PO_2 Using Table 2, we will find that a mix containing 14% oxygen will provide a TOD of 1.33ata. PO_2 and a MOD of 1.5ata PO_2. From this table, we have determined the bottom mix FO_2 of 0.14 or 14%. If we reference Chart 4 that had we used an actual PO_2 of 1.4ata the oxygen would be 14.8%.

Part Two:

To avoid hypoxic mixtures, the dive gas cannot be breathed until the partial pressure of oxygen is at a normal value. To provide a better decompression profile, many times a travel gas will be used. In the current example using the above FO_2 for bottom mix, refer to Table 2 to discover the minimum safe depth to switch to bottom gas. This is 20 feet (6 meters) - actually between 15 and 20 feet (4.5 and 6 meters). For a decompression advantage, we will remain on the travel gas of EAN 40 until we reach a PO_2 of 1.37ata. Refer to Table 1 and it will determine that a switch from EAN 40 to bottom mix will take place at 90 feet (27 meters).

Diving with Trimix produces more variables than diving with EANx mixtures. In addition to selection of the oxygen in the mix, a desired narcosis value must be determined. The amount of helium added to the mix will displace sufficient nitrogen to yield the desired narcosis loading. If we wanted essentially zero nitrogen narcosis, all we need do is to mix helium and oxygen in the mix. The disadvantage of a mix of this nature would be extended decompression times unless the bottom time exceeds two hours. A second disadvantage is a higher probability of HPNS (high-pressure neurological syndrome). Typically, a mixture is derived to give an equivalent narcosis depth (END) value of 80 feet (24 meters) to 130 feet (39 meters). The most recommended and common END is 130 feet (39 meters) for the TOD value. The maximum MOD should not exceed 160 feet (48 meters).

Part Three:

We will use a Trimix mixture with a FO_2 of 0.14 (14%). The helium content is not known yet. To be safe, an END is desired that will not exceed a maximum of 115 feet (34.5 meters) at the TOD depth. As a safety buffer, our MOD END is to be no greater than 160 feet (48 meters).

Using the END Chart 4, it is assumed that the FO_2 is 1.4ata. Go across the bottom of the page to the TOD of 280 feet (84 meters), then go up the page until you match the desired END of 115 feet (34.5 meters); next, follow the diagonal line to the top of the page. This will produce a Fh_e of .48. Now check that the MOD END will be within the planned value of 160 feet (48 meters) Follow the diagonal line at 48% helium until it crisscrosses the depth of 320 feet (85.6 meters); at this point, record the END value.

From this the MOD END is approximately 140 feet (42 meters) and is acceptable for the planned dive. The final bottom mix then will be Trimix 14 (oxygen %) 48 (helium %). With this mix, plan a dive for a 20 minute bottom time at 280 feet (84 meters). Use the IANTD Tables for this dive.

Note: If Chart 3 was not available, the END determinations could be found by working the END and EAD equations.
Imperial-US: END = (target END + 33) (0.79) / (D + 33) ➤ (115 + 33) (0.79) / (280 + 33) = 0.3735 FN_2.
Metric: END = (target END + 10) (0.79) / (D + 10) ➤ (34.5 + 10) (0.79) / (84 + 10) = 0.3739 FN_2.

Total gases other than Helium, (37% N_2)+ (**14%** O_2) = 51%. Balance is 49% (He)lium.
*An **error** of 1% occurs due to the FO_2 actually used being **14%** FO_2 **versus** the chart value PO_2 of 1.40ata that provides a FO_2 of 14.8%.*
For the MOD END on this mix of 14 48 use the EAD formula. FN_2 = 1.0 - (0.14 O_2) - (0.48 He) = 0.38% N_2.
Imperial-US: MOD END = [(FN_2)(D + 33) / 0.79] - 33 ➤ [(0.38)(320 + 33) / 0.79] - 33 = MOD END of 136.79 or 137 ft.
Metric: MOD END = [(FN_2) (D +10) / 0.79] –10 ➤ [(0.38) (96 + 10) / 0.79)] – 10 = MOD END of 40.98 meters.

Trimix Dive Using IANTD/IAND, Inc. Runtime Trimix Dive Tables – Imperial-US

FSW MSW	MIX	ATA	END	TIME	PO_2	%CNS	OTU	NEEDED
280 84	**14% 48%**	**9.48**	**118**	**20**	**1.33**	**12.12**	**31.07**	**114.00** 5.7 x 20
200 60		7.06						
190 57		6.76						
180 54		6.45						
170 51		6.15						
160 48		5.85						
150 45		5.55						
140 42		5.24						
130 39	**14% 48%**	4.94	**46**	**1 (24)**	**.69**	**.18** .18 x 1	**.47** .47 x 1	**2.50** 2.5 x 1
120 36	**14% 48%**	4.64	**41**	**1 (25)**	**.65**	**.16** .16 x 1	**.37** .37 x 1	**2.30** 2.3 x 1
110 33	**14% 48%**	4.33	**36**	**2 (27)**	**.61**	**.32** .16 x 2	**.74** .37 x 2	**4.40** 2.2 x 2
100 30	**36%**	4.03	**75**	**1 (28)**	**1.45**	**.72** .72 x 1	**1.70** 1.70 x 1	**2.00** 2.0 x 1
90 27	**36%**	3.73	**67**	**2 (30)**	**1.34**	**1.22** .61 x 2	**3.10** 1.55 x 2	**3.80** 1.9 x 2
80 24	**36%**	3.42	**59**	**2 (32)**	**1.23**	**1.02** .51 x 2	**2.8** 1.4 x 2	**3.40** 1.7 x 2
70 21	**36%**	3.12	**51**	**4 (36)**	**1.12**	**1.76** .44 x 4	**4.96** 1.24 x 4	**6.40** 1.6 x 4
60 18	**36%**	2.82	**43**	**4 (40)**	**1.01**	**1.48** .37 x 4	**4.32** 1.08 x 4	**5.60** 1.4 x 4
50 15	**36%**	2.52	**35**	**6 (46)**	**.91**	**1.88** 1.57 + .31	**5.50** 4.58 + .92	**7.80** 1.3 x 6
40 12	**36%**	2.21	**27**	**8 (54)**	**.80**	**1.77** 1.11 + (.22 x 3)	**5.22** 3.27 + (.65 x 3)	**8.80** 1.1 x 8
30 9	**80%**	1.91		**11 (65)**	**1.53**	**12.22** 11.11 + 1.11	**20.36** 18.51 + 1.85	**11.00** 1.0 x 11
20 6	**80%**	1.61		**6 (71)**	**1.28**	**3.34** 2.78 + .56	**8.87** 7.39 + 1.48	**4.80** 0.8 x 6
15 4.5	**80%**	1.45		**45 (116)**	**1.16**	**21.43** 19.05 + 2.38	**59.50** 52.89 + 6.61	**31.50** .7 x 45
	14% 48%			**3**		**2**	**2**	**17.18** 5.7 x 3

*Add travel time to first deco stop into bottom time and use 2 + 2 Rule for CNS and OTU calculations.

TOTALS (include residual values): CNS%: 61.62 OTU 150.98

Run Time 116 Gas Needed: Bottom Mix (114 + 2.5 + 2.3 + 4.4 + 17.18) x 1.5 = 210.57

Travel gas (2 + 3.8 + 3.4 + 6.4 + 5.6 + 7.8 + 8.8) x 1.2 = 45.36 Deco (11 + 4.8 + 31.50) x 1.2 = 56.76

Trimix Dive Using IANTD/IAND, Inc. Runtime Trimix Dive Tables – Metric Version

FSW MSW	MIX	ATA	END	TIME	PO_2	%CNS	OTU	NEEDED
280 84	**14%** **48%**	**9.5**	**35.7**	**20**	**1.32**	**12.12**	**31.07**	**3200.0** 160 x 20
200 60		7.0						
190 57		6.7						
180 54		6.4						
170 51		6.1						
160 48		5.8						
150 45		5.5						
140 42		5.2						
130 39	**14%** **48%**	4.9	**13.6**	**1 (24)**	**.69**	**.18** .18 x 1	**.47** .47 x 1	**69.0** 69 x 1
120 36	**14%** **48%**	4.6	**12.1**	**1 (25)**	**.64**	**.16** .16 x 1	**.37** .37 x 1	**64.0** 64 x 1
110 33	**14%** **48%**	4.3	**10.7**	**2 (27)**	**.60**	**.28** .14 x 2	**.52** .26 x 2	**120.0** 60 x 2
100 30	**36%**	4.0	**22.4**	**1 (28)**	**1.45**	**.72** .72 x 1	**1.70** 1.70 x 1	**56.0** 56 x 1
90 27	**36%**	3.7	**20.0**	**2 (30)**	**1.34**	**1.22** .61 x 2	**3.10** 1.55 x 2	**104.0** 52x 2
80 24	**36%**	3.4	**17.5**	**2 (32)**	**1.23**	**1.02** .51 x 2	**2.8** 1.4 x 2	**96.0** 48 x 2
70 21	**36%**	3.1	**15.1**	**4 (36)**	**1.12**	**1.76** .44 x 4	**4.96** 1.24 x 4	**172.0** 43 x 4
60 18	**36%**	2.8	**12.7**	**4 (40)**	**1.04**	**1.48** .37 x 4	**4.32** 1.08 x 4	**156.0** 39 x 4
50 15	**36%**	2.5	**10.3**	**6 (46)**	**.91**	**1.67** 1.39 + .28	**4.98** 4.15 + .83	**210.0** 35 x 6
40 12	**36%**	2.2	**7.8**	**8 (54)**	**.80**	**1.77** 1.11 + (.22 x 3)	**5.22** 3.27 + (.65 x 3)	**248.0** 31 x 8
30 9	**80%**	1.9		**11** **(65)**	**1.53**	**12.22** 11.11 + 1.11	**20.36** 18.51 + 1.85	**297.0** 27 x 11
20 6	**80%**	1.6		**6** **(71)**	**1.29**	**3.34** 2.78 + .56	**8.87** 7.39 + 1.48	**132.0** 22 x 6
15 4.5	**80%**	1.45		**45** **(116)**	**1.16**	**21.43** 19.05 + 2.38	**59.50** 52.89 + 6.61	**913.5** 20.3 x 45
	14% **48%**			**3**		**2**	**2**	**480.0** 160 x 3

*Add travel time to first deco stop into bottom time and use 2 + 2 Rule for CNS and OTU calculations.

TOTALS (include residual values): CNS%: 61.37 OTU 150.24

Run Time 116 Gas Needed: Bottom Mix 3933.0 x 1.5 = 5899.5

Travel gas 1042.0 x 1.2 = 1250.4 Deco 1342.5 x 1.2 = 1611.0

To determine END's and mixes at depths shallower than 200 feet (60 meters), use Chart 6 if the planned PO_2 is 1.4. In this instance plan a dive with an END of 100 feet (30 meters) at a actual depth of 180 feet (54 meters). By going across the chart to an END of 100 feet (30 meters), go down the page to the actual depth on the left and the mixture will be Trimix 22 29 (22% oxygen and 29% helium). If the planned PO_2 is to be 1.3 for the same depth then refer to Chart 7 and the mix will be Trimix 20 31.

On dives deeper than 200 feet (60 meters) down to 300 feet (91 meters), if the PO_2 is 1.4 use Chart 4 as in the earlier example. When the mix is to be planned with a bottom mix PO_2 of 1.3 use Chart 5. To illustrate the use of Chart 5, plan an END of 130 feet (39 meters) on a dive to 300 feet (91 meters). First locate the END of 130 feet (39 meters) at the top of the page then go down to the actual depth of 300 feet (91 meters). The required mix will be Trimix 13 48.

Patti Mount enjoys exploring the *Pilotfish* submarine in Bikini Atoll.
Photo: Tom Mount

The most simple and accurate means of insuring an accurate mix is to mix Heliair, which is a combination of helium and air. The disadvantage of this mix is that while the PO_2 is easily controlled, the END level is often quite deep. By referencing Table 7, it can be noted that from an oxygen exposure point of view, this mix can be made for all depths a diver wishes. However, if the PO_2 is maintained at a depth where it equals 1.40ata, the END will always be 187 feet (57 meters). Thus, a limitation of Heliair is high END levels. A second means of being certain of correct mixes is by blending helium and a premixed EANx. Again, by referring to Table 7, note a mix that combines helium and EAN 30. In this mix, if the diver uses a PO_2 of 1.4ata, the END will always be 103 feet (31 meters).

Let's look at a mix of helium and EAN 26. If we dive to a depth of 296 feet (90 meters), using a PO_2 of 1.4ata, the END will be 133 feet (40 meters) and the oxygen content is 14%. Another advantage of mixing helium with EANx or air is that anytime the O_2 is analyzed, it is easy to determine the inert gas content. Chart 3 is valuable for preparing these types of mixtures. As an example, let's say the gas was analyzed at 14%, and we knew it was mixed with EAN 28. Go to the FIO_2 and then across the page until it crosses the EAN 28 line from the opposite side of the page. At this point follow this intersection down to the bottom of the page and read the helium content that is 50%. This mix then is Trimix 14 50.

Personal Planning

Personal planning is the most important part of the dive plan. It is the individual and his/her perception and interpretation of the planned dive that yields an acceptable or unacceptable performance. There are many aspects involved in personal planning, and the key is being comfortable with one's role in the accomplishment of the dive. In this area, we will be discussing the key components of a personal plan.

- Risk analysis, acceptance and management
- Personal comfort
- Individual "What ifs "situations
- Responsibility
- Personal gas planning

Risk analysis, acceptance and management is the major portion of a personal dive plan. This should begin with an introspective look into oneself to determine how one truly feels about the dive. During this phase, basic questions should be raised and answered honestly.

Each phase of the dive should be mentally reviewed and the following questions answered:

1. What are the specific risks involved in this dive?
2. Do I understand the dive plan?
3. Am I comfortable with the parameters of the plan and my responsibilities within the dive plan?
4. Can I be depended upon - and not be dependent on - others?
5. Have all the "What ifs" of this dive been covered, and have I established a personal management procedure for these variables?

In the process of answering the above questions, all items of the personal dive plan should be reviewed. As part of the risk analysis process, the diver should also review past histories of similar dives. The diver should determine if threatening situations have occurred on similar dives or if accidents have taken place. If either of these has been encountered, analyze what caused those events.

Once the cause has been discovered, develop a reaction response to compensate for the recurrence of a similar situation. List all the possible things that could effect dive safety and develop a response action to these possibilities. Decide if each risk to be encountered is worth the benefit of performing the dive. Prior to the dive, complete the following checklist:

RISK	*CORRECTIVE ACTION / MANAGEMENT*	*BENEFIT*	*VALUE* .
1.			
2.			
3.			
4.			
5.			
6.			
7.			
8.			
9.			
10.			
Etc.			

When filling out this table, it may be prudent to discuss your evaluations with other dive team members. Under the value column, a simple yes or no is sufficient. If the no's outweigh the yes answers, you may wish to revise the dive objectives. If, in some instances, an overpowering *no* is encountered, this may be grounds to dismiss yourself from the dive. In addition, listen to your intuitive voice; if you experience bad sensations about the dive, either postpone or cancel the dive, and limit your participation in this type of diving.

Personal comfort must be taken into consideration. While it is true that unfamiliar situations may lead to an expansion of personal capabilities, for safety's sake, a diver should not be pushed too far from his present comfort level. Anxiety from overextending the comfort level of a dive may cloud good judgment. If a diver is forced to function outside his personal comfort level, anxiety will add to the stress and overall risk potential of the dive.

If you are in the process of expanding your comfort level, do it in small and personally acceptable increments. Do not depend on someone else to maintain your safety or establish your limits. Even with the best of intentions, other divers cannot enter your mind and evaluate your mental capabilities for a dive. Dive buddies are limited to watching your performance and your verbal and body language communication for interpreting your comfort level. Remember, the three basic ingredients that ultimately evaluate your survival and comfort potential. These are:

Only you can swim for you, only you can breathe for you, and only you can think for you.

Any time you have the slightest doubt in your ability to do any of these three, slow your progression toward more involved dives. A skilled buddy may be able to assist you for a short time if a swimming problem exists, but they cannot maintain that function indefinitely. No one can think or breathe for you, so avoid situations that cast doubt on your ability to complete the dive.

An additional factor that determines a diver's personal comfort level is the combined mental and physical fitness he maintains. A degree of physical fitness is needed to manage the equipment on land, and fitness is needed for propulsion skills.

Perhaps one of the most important aspects of fitness, however, does not become apparent until the diver is faced with adverse conditions. In this type of situation, watermanship and fitness may be the determining factors in survival. Even with superb physical fitness, a diver must also develop confidence and discipline combined with the ability to maintain mental focus. The mental fitness of a diver will be the determining factor in development of these attributes. Be sure you remain within both your physical and mental conditioning.

Individual "what if" situations are in addition to the team plan, but they should also be addressed before the final dive plan is agreed upon. These must be placed in the risk analysis table when deciding how to most efficiently deal with them. Exploration of the "what if" scenarios includes both the environmental factors and risk associated with equipment dependency.

Listed below are sample "what ifs" that may be encountered on a dive. This can be expanded on by analyzing the individual risk associated with a dive. List these in the Risk Table featured earlier in this chapter.

1. **What if...** I get lost? Determine a means of finding your way out or in being located by a surface crew/boat. The exact solution will depend on the type of dive, the location, and the community standard for locating lost divers.
2. **What if...** I lose a decompression stage cylinder? In this case, if it is an air dive, you may bail out to an air table or air dive computer. If this is a mixed gas dive, it is recommended that a backup schedule be used, reflecting stops if either deco gas is lost. When tables are not available, then, as a rule of thumb, if the EANx was lost at the stops requiring the higher EANx, double the remaining decompression while breathing the remaining lower EANx mixture. If other divers are present, once they have completed their stops, have them leave the higher decompression mix and complete the stop on this mix. Once on the surface, breathe oxygen for at least 30 minutes. Under ideal conditions, the dive will employ safety divers who may be able to respond to this situation. In this instance, the support divers would bring decompression cylinders to the diver. In addition, a backup decompression gas supply can be used, such as surface supplied gas on a boat, or, on inshore based diving, safety deco stage cylinders placed at central points along the return path to the entry point. In a worse case scenario, share gas with a dive buddy providing sufficient gas is available. (The last means is to use up the

remaining decompression gas from a buddy once they are finished with his/her personal gas needs for decompression.)

3. Think and continue this list until you have developed 10 or more personal "what if" scenarios.

Once your personal "what ifs" are listed, determine the solution to each situation and visualize a method for overcoming them. Once you have identified the problem, developed the solution, and visualized its accomplishment, do not dwell on it. You have achieved the goal of overcoming this specific problem. Dwelling on problems has two negative effects. First, you begin to worry about it. Worry creates stress and may lead to apprehension and result in either an incident or a dive that you do not enjoy. Secondly, by continuing to think about the problem is, with so much emphasis on the problem, the mind may in fact create the circumstance.

Responsibility: Evaluate both your physical and mental conditioning. Determine if you have what it takes to do this dive. This evaluation must be honest. Don't do a dive out of false bravado. Know in your heart that you can deliver 100% effort. Be certain the team can depend on you. The importance of both physical and mental conditioning cannot be overemphasized in technical diving. If you are going to participate, accept and pay the price of staying in good physical and mental condition. Understand in your own mind that you will not be a person that is dependent upon the other team members.

Technical diving is a hostile environment for dependency divers.

Another important aspect of responsible dive planning involves **awareness**. Are you absolutely aware of the dive's objectives and the technical components of the dive? While a level of trust is needed for every dive, there's a big difference between trust and a "trust me" attitude. The "trust me leader" expects you to put your life in their hands and follow him wherever he decides to go. **Never, ever get yourself in this position.**

If a dive is completely or partially exploratory, this fact needs to be established at the outset. If one member of the team is made the leader, their role must be defined. Responsibilities must be established. Conditions for dive termination must be fully defined. And, never forget one simple rule.

Always trust in yourself first and dive within your personal survivability.

When planning a dive, it's easy to get wrapped up in the technicalities and overlook the reasons why you're doing the dive in the first place. Anticipate the fun you're going to have. **Visualize** what you may see. Imagine how the members of your dive team will react to these aesthetic elements. As part of this exercise, develop an understanding that you are both a team member and a **solo diver**. Estimate the abilities of others in your dive team but always mentally prepare yourself as if you are diving solo. This approach virtually guarantees that you will not exceed your personal limits and expose yourself to extraordinary risks. Besides, if you become separated or find yourself faced with a life-threatening event, you will most certainly face the situation alone. We repeat, when "the chips are down," **only you can think, breathe and swim for yourself**. Bearing this in mind, it is obvious that dives must be planned within your personal limits and abilities to rescue yourself. Not quite as apparent it is also crucial that you remain within your abilities to assist or rescue a dive buddy. As a team member you are responsible to the other divers on the team. In return ascertain that each of the team members also are capable of rendering help to you.

Personal gas management: In this planning stage, the diver will become aware of their Surface Air Consumption (SAC) rate and the amount of gas in psig/bar they use when switching tanks. First, one must determine the SAC rate at a moderate swim pace. This can then be used as the normal swim rate SAC. To do this, swim at a predetermined constant depth for a period of at least 20 minutes. It is recommended that this be performed when a tank is between 1/2 and 2/3rds of its rated pressure. In addition, this provides a more realistic value if done once the diver has been in the water diving or doing skills for a long enough duration to add some degree of fatigue.

To calculate a heavy work load modifier, repeat the above drill when swimming at full speed. On this second drill, note the following, Divers who are in good cardiovascular condition will have a slight increase in gas consumption and will be able to retain a more constant swim pace. Divers who are not in good cardiovascular condition will usually have a more dramatic increase in gas consumption and tend to reduce the pace over time.

Table 9 may be used to convert SAC to respiratory minute volume (RMV) values. To do this, locate the table and find the tank size from which you were breathing Go down the column until you reach the single tank consumption rate. This will give you RMV values for gas planning. Should you decide to switch to a different tank size simply match the new tank volume to the RMV value and then go to the left side of the page and discover the psig/bar per minute value on the new cylinder. Remember to convert to double tank values if applicable.

Note: If the drill was in double tanks, to use the table which is based on single cylinder values, one must double the gas consumption minute value.

Example:

If using a cylinder where the psig/bar per minute is known, gas calculations may be completed from Table 10. For instance, a diver breathes at a SAC rate of 10 psig (0.6 bar per minute). If the dive is planned to 300 feet (91 meters), the diver will use 101 psig (6.8 bar) per minute. This means that on a 20 minute dive the diver would use 2020 psig (137.4 bar).

Table 11 may be used when planning the total volume of gas needed for a dive. This can be applied individually or to the group. By knowing ones gas consumption in cubic fee (free liters) per minute, a total gas need calculation is made. For instance, the planned depth is 130 feet (39 meters). The diver uses 0.60 cubic feet (16.99 or 17 free liters) per minute at the surface. Go down the table and you will discover that 3.0 cubic feet (84.96 free liters) per minute of exposure are needed. For decompression purposes, each gas and stop depth gas supply need can be determined in the same manner. This table is especially beneficial when planning Trimix dives due to the multi gas switches and the duration of the dives.

Remember to add the Rule of Thirds safety reserve to the total volume.

Group Planning

Group planning is the process used by the overall dive team to determine understanding and acceptance of the objectives of the dive and the responsibilities of each diver. The specific items addressed include but should not be limited to:

- **Establish gas management procedures**
- **Decide on the limits of the dive**
- **Determine the size of team and responsibilities of members**
- **Determine team member compatibility**
- **Ensure each diver is aware of the configuration of fellow divers**
- **Plan for the "what ifs" that affect team safety**

Gas management is a crucial portion of any dive. The more involved the dive, the broader its objectives, the more important gas management becomes. Maturity and judgment reinforce the concept of **proper** gas management. Most technical divers, and all overhead environment divers, observe the gas management rule known as the **Rule of Thirds**. The cave diving community developed the Rule of Thirds after analyzing their accident history. The Rule of Thirds is conservative. It was designed to be so. More importantly, experience has taught us it works.

Every gas management rule devised depends on individuals functioning "normally". They must **swim normally, breathe normally and function as expected**. For a rule to be valid, unanticipated variations caused by the environment or changes in divers' abilities cannot occur. This means that events such as unexpected currents or having to maneuver through restrictions must not deter the divers proficiency.

If divers are forced to increase their swim pace, they will also increase gas consumption. Other changes in respiratory patterns, such as response to mental and physical stress, will also increase gas consumption. When divers slow their pace, gas consumption is reduced. However, you must never forget that your return speed must match your travel pace. You must cover the same amount of ground in the same time "coming back" as "going to" in order to ensure you won't run out of gas.

Once again, this is where mental and physical conditioning come into play. With mental discipline and good physical fitness, it is much easier to remain "normal" during a stressful event. A physically conditioned person will have much less increase in gas consumption with increased workloads than an out of shape diver.

A diver who does not maintain good cardiovascular efficiency will experience tremendous changes in his/her gas consumption when going from light effort to harder work loads. A diver who maintains a cardiovascular training program will experience significantly lower changes in his/her respiratory minute volume when switching from light to heavy exertion than a comparable individual who does not train on a regular basis. The diver who is a weekend warrior and a couch potato during the week will also have less endurance and is more likely to experience increased use of gas when fatigued.

Changes in buoyancy will also affect gas consumption. Environmental changes such as silting or changes in current flow and direction will modify the swim pace. Alterations to swim posture can increase drag. Additional gas is needed to anticipate these changes, too. By now it should be obvious that every phase of a technical dive must be anticipated to ensure the effectiveness of the team and personal gas management rule.

Since dive teams are obviously composed of individuals, a "team gas management" rule must be established. This rule incorporates all the factors involving individual considerations with another dimension. People working together create this dimension. When you dive alone, you dive differently than you would as a member of a buddy or dive team. To understand these differences, think of dancing. You dance differently when holding someone in your arms. An effective team gas management rule takes time to develop. The team must do a lot more than just shake hands. Each member must learn other team members' dive style and ability. They must also practice emergency management skills.

The size of the dive team will dictate effective gas management. Obviously a two person dive team is the most efficient from a dive performance standpoint. It needs less communication and requires less choreography. Both divers know where each other are. Swim pace is easier to regulate. A small team reduces the level of environmental management needed. For example, silting is just one of many factors that's easier to anticipate and prevent.

On the other hand, there are strong arguments to support the advantages of a **three person dive team**. The group gas supply can go much further when shared between three people. Two people are usually better able to rescue an individual in trouble.

When computing a team gas management model, compensate for variations in both breathing volume (respiratory minute volume RMV) and varying tank capacities. In addition, plan out the known gas volumes for the dive. If a dive has a three-person team, the dive gas is matched automatically provided all use an honest Rule of Thirds. If a two-person team is used and the diver who uses the least gas also has the smallest gas supply, the divers must match gas. Gas matching ensures that if a gas failure occurs at the farthest point form the return area, both divers can safely travel on the lowest volume of gas in the team.

When planning with known gas volumes, refer to IANTD Table 12. This table will allow you to determine the actual volume of gas available to you. For example, a diver has 2,000 psig (136 bar) in double 121s (double 19 liters) rated at 2640 psig (180 bar). By checking the tables, you can see the diver actually has the equivalent gas volume of double 91.7s (13 liter tanks at rated volume).

This process provides the ability to plan gas duration based on the diver with the greatest RMV being able to exit a dive while sharing gas from the smallest gas supply on the team. To provide a realistic and practical means of gas matching in the field, IANTD developed comprehensive *Gas Management Tables* that eliminate complex mathematical computations. These **waterproof tables** are easy to read and fit into your BC pocket.

To use the IANTD Tables, divers simply need to determine their personal *RMV* (See IANTD Table 13). Most divers determine their RMV while swimming at a moderate pace at a fixed depth for 10 minutes. This value is then converted in to a *surface rate.* A "resting rate" can also be determined. To develop a resting rate, simply breath on SCUBA for 10 minutes while at rest. Variations can be developed by adjusting the surface rate to account for different energy outputs. For example, gas consumption will be greater with a current than a dive in calm water.

The gas plan you use must be developed from a swimming-based surface rate (vs. a resting rate). It must be fine tuned by adjusting anticipated gas consumption against the environmental factors you expect to encounter. Experience has taught us this method is consistently accurate for planning dives involving a lot of swimming. To do this correctly, all dive team members must know their individual RMVs.

Developing a gas management profile for a hypothetical team:

Diver #1, "Jan," has a low RMV. Jan determined her breathing while diving in double 80s (twin 10s) at 3500 psig (238 bar). When using these tanks she breathed 8 psig (5 bar) a minute. If we refer to the psig (bar) per minute to SAC Table 9, and double this figure to match the single tank values presented in the table, it will be determined that Jan uses 0.37 cubic feet (9.9 free liters) a minute. Jan will use double 100 cubic foot (twin 18 liter) steel tanks at 3500 psig (238 bar). As a reference, on double 100s (twin 13 L), Jan will breathe (using the same chart) 6 psig (0.4 bar) a minute (half the single tank value).

Diver #2, "Bill," consumes 1.13 cubic feet (32.6 free liters) a minute. He uses 121 cubic foot (20 liter) steel tanks at 2640 psig (180 bar).

When using the Gas Matching Table, Table 13, **round** to the most conservative value. This means round down for the diver who consumes the least gas and round up for the diver who consumes the most gas. In this example, round Jan down to 0.35 (9.91) and round Bill up to 1.15 (32.57).

Using the IANTD Gas Management Tables 13:

1. Follow the left margin side until you reach Jan's RMV, which is calculated at 0.35 (9.91).
2. Go across the top of the table to Bill's RMV of 1.15 (32.57), column #1.

At this point, follow Bill's RMV down the column until it's adjacent to Jan's. Note the value 0.81. The number 0.81 represents a conversion factor of 81%. This means that Jan, instead of turning at 66% (0.66) of her gas supply, needs to turn at 81% (0.81). This should provide Jan with an adequate safety margin in case Bill needs to share gas on the way out.

Convert this safety margin into a usable number; Use IANTD Gas Management Table 14:

1. Go down the Starting Cylinder Pressure Column along the left side to 3,500 psig (238 bar).
2. Go across the top of the table showing SRFs from 0.67 to 0.81. The last column is labeled 0.81.
3. Go down this column until it intersects with 3,500 psig (238 bar).

The chart shows Jan's turn pressure to be 2,835 psig (193 bar). Normally Jan would turn at 2,310 psig (157 bar). The chart shows she must hold an additional 525 psig (36 bar) in reserve to compensate for Bill's increased RMV.

Miria Denlay making last minute checks prior to a dive.
Photo: Kevin Denlay

Even with proper gas matching, it is still imperative that all dives remain within normal parameters for these rules to work. When you start diving with new buddies, it's advisable to add a couple of hundred psig (extra bars) to any cutoff point. This practice should be continued until divers have sufficient experience to develop the discipline to function normally under stress. Many experienced divers develop the ability to actually reduce their RMV under stress and to maintain a normal swim pace under the most demanding of situations.

Gas duration required for the dive plan should be figured by anticipating the planned distance traveled, coupled with gas consumption. In this case, let's look at two divers who are planning a dive into a moderate outflow cave. This example employs a cave dive because cave dives generally employ more consistent swimming than open water dives.

Example:

Note for metric users: Table 16 comes in both imperial-US and metric versions. For convenience, the metric Table 16 works with whole numbers that **do not directly correspond** with the imperial-US Table. For this reason, the answers worked in metric differ slightly from the imperial-US answers. Example: 25 feet actually equals 7.65 meters but the Table 16 metric uses "10."

1. Swimming into a dive, the divers will swim at a pace of 50 feet (15 meters) per minute.
2. From gas planning, it has already been determined that the turn pressure will be 2400 psig (160 bar) from a starting press of 3600 psig (240 bar).
3. It has already been determined (through steps explained earlier in dive gas planning) that the divers use 30 psig (2 bar) a minute at the planned dive depth of 90 feet (27 meters).
4. To determine the turn pressure time,
   First, compute the gas available: 3,600 psig – 2,400 psig =1,200 psig (240 bar - 160 bar = 80 bar).
   Next, compute the amount of time unto reaching turn pressure:
   Imperial-US: (1,200psig) / (30 psig per minute) = 40 minutes
   Metric: (80 bar) / (2 bar per minute) = 40 minutes
5. Using Table 16, "Distance Traveled in Feet (Meters)," one finds that the divers, traveling at 50 feet (15 meters on metric Table 16) per minute, will penetrate 2000 feet (600 meters on metric Table 16).
6. From Table 16, should the divers exit at 75 feet (20 meters on metric Table 16) per minute, it will only take 27 minutes (30 minutes on metric Table 16) to return. This will increase the safety of their gas management procedures.
7. However, what happens if the divers slow their return due to an emergency such as a silt out or gas sharing problem? In this event, let's say the exit speed is at 25 feet (10 meters on the metric table) per minute. Using Table 16, the exit will take 80 minutes (60 minutes on metric Table 16. See note above).
8. In this delayed exit event, it will take (80 minutes) x 30 psig (2 bar) per minute = 2400 psig (160 bar) to exit.
9. If this is a not a gas sharing emergency, there is still a sufficient quantity of gas to exit with reserve. If a gas sharing emergency did take place at the maximum point of penetration, it would require 2400 psig (160 bar) x 2 = 4800 psig (320 bar). Both divers combined gas needs to exit. **This is not sufficient gas to return to the surface.**

Under stress, divers often slow their swim rate. From the above example, the results are quite vivid.
Gas Matching & the Rule of Thirds rely upon maintaining a constant swim rate!

Another common problem in out-of-gas situations is that the divers' breathing rates increase. Let's assume the divers use some discipline but, due to stress, they increase their combined breathing rate from 30 psig (2 bar) per minute to 60 psig (4 bar) per minute. Let's allow for a normal swim rate equal to the penetration rate of 50 feet (15 meters) per minute. The divers will exit in 40 minutes if gas has been matched. It will now take 60 psig (4 bar) per min. x 40 min. = 2400 psig (160 bar) per diver, 4800 psig (320 bar) for both divers sharing gas to exit. **This is more gas than is available!**

Divers under stress often increase their breathing rates. The results are final.
Gas Matching & the Rule of Thirds rely upon maintaining a constant breathing rate!

From these examples, it is apparent divers must function in a normal fashion even when responding to an emergency. Table 15 may be used for assisting in determination of turn time referencing gas used per minute and gas available for a diver. Planning gas needs for decompression is also vital to a safe dive plan. A separate gas supply should be planned for decompression purposes. This gas supply must include the amount of gas needed plus a 1/5 reserve. In this case determine the gas needed and multiply by 1.2 for the correct volume of gas to carry.

Avoidance is a key principle of technical diving. In this case, however, avoidance does not mean ignoring a potential problem. It means knowing what constitutes a small problem and what doesn't. It means knowing that a "tiny" free-flow could become a major problem. It means having the common sense to know if one part of your gas supply is not working properly, turn it off and use your alternate source. It means having the discipline to anticipate, to think ahead, and to immediately neutralize the source of problems.

By taking corrective actions with gas supply problems before those problems escalate, divers can begin sharing gas before the diver with the problem actually runs out. This is good stress management, because it allows the distressed diver to use their own gas whenever a restricted or hazardous point in the dive is reached, and to share air in the long, unobstructed passages.

Once any member of the dive team is using a back up regulator, the dive should be terminated. All divers should begin their pre-planned exits.

In a **3 person team,** the "out-of-gas diver" should be sandwiched **between** the two divers with gas. Every few hundred psig (free liters/bar), the out-of-gas diver is rotated between donors. This allows the two divers with air to deplete their gas supplies somewhat evenly. When exiting an overhead environment dive, certain **problem management techniques** have been developed. For example, in three person teams, one of the "donor divers" negotiates a problem area, such as a restriction, ahead of the "recipient diver". Once the lead donor diver has safely reached a clear passageway, the "recipient diver" switches over to their own gas supply and swims to the lead donor diver. They resume sharing the donor's gas while waiting for the third member of the team to join them. This, of course, assumes the "recipient" is *not* out of gas.

In a true out-of-gas situation, the recipient would share gas with a buddy while the buddy goes through the restriction. At this time, the recipient will go into the restriction to a point where the long hose is dropped and continues until they reach the awaiting second stage of the diver who has already negotiated the restriction.

Two person teams must handle a gas supply problem differently. When negotiating a problem area, the "recipient diver" stops, takes 3 breaths (inhaling slowly and deeply) followed by 3 hyperventilation breaths and waits for the "donor diver" to reach an unobstructed area. Once the donor signals "clear," the recipient swims to the donor and shares gas. There's a good reason why the donor leads. At the point of separation, the recipient has adequate gas in their lungs to reach the donor. Moreover, there's a psychological edge provided by swimming toward a gas supply rather than away from it.

Gas management rules are occasionally modified when conditions warrant a change. Specialized equipment may mean altering normal gas turn around points. For example:

- When diving into caves with "siphons" or downcurrent on wrecks and other circumstances which will require an upcurrent swim to the exit or ascent point, gas management rules should be modified to account for the challenge of overcoming the in-flowing water. In this case, more conservative rules are implemented. This may be nothing more than adjusting to a different gas turn-around percentage or fraction. A good starting point for mild to moderate siphons is the **Rule of Fourths**. This is also a good starting reference when you first begin using a Diver Propulsion Vehicle (DPV).
- With experience in both technical diving and at a given location, it may be acceptable to make modifications to the basic thirds gas management rules. For example, a diver may use 40% of his gas supply swimming into a dive with a strong outflow. By riding the current out, the diver will not work as hard and will consume less gas. The "turnaround point" might then be adjusted to allow the dive team to adhere to the Rule of Thirds as it applies to this environment.

Such interpretations of gas rules can only be performed by accumulating experience. This experience comes from both the total number of dives logged and the number of dives performed at the specific location where the modifications are being applied. Modifications to gas management rules should be made in gradual increments. Each dive is followed by careful evaluation to determine if the modification did, in fact, allow a true 2/3rd's reserve gas for exiting the system. Regardless of the current, **no more than 40% of the gas** should be used when traveling into a dive.

We suggest you be very conservative before making changes to gas management rules. We recommend you make **at least 100 total dives and 25 dives at a specific site before considering such modifications.** Again, you must be able to prove that the modified turnaround point does provide 2/3rds of the available gas is actually available for exiting. This availability is defined within a relationship of time, distance, and duration of gas.

A specific example of a modified Rule of Thirds could involve a dive into a strong current. After completing numerous dives at this location, you realize it's apparent that upon exiting, you and your buddy team will finish the dive with half your gas. In this example, the management rules can be modified. If, for example, you had started with 3,600 psig (245 bar), the exit would be completed with 1,800 psig (122 bar) remaining in the tanks. Thus, 1/3rd of the gas was used going in and only 1/6th of the gas was used on return. In psig (bar) this equates to 1200 psig (82 bar) going in and 600 psig (41 bar) exiting. The Rule of Thirds allows for the use of an additional 600 psig (41 bar).

The key is that all dives must be planned with the diver arriving at the surface with a minimum of one third of the original gas supply.

The experienced diver who is familiar with the dive site may now begin to modify the turnaround point to allow for a safety factor of one third. By familiar, we emphasize that it means you have made numerous dives at the site and encountered the same or very similar conditions.

In the above example, if a diver turns with 60% of the gas remaining, a turn around at 2,160 psig (147 bar), the dive will reflect 1,440 psig (98 bar) used going into the dive. It will require 1/2 of that to exit, or 720 psig (49 bar) with a remaining 1,440 psig (98 bar). This works out to more than a 1/3rd reserve as the true "3rd reserve" would be 1,200 psig (82 bar).

If a diver does not carry extra gas for decompression, it is necessary to plan for sufficient gas supply into the dive plan. In this instance, the diver must incorporate two phases of dive planning into the primary gas supply. These involve **bottom gas** and **decompression gas**.

Anticipated need for decompression gas must be planned. When planning the necessary gas, subtract the gas needed for the decompression stops and plan the dive as if that gas did **not** exist. For example, after careful planning, you determine that 30 cubic feet (850 free liters) of gas is necessary for decompression. You would then multiply that value by 1.2 for reserve. Finally, you would subtract the deco gas from your primary gas supply and plan accordingly.

Whenever possible, decompression should be made using Enriched Air Nitrox (EANx) of **50% or more**. Doppler studies have discovered bubble formation decreases as the oxygen level in the EANx mixture is increased. Many experts consider the practice of decompressing on bottom mix to be unsafe from a DCS (decompression illness) standpoint.

Another consideration is the "solo" diver. In this instance, in addition to diving using the Rule of Thirds, it is recommended that the diver must also carry a stage bottle (referred to as the buddy cylinder) that is equivalent to one third of the back-mounted gas. This tank is reserved for emergency use only. It is only used if a failure of the primary gas system takes place. As an example, a diver with double 100s (15 liters) has a total of 200 cubic feet (38 liters) of gas. The safety gas supply must be at least 66 cubic feet (12.5 liters).

In summary, prior to commencement of the dive, review all the objectives. During this phase of the plan, ascertain that each diver is aware of the responsibility assigned to them. If it is a complex skill, rehearse it through land drills as a team and visualize it. At the same time, discuss the absolute limits of the dive. In addition to gas management, consider factors such as partial pressure of oxygen, narcosis loading, gas density, and decompression duration and contingency factors.

Under no circumstance should a bottom mix PO_2 exceed 1.4ata, and it is prudent on longer dives to drop to 1.3ata. For decompression, a maximum of 1.6ata is to be observed. On exceptional exposures, the dive gas design must allow for a total exposure to remain within team and physiological safety standards. Some projects actually limit the bottom mix to less than 1.35ata and decompression mixes to 1.50ata. Usually, these projects use multiple gas changes on stops and stay close to a range of 1.2 to 1.45ata throughout the entire stop times. Remember, to plan both the MOD (maximum operating depth) and TOD (target operating depth) limits for oxygen, nitrogen (narcosis limits) and gas density.

Define other limits such as penetration on a dive, duration, burn time of DPV's lights and other support equipment used on the dive. Basically, sit down and detail all the events in the proposed dive and define the minimum and maximum risk values of each. The limits should remain within the agreed on team values, provided they are all within the personal risk acceptance of each individual.

Be careful not to challenge egos when planning complex dives. This is a time when each diver's self and team honesty is paramount to the safety of the project. Be certain the team members are compatible. On technical diving projects, one must be comfortable with the abilities of the team, have trust and respect for the members, and they should have compatible personalities. Remember that each of the members should be self-sufficient, yet aware that in unusual circumstances their lives may depend on a coordinated team effort.

Prior to entering the water, make certain that each diver is totally aware of each other's equipment configuration and its operational parameters. Each portion of the system is to be pre-dive checked and verified by a team member (buddy). When it is possible, do an in-water safety drill to ascertain that all components operate correctly and that each diver can use the buddy system. Divers must breathe from each other's second stage to be handed off and verify the functionality of equipment of the buddy diver. This act is a vital part of pre-dive checks. It should be approached in a check list fashion.

A list of all the "what ifs" that affect team safety is to be laid out, and the corrective factors defined and rehearsed mentally and physically if possible. This list must include all safety parameters and all possible problem areas the team can identify. Be creative as you make up the list. Once the list is developed and each diver has had input on it, discuss all solutions and develop a "What If" plan of action for each. After this, verbally go through each item at least three times and then have the team visualize safely correcting the "What If" situations. Once this is accomplished, put it to bed and then visualize and enjoy a safe and productive dive.

- **Changes in current**
- **Changes in visibility**
- **Changes due to upline problems**
- **Changes due to team reaction**

The final aspect of dive planning is **in-water updates**. Mr. Murphy is always with us in all endeavors of life. Frequently, dive plans need alternation due to changes in the anticipated water conditions. Therefore, one must remain open-minded when beginning a dive and be prepared to modify the dive performance as dictated by environmental conditions.

Once the dive begins, allow for flexibility in performance. "Mother Nature" is often fickle. The dive may offer the unexpected, and you must be prepared to adapt and to modify the dive plan. A degradation of visibility may provide grounds for altering the dive plan while in the water; if so, have that included as an agreed dive plan objective. Changes in the type of, the severity of, or the direction of current may be a sufficient cause for modifications in an existing dive plan. If a boat breaks anchor, or a guideline is broken, or other factors that influence either the exit or ascent of a dive, these are grounds for modification or cancellation of a dive.

You will also need to anticipate behavioral changes within the dive team. Simple things such as one diver becoming uncomfortable will modify the dive plan. Accident potential increases when you fail to modify the dive plan because of a diver's behavioral changes.

Awareness is the critical component in making a command decision to modify the plan of a dive already in progress. As you explore and discover, don't forget to periodically observe the members of your dive team. Set up a plan of intermittent contact.

Observation and *communication* play key roles. Observation helps you to know when a diver starts "slipping". Communication overcomes the hesitancy of divers to tell you they are having a problem.

Guilt associated with failure is a key threat to dive safety. Divers will frequently feel guilty if they cause a dive to be terminated. Feeling of guilt, combined with a "threatened ego," produce a potentially dangerous combination if the dive is allowed to continue. When diving, not every change is obvious. You must be aware of **subtle changes** that may occur. These would involve recognizing changes in coordination, swimming style or rhythm, and breathing patterns.

Maturity and **sound judgment** play key roles in personal success and diving ability. The smart diver knows that cancellation is not the end of the world. Once they learn a dive cannot be accomplished as planned, they will terminate the present dive. They understand that a new plan must be developed to incorporate what has been learned. He/she knows that the price of continuing an unsafe dive skyrockets. It's not only foolish; it's deadly to continue diving with a marginal safety factor.

In summary, a safe dive plan requires divers to gather all information pertinent to the dive site. The entire dive team needs to discuss the dive comprehensively and establish a team plan. Each participating diver must search his/her mind and develop a personal plan of action. This personal plan should be based on self-sufficiency. It must allow for self-rescue ability and team rescue capabilities. Gas Management Rules must be carefully and comprehensively developed from actual field experience.

CHAPTER 4
Dive Technique

Tom Mount

When asked what the *tech* in the phrase *tech diver* stands for, most would answer: technical. True, but by the same token, tech could - and should - refer to technique. Proper underwater posture and swimming technique is probably the most overlooked yet critical ingredient of safe and enjoyable diving.

All too often, tech divers get caught up in the technology of the sport, but ignore the technique. Imagine a poorly trained diver, struggling to control his heavy double tanks and redundant scuba equipment while clumsily kicking his way through a silty, fragile wreck or cave environment. He is a hazard to himself and to everyone in his dive team.

Now, visualize a well-trained diver, comfortable with his equipment, confident in his abilities, and practiced in the art of gliding through small passageways with no clang of tanks against the ceiling, no silty upwellings caused by poorly executed kicks. Like an expert rock climber, our well-trained diver considers every action, then performs each move with flawless precision.

Good underwater technique combines a variety of skills and methods. These include the use of the correct kick, the ability to read and utilize the underwater environment to minimize work and aid in the propulsion effort, the adoption and maintenance of the correct superb body positioning, and the ability to maintain precise buoyancy control. An accomplished diver knows instinctively when to apply specific techniques as the environment changes, and is a master of these techniques.

Developing the techniques needed for safe, effective technical diving requires training, practice and the ability to read the underwater environment. The specific techniques and swimming styles that are unique to technical diving will be introduced and practiced during formal training. One way to facilitate the learning and ongoing improvement of these techniques is by visualizing your desired swimming style between practice sessions, and prior to dives.

The ongoing enhancement and refinement of your diving technique should come from within, and will be driven by a constant desire for self-examination. All dives should be performed as if you were in the most demanding of environment, where every move counts, and every mistake matters. If you approach all of your dives with this mindset and attention to detail, you will find that your abilities and comfort level will improve with remarkable speed.

Body posture is an extremely important aspect of underwater technique. Ideally, you should swim horizontally to the bottom. This position minimizes drag and maximizes efficiency. It also helps you to avoid silting problems when swimming near the bottom.

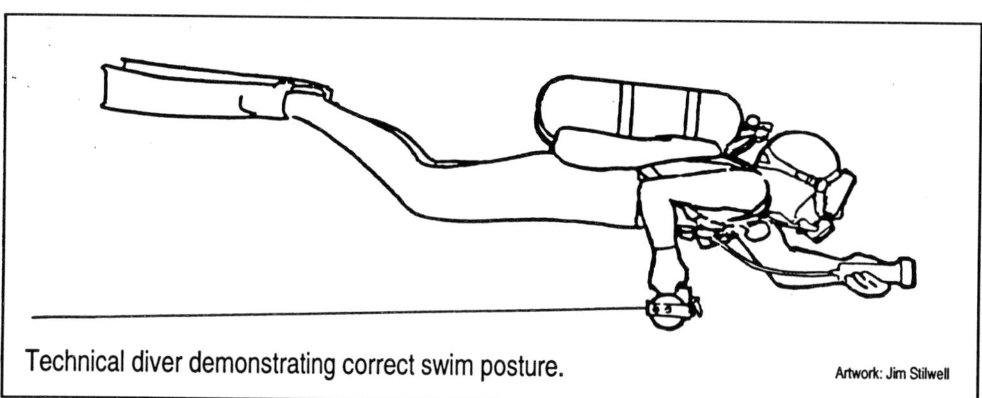

Technical diver demonstrating correct swim posture. Artwork: Jim Stilwell

To picture the ideal swim posture, imagine yourself lying on your stomach with your legs extended. From this position, no kick should extend more than 10 degrees below your mid line. Because your head must be held up to see where you're going, you will be required to arching the neck and back. At first, this may result in some sore neck and lower back muscles, but as your muscles become accustomed to swimming in this position, any feelings of awkwardness will quickly fade.

Buoyancy control is the second element of good dive technique. Your buoyancy needs to be so precise that you can become totally relaxed when hanging in a fixed position, rising slightly upon inhalation, then sinking slowly with each exhalation. In some situations, you may be required to remain either negatively or positively buoyant, but in the majority of situations, you will be neutrally buoyant.

It is imperative that you reestablish your buoyancy at each "change point" in the dive. Change points occur when you add or remove stage bottles, enter an overhead portion of a dive, add or remove reels or other equipment, deplete a significant portion of your gas supply, or encounter silting surfaces.

Cave and wreck divers refer to the position of their body relative to the ceiling and floor (deck) as "placement". Placement should be dictated by the structures one is diving in. During the course of instruction, you will begin to develop an awareness of correct placement. Gradually, your placement will be governed by instinct. Your instructor will help you learn this important skill.

Propulsion Techniques

Technical divers use an assortment of swimming kicks not usually employed by recreational, open water divers. Collectively, they are referred to as "propulsion techniques". The kicks you will learn to use include a variety of frog kicks, modified flutter kicks, and one-legged kicks. You will also practice "fin sculling" and heel-toe kicks. The finning techniques described in this manual and workbook will be demonstrated by your instructor.

KICK Techniques

Technical diving involves **precision swimming**. You will also be required to swim longer distances than in most open water dives. These kicks will provide the necessary precision, and help you with your endurance:

Frog kicks (right) consist of the cave frog kick, a modified frog kick, and the power frog kick. The most common of these is the cave frog kick.

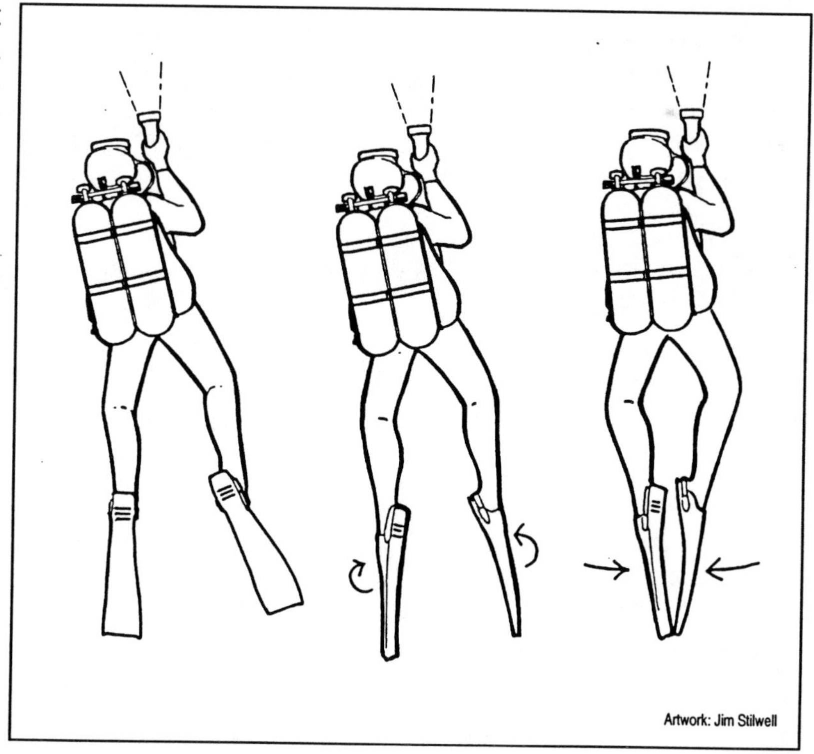

Artwork: Jim Stilwell

A cave frog kick is performed with your body in a horizontal posture. First, the fins slide gracefully - without power - outward to a full extension. In most cases, the legs will remain slightly elevated to maintain maximum distance from the cave floor. The fins are then cupped by twisting the ankles and the power stroke is on the inward travel portion of the kick. It will place demands on your leg muscles as you deliver the kick in powerful, continuous strokes.

The modified frog kick is identical except the range of the kick is shortened. Occasionally this kick will utilize only a range of motion created from the movement of the ankle, i.e. a parallel, horizontal "flutter". A diver using this kick may travel less than a foot in some circumstances.

The power frog kick is another variation of the basic frog kick. In this kick, both the extension and retraction portions of the kick are executed with power.

Modified flutter kicks are the most common of technical propulsion skills. Such kicks involve an up- and down (vertical scissors) leg motion and are executed while swimming horizontally with your body parallel to the bottom. When using this kick, make sure your downward thrust does not extend below your body axis. To execute a modified flutter kick, a diver extends his legs and uses a vertical scissors motion to propel himself forward. To avoid silting, the sweep should not extend lower than the horizontal axis.

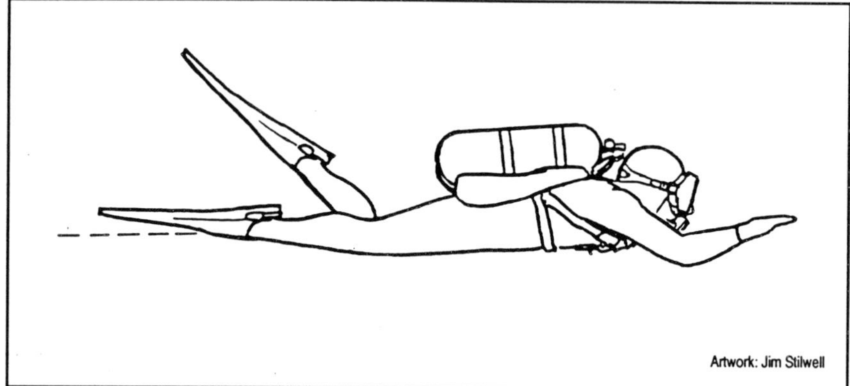

Artwork: Jim Stilwell

Shuffle kicks are another variation of the flutter kick that is most often used in areas where potential silting is a major concern. This kick involves a carefully controlled vertical scissors motion. The kick begins above the diver's back and only travels a distance of ¼ to ½ the distance to the diver's horizontal axis.

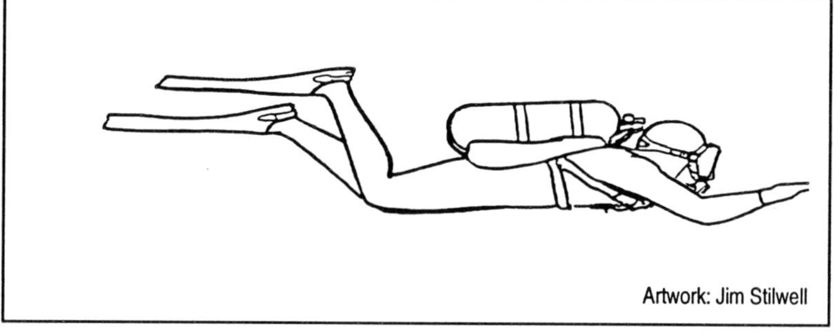

Artwork: Jim Stilwell

The one-legged shuffle kick was developed for use when leg cramps occur. It also works well in silty areas. This kick uses a full range of motion similar to the modified flutter. The difference is that one leg is a kicking leg and the other a resting leg. The kicking leg travels downward until it rests on the diver's other leg, which is extended but not moved. The extended leg serves as a shield to minimize fin turbulence on the down stroke.

Heel toe, or ankle kicks are a very controlled flutter kick. Both legs are extended and the kick is delivered by flexing your ankles up and down. This motion effectively controls silting, provided the diver executes the kick with accuracy and does not extend the kick to exaggerated distances below the horizontal axis.

HAND Techniques

When swimming with fins, a diver's hands are normally kept close to the body. Technical divers should learn not to wave their hands in an attempt to maintain placement or balance. The turbulence caused by this type of reactionary hand sculling may result in substantial silting. Gentle, deliberate sculling, on the other hand, is a tool that is useful to slightly reposition the diver.

Pull and glide is a technique developed by cave divers to pull themselves along a wall with hand and arm motions. This technique is also usable in wrecks and in open water current dives where there is appropriate structure to grasp.

Just as it sounds, this technique involves using the hands to grasp a structure and pull the body forward. A glide is often added when there is mild or no current, or a following current. The pull is not done with the finger tips, but rather by "clamping" with the palm of your hand and the lengths of your fingers. If you persist in using your fingertips to propel yourself, you'll find you've removed most of your fingerprints!

"Finger walking" is a technique used when sandy floors, bottoms or decks are encountered. When "walking," keep your feet high to avoid kicking up the bottom.

Aside from communicating and "manipulating" your equipment, the only other real use for your fingers is to maintain line contact in overhead environments. This is only done when visibility requires you to touch the line.

ADDITIONAL Techniques

When divers are involved in the exploration of overhead environments or engaging in open water night dives, keeping track of dive buddies can become a challenge. Remember, the only light available is that which your dive team creates. As long as the "light distance" between team members remains constant, the pace is probably okay. If you notice a buddy's light dimming, this usually indicates the pace should be slowed. To get a buddy's attention, the customary practice is to sweep your light in a circular motion on the bottom or wall of an overhead environment (not in your buddy's eyes) or along the bottom in open water.

The best way to locate a dive buddy swimming behind you is to dip your head down and look between your legs. This is much more efficient than stopping and turning around. Some times this is the only way to locate your buddy.

When diving at night or in overhead environments, buddy checks must involve all dive team members. OK's are communicated from any diver, but they must be verified starting with the last diver passing the verification forward to the lead diver. As soon as a problem arises, the diver advised of the problem sweeps his light in a vertical motion to the diver in front of him. The signal is passed forward until the lead diver is advised and the team stops.

Stage diving - the use of additional tanks to increase swim time or bottom time - is an activity that requires considerable thought and planning prior to execution. Staging allows the diver to extend the distance of safe exploration but, due to being further away from the return point of the dive, may also produce additional time pressure stress. Training and a gradual increase in penetration distances and bottom times will help offset this stress.

In addition, stage diving is similar to flying an airplane in that the diver must think well ahead of his/her position. By thinking ahead and being familiar with stage techniques, the diver avoids delays during stage drops and retrievals, and will avoid sudden changes in buoyancy. Your instructor will introduce you to stage diving techniques as applicable to either decompression stage management or penetration staging.

DPV diving is the closest thing to space travel one can imagine. A DPV diver must think in terms of minutes ahead of his present position. Prior to enrolling in the IANTD DPV course, you must become proficient in all the relevant skills of the technical diver and should be completely comfortable with stage diving, long swim distances, orientation and the ability to read the environment.

Once DPV diving becomes a part of your repertoire, it would be prudent to periodically make long swim dives to keep track of the amount of gas used per distance traveled when swimming as opposed to riding the DPV. With modern DPVs, it is possible to attain penetration distances that the diver could not return from in the event of a DPV failure. Constant physical training and periodic long stage dives will provide an understanding of your swim limits, and can assist the diver in the development of the proper disciplines needed to cope with DPV emergencies.

It is very important that you learn all of the techniques discussed in this chapter. It takes practice and experience to develop the combinations of techniques that yield the best performance with a minimum of effort. Good technique, the maintenance of an acceptable level of physical conditioning, the development of mind control and ongoing practice will result in lower gas consumption, less drag in the water, increased forward momentum, less fatigue and generally more enjoyable diving.

PRACTICE... PRACTICE... PRACTICE...
and you will become a master of technique.

CHAPTER 5
Respiration, Circulation and Breath Control

Tom Mount

Simply stated, we breathe to stay alive. The importance of breathing is defined better in Eastern philosophies than in most Western belief systems. In fact, none of our belief systems in the West discuss breathing as a vital component of health and healing. So, to help us do a better job of controlling our breathing, we need to combine a little Oriental philosophy with Western physiology.

In Eastern thought, the substance by which the universe is known is *Akasha.* Akasha is simply the "stuff" from which the universe flows. In its simplest definition, it is infinity. Akasha contains all - all thought, all knowledge.

Prana sustains *Akasha.* The universe is, itself, a living, breathing entity. *Prana* is the name for "universal breath". Like us, the universe breathes to survive, but obviously on a grander scale. Interestingly enough, western scientific thought has recently embraced theories that coincide with traditional Eastern descriptions of the universe. The universe does, in fact, expand in pulsating rhythms, scientists now tell us.

According to Eastern thought, the practice of correct breathing enables one to control his/her own being. In our own world, athletes increase their performance by improving their breathing skills. Biofeedback and meditation regularly lower stress levels and increase overall feelings of well being.

Obviously, comparing breath to energy is valid in any culture. If you don't breathe, you die. But, breathing is more than "sucking in air" and releasing carbon dioxide and nitrogen. Breathing supplies our cells with oxygen. Oxygen is a key component that allows us to convert food into energy. Since our bodies only use a small portion of the oxygen in a complete inhalation, our bodies are able to function on altered or less-efficient breathing patterns, but may not be able to perform at our highest potential level.

By learning simple breathing exercises and developing correct breathing patterns, we can enhance our bodies overall respiratory efficiency, learn to cope with stress and emotions and live more relaxed, healthy lives. In addition, breath control can help us become better divers! Meditation combined with controlled breathing does, in fact, give you additional control over your mind and body.

Proper breathing and good dive techniques go hand-in-hand. Technical diving involves the proper management of a finite and often quite limited supply of air (or alternate breathing mix). If, to quote from a popular TV show, you plan to explore strange new worlds, seek out new forms of life, and boldly go where no one has gone before, you will need to manage your air supply every minute of the way.

In the course of your explorations, you may encounter stressful or threatening situations. In many such cases, the ability to take immediate control of your breathing rate and your mind are essential to your survival. Incorrect breathing produces stress, and stress can lead to accidents and panic. In addition, improper or uncontrolled breathing depletes the air supply rapidly, fails to provide adequate ventilation to your lungs and increases your carbon dioxide levels. To develop an understanding of breathing, we must review some basic physiology and learn to breathe as we did at birth... **correctly.**

The Circulatory System

The circulatory system is a closed-loop system consisting of the heart, arteries, veins, tissue capillaries and lung capillaries. The heart is the pump propelling blood through the circulatory system. The heart's contractions produce blood pressure. This pressure is the driving force propelling the blood and gases throughout the body. Blood pressure is determined by the work the heart has to produce to insure adequate circulation.

The amount of work performed, the health of the blood vessels and other factors influence the resistance of blood flow and the need's of the entire body. The heart adjusts its blood pressure to meet these needs. The carotid sinuses are pressure-sensing nerves that aid in regulating blood pressure by informing the brain, via impulses, about pressures.

Blood carries oxygen to your cells by bonding it to *hemoglobin.* Oxygenated hemoglobin is transported to the body's cells via arteries and capillaries. Your tissues absorb the oxygen, use it, and give off carbon dioxide. Carbon dioxide is then combined with the de-oxygenated hemoglobin and is returned to your lungs via your veins. Correct breathing technique insures that the hemoglobin maximizes its capacity to transport oxygen efficiently. Improper breathing such as shallow or erratic breathing results in clumbing of oxygen in the RBC, vs a smooth distribution of oxygen molecules.

Plasma and **serum** are important components in blood and also determine overall blood volume and hydration level. When you become dehydrated, you have basically reduced your blood volume. For this reason, it is imperative to maintain proper levels of hydration in order to ensure adequate gas exchange on dives.

Platelets and **fibrinogen** are important clotting mechanisms in blood. They are essential for healing injuries. Unfortunately, when bubbles form they can contribute to bubble mass. The circulatory system functions as one system containing two separate subsystems, the *pulmonary* and the *systemic.* The pulmonary system supports the circulation dedicated to the lungs while the systemic services the body tissues. These systems are controlled by nervous impulses that respond to the body's needs.

By studying the illustration, we can see that the circulatory system functions as a highway or transport mechanism for gas to travel to and from the tissues. The overall health of a person depends on the body's ability to maintain a healthy circulatory system. Any alteration to the circulatory system will have a corresponding effect on gas transport. These alterations can include blood vessel injuries, fat concentration, blood vessel disease, or even the effects of prescription or common across-the counter drugs.

The transport of oxygen, which is vital to metabolism, is among the circulatory system's most important functions. If the oxygen tension and concentration within the circulation varies outside of a known limit, it will produce adverse effects to the organism. Virtually every cell in our bodies require oxygen, nutrition, and waste removal in order to survive. Diseases such as hardening of the arteries reduce the supply of both oxygen and nutrients to every cell, including the brain. Our memories, learning skills, and virtually all our mental cognitive skills depend on a steady supply of oxygen and nutrients.

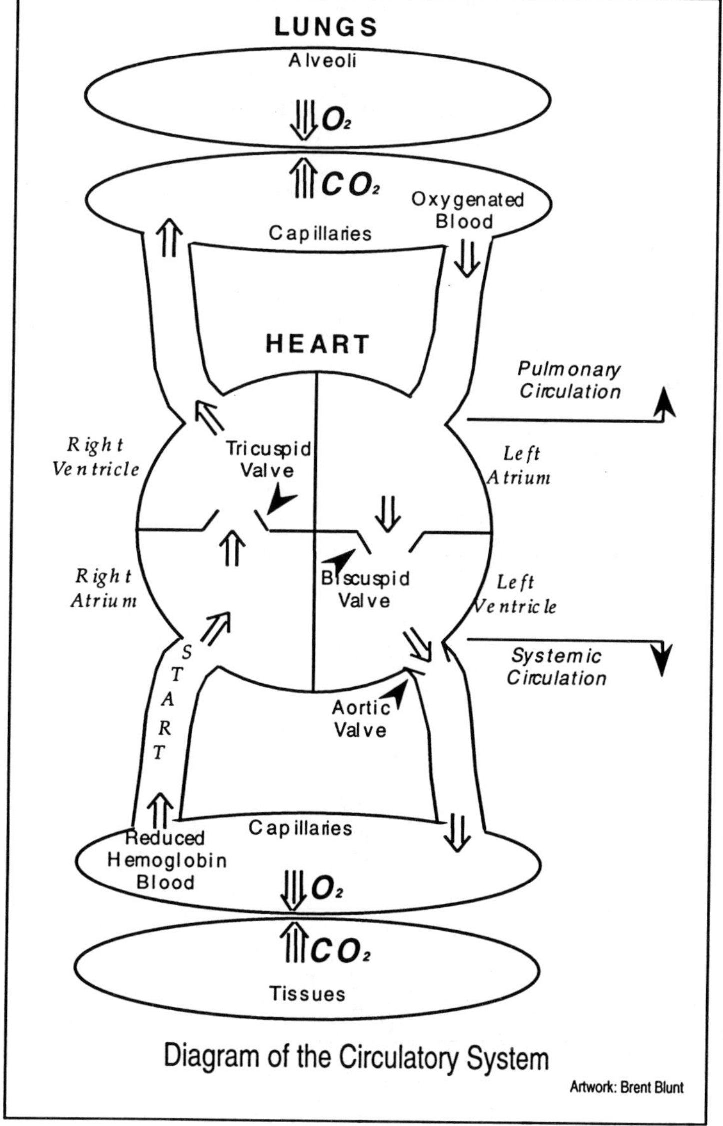

Diagram of the Circulatory System

Artwork: Brent Blunt

Maintaining Circulatory Health through Diet and Exercise

Diet is a vital aspect of overall health. We really are what we eat. A fitness program that disregards the importance of diet will provide minimal results. Our diets should feature a balance in five essential areas: water, grains, fruits, proteins and vegetables. Ideally, each of these will be included in every meal. Maintaining the correct amount of protein, carbohydrates and fat is extremely important for our long-term health.

The USDA recommends that a normal diet for human beings be composed of 14% protein, 25% fats and 60% carbohydrates. It is interesting that the USDA recommends almost the exact same diet for fattening hogs. When selecting fats to be included in a diet, emphasize the Omega 3 group and avoid as many Omega 6 fats as possible. The fat in the daily diet should not exceed 30% of the total calories and should represent at least 10% of our daily intake. (I recommend 20 to 25% of good fats). Protein should be between 20 to 40% while the balance of fat and protein should be 60 to 70% of the daily diet. Carbohydrates provide our natural sugars and are essential for energy. Carbohydrates may range between 15 to 45% of our total calories. Your activity level and individual physiology will dictate the exact distribution of calories. Processed sugars are to be kept at a minimum. Too much sugar will have adverse effects on our circulatory system and our bodies in general. Moderation is the essential word in maintaining a healthy diet.

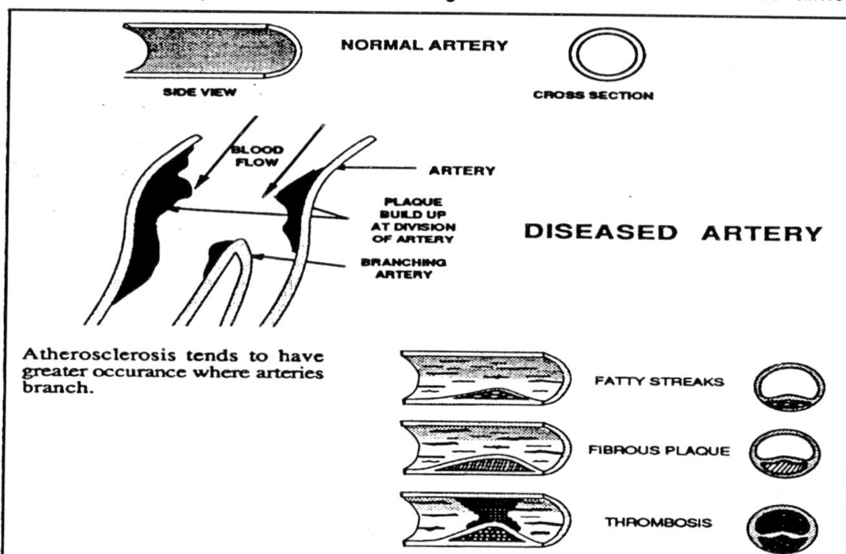

Most adults in the USA have some degree of circulatory disease due to poor dietary and exercise habits. Yet even though this is true for most of us, it is a reversible situation. The factors that may reverse this adverse effect include good eating habits, supplementing the diet with nutrients and vitamins, and a cardio-vascular exercise program.

One of the most common diseases of the circulatory system is arteriosclerosis. This condition is brought about by plaque buildup in the blood vessels. As the plaque accumulates, the vessel is clogged and its effective diameter is reduced. This condition will result in less circulatory efficiency and will cause the heart to work harder. Reduced circulation means less oxygen to tissues. The three areas that are hypersensitive to a decreased PO_2 are the heart, the legs and the brain. One of the theories for the beginning of arteriosclerosis is that tiny injuries are incurred in the blood vessels by *free radicals.*

Free radicals are volatile, short-lived chemicals that are produced by the process of metabolism, the diet, and a lack of exercise. Diet has a pronounced effect on the development of free radicals. The following foods are producers of free radicals in the human organism: fried foods, cooked fats, cooked cholesterol, alcohol, and tobacco smoke.

The free radicals such as the superoxide radical have one missing electron with a single covalent bond. These radicals attack any double bond within the system, such as fatty acids and intracellular membranes.

Once they produce an injury site, plaque is formed and, eventually, cholesterol attaches to it producing disease of the circulatory system. Divers who consume a high fat diet (the standard American diet (SAD) contains 40% fat) are at high risk of increased free radical development and low-density cholesterol. This is the combination that leads to circulatory disease.

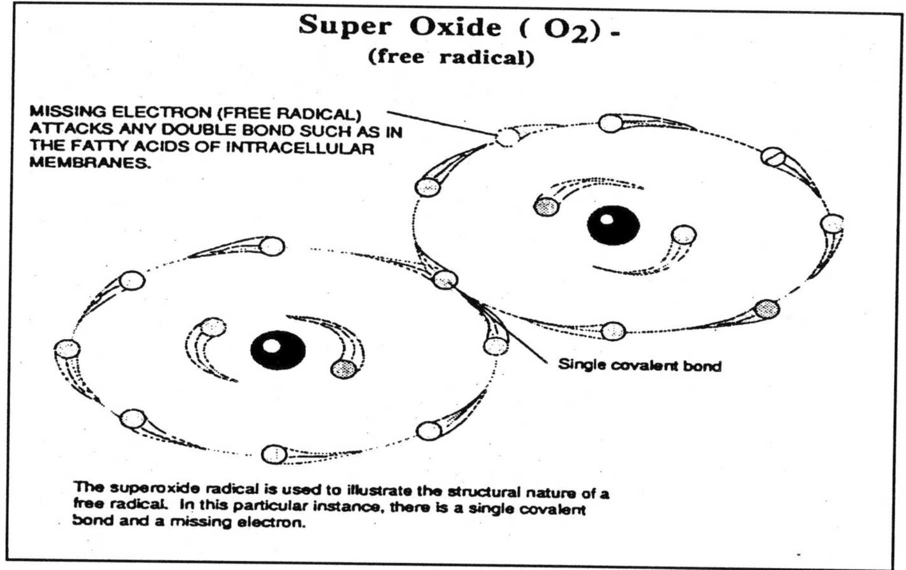

Fats

When fat and cholesterol are combined, especially if the cholesterol has been exposed to air and heat such as in the preparation of red meat, the result is the formation of cholesterol oxide which acts as a free radical and produces damage to the lining of the arteries. High-density cholesterol helps return cholesterol from the arteries to the liver for metabolism.

A fatty meal produces immediate changes in the circulatory system. Normally blood cells within the vessel flow freely and tend to bounce off each other. The red blood cells must remain flexible to be able to carry oxygen and nutrients through capillaries and to eliminate waste and carbon dioxide. Within an hour of completing a fatty meal, blood cells begin to stick together and form clumps.

As this process continues, it slows down circulation and creates a phenomenon described as sludging. About six hours following the meal, the sludging is severe enough to virtually halt circulation in the smallest of blood vessels. This has several effects on the body, including reduced oxygen to the tissues and a lessened ability to remove carbon dioxide and waste from the system. The illustration at right shows the time release effects of fatty food intake and sludging.

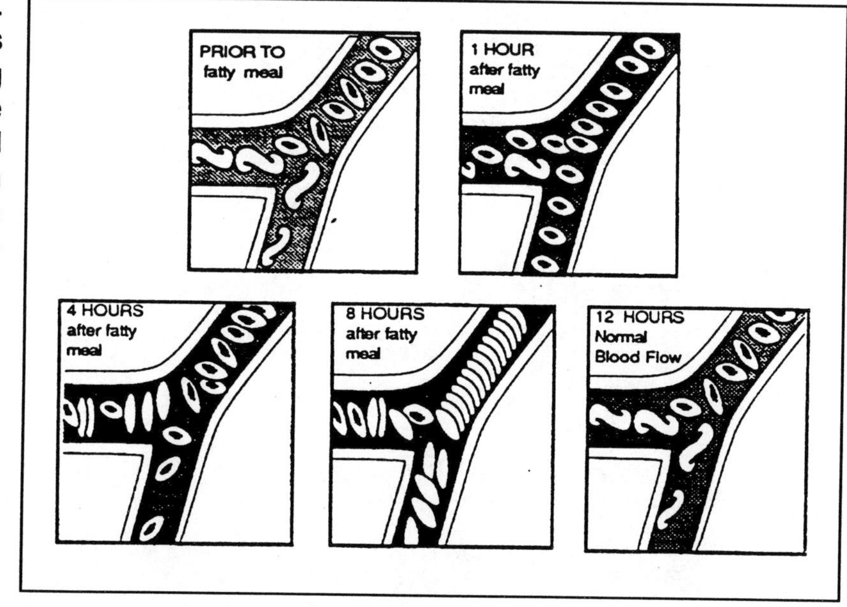

In diving, we are concerned with the transport of inert gas as well as metabolic gases. Circulatory diseases, circulatory inefficiencies and the physiological changes associated with fat ingestion will all interfere with the elimination of inert gases while diving. In the case of circulatory disease and the corresponding decrease in the diameter of the blood vessel, it is easy to see that gas transport will not be efficient. It is also probable that when a bubble is formed, it is more likely to become lodged in the blood vessels with less chance of being filtered out by the lungs.

The circulatory changes that follow a fatty meal include an increased resistance to gas transport and elimination due to the sludging effect. In addition, this sludging appears to be associated with decompression sickness (DCS). If it is already present, there will be a predisposition towards DCS. The blood gas changes will also contribute to carbon dioxide retention and play a role in susceptibility to oxygen toxicity, inert gas narcosis, helium tremors and its own set of problems, including a change in pH balance. All fats are not bad, and so we need to mention good fats as well. Good fat lubricates the system and, in the proper quantities, is good for us. Fat can be grouped into Omega 3, which is good fat, and Omega 6, which is bad fat. In general, one should avoid the Omega 6 fats and insure some Omega 3 fats are in the diet. The "Trans Fats and Oxidized Fats" chart shows the type of fats and their effects.

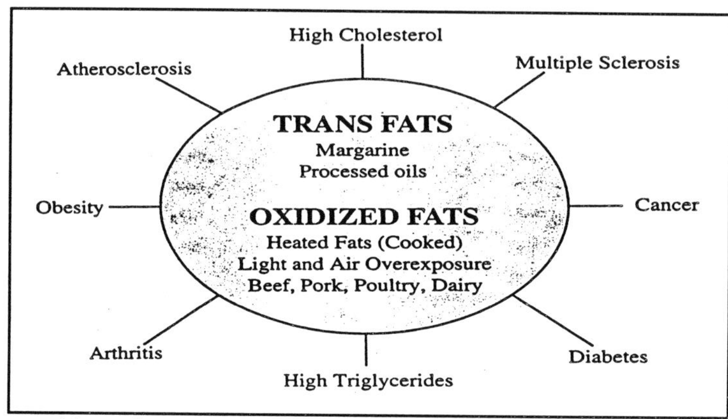

Many diseases have their origin from fats. Trans fats are the primary factor as these are biologically inactive. They separate from the cis (biologically active) portion of fat and block the production of healthy cells. Trans fats occupy space and provide no vital function. This leads to unhealthy situations making tissues permeable to viruses and other illnesses.

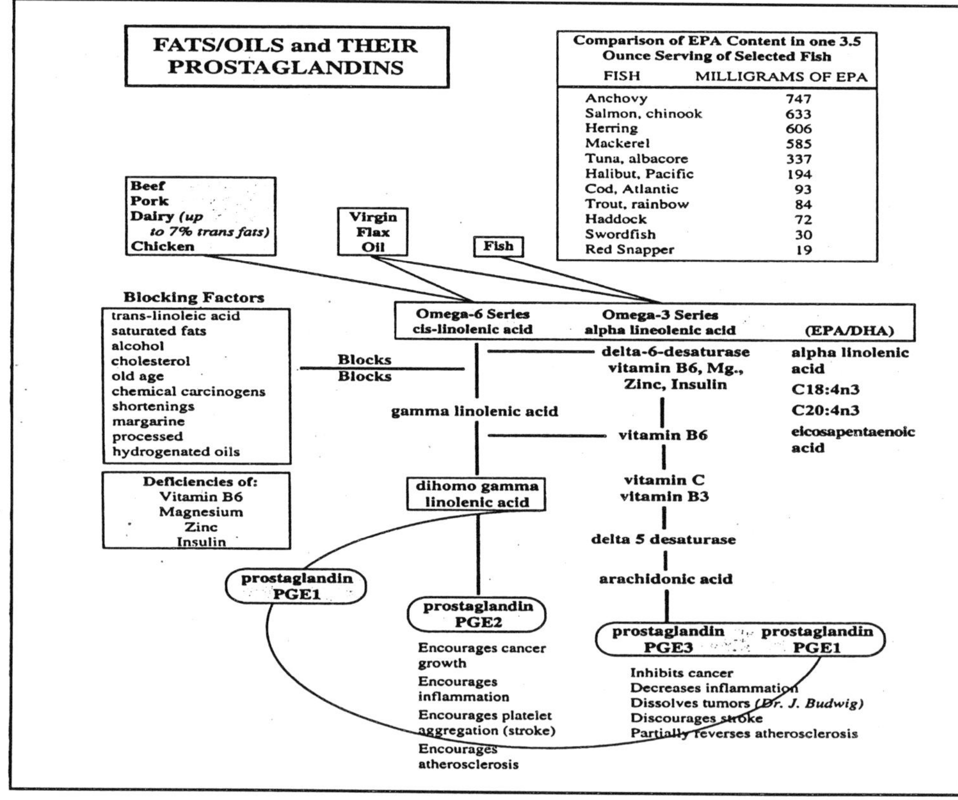

Much of the trans fats in the American diet come from hydrogenated vegetable oils. Other sources include red meats and margarine. If you need the flavor, use butter which is a cis (good) fat. Trans fats cause swelling of the mitochondria, the sub units where metabolism occurs; thus, it interferes with metabolism trans fatty acids can increase blood cholesterol up to 15% and triglycerides by 47%.

Cis fats are good and are needed for vision, nerve function, coordination, memory and the vital functions of life itself. Cis fatty acids may reverse the effects of trans fats. Oils such as olive, fish, flax, corn, and sesame all represent forms of cis fats and are beneficial to cells.

Antioxidants and Fiber

Antioxidants such as vitamin E do much to reverse the development of free radicals in the body. Vitamin E elevates HDL levels and provides numerous health effects. Other antioxidants include vitamin C, beta-carotene, CQ_{10}, and Melatonin. These substances, when combined with nutrients and vitamins, especially the B's, are effective in promoting a healthier body and circulatory system. Fiber is also needed to maintain a healthy circulatory system.

> **IANTD** feels that the value of antioxidants to the diver is significant enough that it produced the "Diver's Antioxidant Plan" formulated and distributed by **IANTD**.

Fiber (i.e. whole grains, fruits and vegetables) is an excellent body cleansing agent and should be in all divers' diets. Fiber has been shown to be effective in preventing some forms of cancer, and it is excellent for our heart and blood vessels. Fiber is also needed to maintain a healthy circulatory system, which will in turn reduce a diver's predisposition towards diving related injuries to the system. Figure "Fats/Oils and Their Prostaglandins" shows some interesting effects of fiber on cholesterol levels in the blood.

Sugars

Sugar is needed for immediate energy expenditure and for prolonged endurance. A warm muscle will burn fat and use the sugars gained from the carbohydrates we eat. Explosive action by muscles not properly warmed up tends to burn only sugar. Thus, prior to exercise or a dive, it is wise to take a few moments to stretch and warm the muscles up before placing a demand on them.

Too much sugar, especially processed sugars, is harmful. Excess sugar creates an increase in insulin from the pancreas, which attempts to transport the insulin to tissues throughout the body. Chromium is an intricate part of the biochemistry of this process. It gets sugar from the blood to the cells. The more sugar digested, the lower the chromium, because sugar depletes the chromium levels.

Aortas examined by Howard A. Neuman Ph.D. disclosed that in areas where the sugar intake is low, people have high chromium levels and a lowered incidence of arteriosclerosis. In the USA, where sugar uptake is excessive, it was found that a higher incidence of arteriosclerosis is present and that the chromium level is low. This means that insulin is unable to work up to par and the blood fats do not get cleared from the circulatory system efficiently. (Chromium is an excellent supplement to take when combined with vitamin B3.)

Increased sugar also has the side effect of weakening the immune system's ability to fight off bacteria. In one test, individuals given sucrose and fructose experienced a depression of white blood cells that lasted for up to five hours. If you are becoming ill, avoid all sweets. High levels of sugar are also bad for the heart. By now, you should realize that a combination of excessive sugar and fats could be very damaging to the circulatory system.

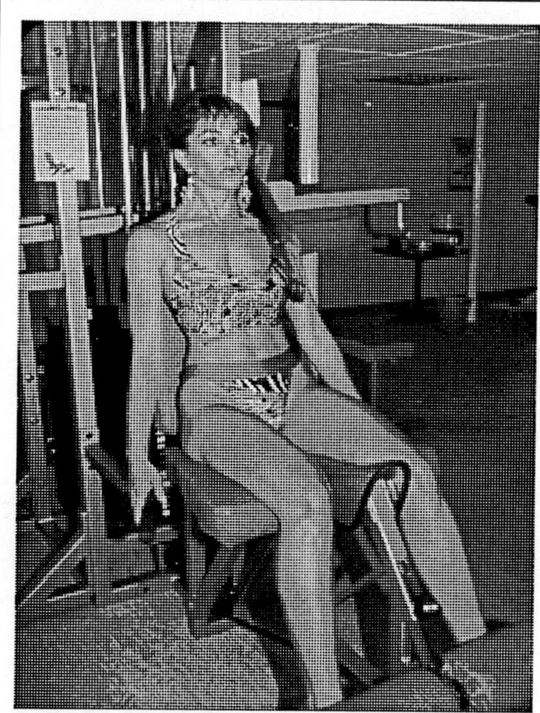

Patti Mount working out to stay fit for technical dives. Photo: Tom Mount

The second prime need for a healthy circulatory system is cardio-vascular exercise. Exercise benefits the respiratory system by producing healthier lungs. Healthy lungs in turn provide better ventilation. The in-shape diver's VO_2 max, the ability to utilize oxygen efficiently, is higher than a non-fit counterpart. This increased VO_2 max allows the conditioned diver to work harder without a dramatic increase in RMV. In life threatening situations, this respiratory efficiency may prove to be the dividing line between survival and non-survival.

Another advantage of regular exercise is that it places demands on every organ in the body. The liver responds to exercise by producing glycogen more efficiently. Insulin and glucose regulation is fine-tuned by the pancreas as a reaction to exercise. The heart and lungs deliver more oxygen, and the circulatory system builds more capillaries. LDL cholesterol drops while the good cholesterol, HDL, levels elevate. The mitochondria enlarge and produce additional adenosine triphosphate (ATP), thus providing us with more energy. As an added benefit, the body also begins to burn more fat.

Some benefits of having a high rate of oxygen uptake due to an increased VO_2 max from exercise include:

- Lower blood pressure
- Better heart regulation
- Stronger tendons and ligaments
- Thicker cartilage
- Larger muscles
- Greater blood volume
- More hemoglobin
- Less body fat
- Denser bones
- More efficient lungs
- Heart pumps more blood with each stroke
- More oxygen extracted from the blood
- More capillaries
- Lower heart rate

The more intense the aerobic program, the better the VO_2 development. Tour-de-France cyclists have among the highest VO_2 max of all athletes. It is this high pulmonary efficiency that allows them to perform well on a long enduring race. A diver who needs endurance to swim a given distance, to assist another diver, or to get out of a bad situation will be more prone to success if they are in good physical condition.

If started in time, the combination of exercise and prudent diet habits will produce a healthier body, reverse circulatory problems that may already exist, and act as a preventative step for most diving-related illnesses. In short, it is not logical to eat a fatty diet, be a couch potato, *and* participate in a strenuous form of diving or other activities.

In numerous studies, regular exercise has been shown to lower the instance of heart disease. It is effective both in lowering blood cholesterol levels and in conditioning the heart. Exercise stimulates collateral circulation. If blood vessels leading to the heart are clogged, collateral vessels can take over the job of supplying the tissues with circulation. Exercise increases the amount of collateral circulation, and thus reduces instances of sudden death from heart attack.

Tom Mount practicing what he preaches.

Photo: Patti Mount

Exercise has also been shown to be a releaser of the good cholesterol HDL. The preferred type of exercise for circulatory conditioning is an aerobic program. To accomplish an aerobic level of exercise, you must work at an elevated heart rate that is safe, yet high enough to effect physical change.

To determine a maximum safe heart rate, subtract your age from 220. During aerobic exercise, your target heart rate should be 65% of your safe heart rate. For example, if your age is 60, subtract 220 - 60 = 160 X 0.65 = 104. If you are 30 it will be 220 - 30 =190 X 0.65= 143. It is apparent that with aging the target aerobic rate is reduced.

Once you are in good shape, increase the target rate in increments of 70% to 75% and eventually to 80%. Once at the 80% value, do not increase the target aerobic rate beyond this value. This translates to a 60 year old settling on a heart rate of 160 *x* .80 = 128 and a 30 year old would evolve to 190 *x* 0.80 = 152.

The aerobic workout should be performed at least three times a week. The minimum time should be 20 minutes, and an ideal time is one hour. Seek out a training program with which you will be happy. There are many machines on the market that tone both the upper and lower body and some even double as strength exercises. Swimming, cycling, jogging, rollerblading and so forth are all excellent for cardio-vascular conditioning.

For added benefit, and to prevent boredom, incorporate cross training by doing more than one form of exercise. One day go cycling, the next row or swim. This maximizes your exercise potential and prevents boredom. You may even do cross training within an individual workout. Ideally, develop a program you will stick with. Make this an integral part of your normal daily habits. Place its priority above all other items during the time you select as a daily exercise time. Most people are more prone to maintain an exercise regime if they do it in the morning before becoming involved in daily activities.

The circulatory system is vital to our overall health. The recommendations discussed in this section will, if adhered to, prevent circulatory problems and enable us to have better gas transport. This in turn will help protect us from decompression illness and other diving disorders. If you are going to be a serious diver, take serious actions to insure your safety.

The Nervous System

To understand breathing's effects in light of Eastern philosophy, we need to understand what happens when *Prana* is interrupted and its effects on our nervous system.

Our nervous system controls the actions of all other systems in our physical bodies. It is composed of two subsystems. The first is the *central nervous system (CNS),* which includes our brain and spinal cord. The second is the *peripheral nervous system,* which is made up of our parallel cranial and spinal nerves. This subsystem consists of 12 pairs of cranial nerves in the brain and 31 pairs of spinal cord nerves. These nerves spread throughout the body, forming a complex network of nerve fibers responsible for carrying messages outward from the CNS to the nerve endings. *Afferent,* or sensory nerve fibers, transmit information back to the CNS from the arms and legs.

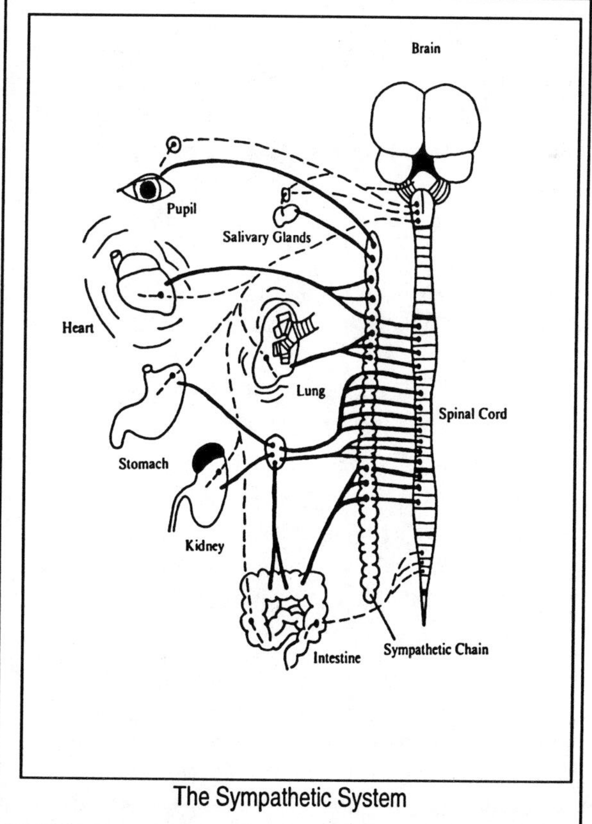

The Sympathetic System

The **autonomic nervous system** *(ANS)* regulates the so-called involuntary functions. These functions include secretion, lung control, heartbeat and control of the "internal environment" (emotions, temperature regulation, etc.). By assuming control over some functions of the ANS, breathing can be controlled and, thus, our internal environment.

The ANS is divided into the **sympathetic** and **parasympathetic** *systems.* The Endocrine System controls the parasympathetic system by hormonal release. These opposing systems insure body/nerve functioning and reaction to stimuli. The parasympathetic system tends to slow the heart. The sympathetic system speeds it up. This action results in normal heart functioning.

The sympathetic system is composed of two vertical rows of **ganglia**, nerve cell clusters, on either side of the spinal column. These branch out to glands and viscera in the thorax and abdomen, forming **integrated plexuses** (energy centers) with nerve endings of the parasympathetic system.

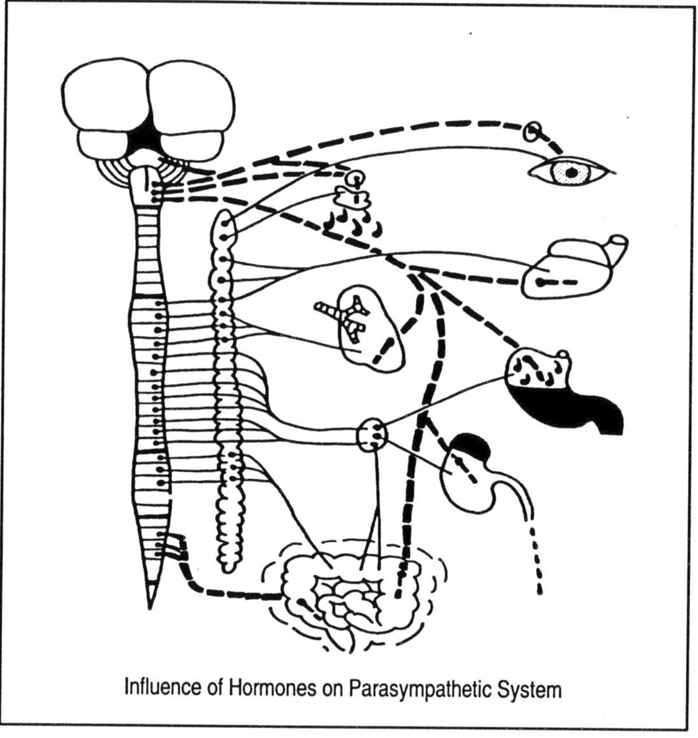
Influence of Hormones on Parasympathetic System

The **vagus nerve** is the 10th cranial nerve and is the focal point of the system. The vagus nerve is connected with the brain's *cerebellum* and extends along the spinal cord through the neck, chest and abdomen, sending out branches to form various plexuses within the sympathetic system. It ends in a plexus that, in return, is connected to the **solar plexus**. In addition, through filaments, it is connected with the lower plexuses.

Most religions and philosophies recognize an inner energy source. They usually refer to it as a spirit body, soul, or "subtle body". This spiritual body, soul, or subtle body has its own anatomy and physiology, and, thus, contains energy. According to these beliefs, the soul's energy (the subtle body) exists after the physical body dies. Scientists have photographed this energy by using electromagnetic-kirlin photography. These scientists say that psychic energy leaves the physical body within 24 hours of death.

In Eastern philosophy, a model for the spiritual body exists that contains its own anatomy and physiology. Acupuncturists tap into these. In this body, thousands of energy channels, referred to as **nadirs**, are portrayed.

Fourteen nadirs are more important than the others are. Six of these are the most valuable for channeling energy. The most prevailing of these are the three which most directly affect energy flow and are within easy access of our direct control. One of these flows through the right nostril. The second one is directed through the left nostril. The third is channeled with the flow of both nostrils. Through meditation, and correct breathing practices, control of these allows freedom from outside distractions and non-directed thoughts from the conscious mind. All three major nadirs originate at the base of the spine and travel upward along the same paths, as do the ANS nerves in their downward journey along the spine.

The junctions where these nadirs crisscross are known as **Chakras**. In addition, other nadirs also cross at these junctions developing them as major energy fields. These Chakras are located in the same areas as our major plexus. Thus, once again, we see the theoretical coincidence of the philosophical model that dates thousands of years prior to the physical being described by Western science. The Chakras are "charged" when directing the breath and flow of energy while the body is in a meditative state.

There are seven principal *Chakras*. They are all highly sensitive to breathing.

- The "**Spleen Chakra**," or ***Swadhisthana***, is located over the spleen in the lower abdomen level with the **hypogastric plexus**. It is the Chakra of emotion and sexuality. Its element is water. It can be used to gain control of emotions and emotional responses and sexuality. The color or associations are those that deal with vital forces of life. Orange is its predominate color.
- The "**Root Chakra**," or ***Muladhara***, is located at the base of the spine at the same level as the **pelvic plexus**. This Chakra, when activated, radiates a fiery orange-red color representing its vitality. This Chakra is associated with survival and is The "Earth Chakra." Divers who wish to develop strong "survival will", may wish to emphasize this Chakra in meditation and breathing patterns.
- The "**Navel Chakra**," or ***Manipura***, is located at the **solar plexus**. It governs personal power and metabolic energy. The element is fire and its color is yellow.
- The "**Heart Chakra**," or ***Anahata***, is located in the region of the heart level with the **cardiac plexus**. As one would suspect, this Chakra deals with love. Its element is air with a color of green.
- The "**Throat Chakra**," or ***Vishuddha***, is located at the **pharyngeal plexus**. This Chakra is affiliated with communications and creativity. The element is sound and its color is blue.
- The "**Brow Chakra**", or ***Anja***, is located in the forehead between the eyebrows level with the **nasociliary plexus**. This all-important Chakra, known as the "third eye," deals with clairvoyance, intuition, and imagination; all-important attributes to exploratory divers. The element for the third eye is light and its predominate color is indigo.
- The "**Crown Chakra**," or ***Sahasara***, is located at the top of the head, **within the brain**. The anterior portion passes through the third eye Chakra. This empowering Chakra is associated with knowledge and understanding. The element is thought and its color is violet.

Meditation uses concentration to bring energy into each of these energy centers.

Research has shown it can energize the body. Indeed, most who practice these techniques report feelings of deeper relaxation and increased intuition as well as increased awareness. The benefits of increased intuition and greater awareness are important aspects for underwater explorers.

If we now overlay the physical body with the "subtle body," we have a complete view of a life/energy system. The subtle body serves as a counterpart to the nerves and plexus. The physical body is developed around the framework of nadirs which coincide with the location of our plexus.

People do not use all of the stored energy, or **Prana**, available to them. Thus, a vast energy potential is stored as a "seed state". This stored energy, with study and practice, can be tapped. In Eastern thought it is called **Kundalini**. If a person successfully cultivates their Kundalini, they experience peace and increased ability to control their lives.

By studying and with the development of breath control, you may realize increased healing powers and greater resistance to diseases. Perhaps, an even greater discovery is that through correct breathing, you control the right side of your brain and the ability to completely control your mind. It is thought that many diseases are due to an imbalance in energy, or loss of Prana. They are caused by improper breathing, stress and negative mental states. If you search your past, you may remember that at times when a great deal of stress existed in your life, there was probably a corresponding lowering of your immune system, and an increase in your susceptibility to colds, allergies and other infirmities.

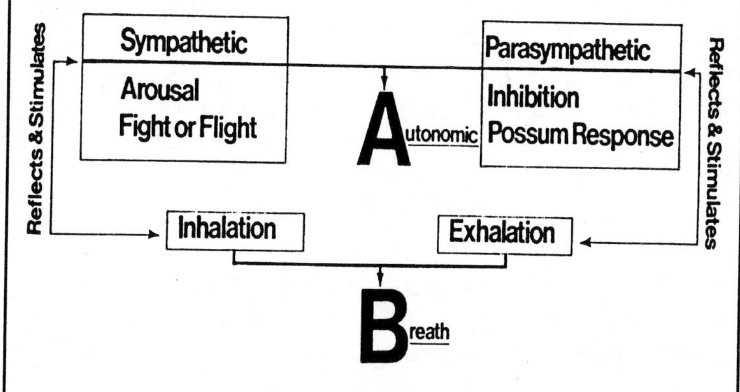

Without altering any of your religious beliefs, we simply suggest that you regularly practice good breathing techniques, meditation, and some form of physical toning, not only to lower your stress levels but also to improve your diving controls. In doing so, you may experience less mental fatigue and, perhaps, a healthier body.

As discussed previously, there are two ways we can gain control over the involuntary nervous system (ANS). The first, and easiest to accomplish, is the control of respiration. This can be accomplished through the practice of breathing exercises, which will not only make us better divers, but can also be incorporated into our everyday lives.

Breath control regulates heart function by bringing the right **vagus nerve** under control. This action allows access to the involuntary nervous system, or ANS, and its conscious direction.

The second means of controlling the ANS is by developing a stronger will. *No,* we don't mean leaving everything you own to IANTD. What we mean is, through meditation, we can sharply focus mental energy, thus gaining access to our minds. To maximize our self-control, we need to incorporate both correct breathing and meditation.

Respiration is a major body function. Breathing is the source of all life-sustaining energy. Breathing dictates emotional stability, health and happiness. A stressed person produces even more stress by breathing incorrectly. This type of individual will tend to breathe shallow and rapidly. You can avoid this pitfall by concentrating on slow, deep breathing to release stress and tension.

The Respiratory System

The respiratory system functions in conjunction with the circulatory system. It provides the hemoglobin with an appropriate environment for gas exchange. When the body is at rest, the breathing cycle starts when the nervous system detects an increase in carbon dioxide (and a corresponding decrease in oxygen) in the blood. Stress and increased exercise levels also affect breathing rhythms. These reduce neuro-chemical stimuli for breathing. Carbon dioxide, which alters blood pH levels, is the primary stimulus for initiating breathing.

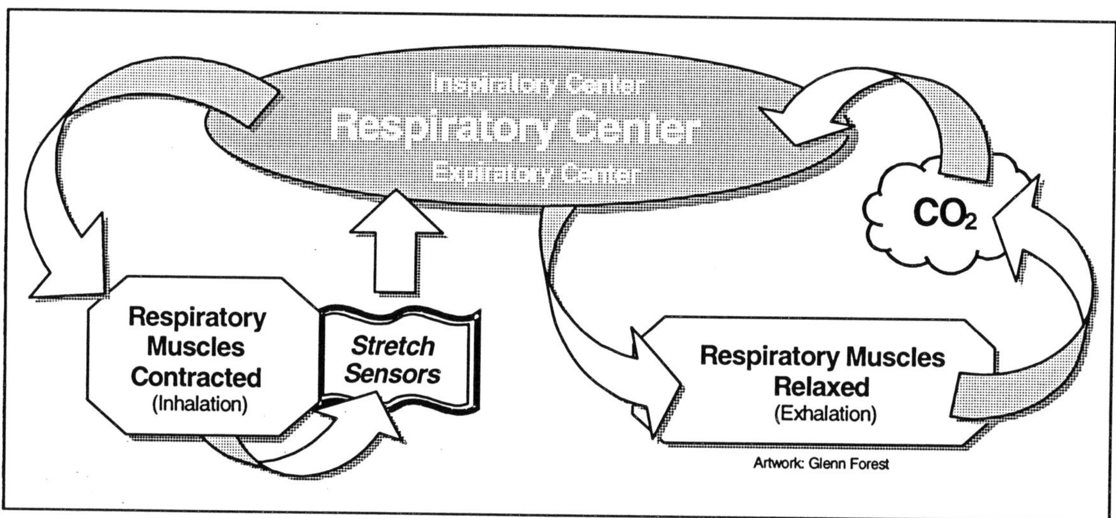

As our CO_2 level increases, a signal is sent to the Inhalation (Inspiratory) Center of the Respiratory Complex located in the *medulla oblongata* portion of the brain. It transmits a signal telling the respiratory muscles to contract. When this happens, the diaphragm causes the lungs to expand. The lungs are composed of billions of **alveoli** that are coated with a *surfactant-type* protein substance. This surfactant increases surface tension. Surface tension maintains the shape of the alveoli as well as the lungs themselves.

In order for inhalation to occur, the contraction of the respiratory muscles must overcome this surface tension. Upon relaxation of the muscles, the surface tension draws the lungs back to a "normal" shape and the chest and diaphragm follow this action. These two actions, contraction of respiratory muscles and relaxation of these muscles, combined with surface tension of the alveoli, produce inhalation and exhalation at rest.

The human respiratory system is a complex system of tissue groups beginning with the nasal and oral cavities and extending to the diaphragm. When air is drawn down the *trachea*, it splits into the **bronchi** that serve the two lungs. The bronchi resemble branches of a tree, becoming smaller until they terminate into the **bronchioles**. They, in turn, end in a series of tiny air sacs (alveoli). As the illustration on page 88 shows, there is a big difference between the lungs of a non-smoker and those of a smoker.

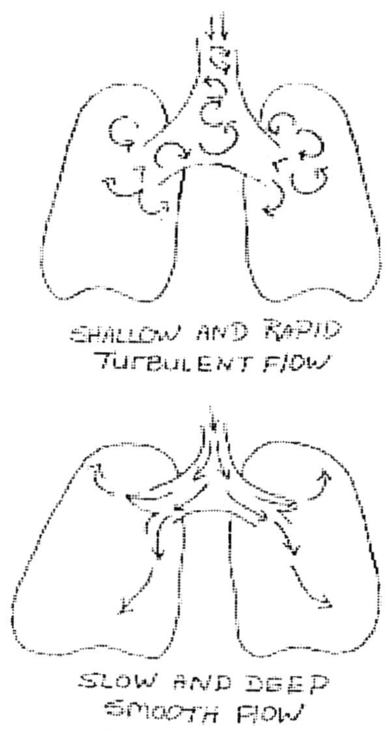

Turbulent versus Smooth Gas Flow

Artwork: Carla Ram

Once initiated, inhalation continues until the **stretch sensors** within the lungs sense adequate expansion. Upon attaining the desired level of expansion, the sensors respond to the Expiratory Center. They, in turn, communicate the need to discontinue inhalation.

During inhalation, gas traveling through an airway will meet frictional resistance caused by the walls of the trachea which will result in gas literally bouncing off the airway's walls. These molecules oppose the flow of additional gas. This results in **turbulent gas flow**.

Breathing (gas flow) that produces turbulence is inefficient and may lead to hyperventilation. Inadequate ventilation generates a sensation of gas starvation. If the autonomic nervous system reacts to this sensation, it will stimulate an increased breathing rate. In divers, this is commonly seen as a "gulping" of gas. This pattern, if left unchecked, results in improper ventilation, produces stress, and, most certainly, ends in panic caused by a perception of gas failure.

To avoid this reaction, it is important that divers be trained to inhale and exhale slowly. The volume should be deep and evenly paced. In other words, the respiratory rate and *respiratory minute volume (RMV)* should be slow and deep. A RMV of this nature avoids turbulence, maintains *Laminar flow*, assuring the diver of proper ventilation. Deep, slow breathing causes a greater fraction of the tidal volume to enter the alveoli. Shallow breathing causes a smaller fraction of the tidal volume to enter the alveoli.

Gas exchange does not begin until inhaled gas reaches the alveoli. A complex network of capillaries surrounds the alveoli, allowing oxygen to be exchanged from the lungs into the circulatory system. At the same time, carbon dioxide is transferred from the bloodstream and exhaled.

Blood is a complex, multi-faceted liquid tissue that has evolved to meet the complex demands placed on the circulatory system. Among it's many functions are the supply oxygen and nutritional materials to the body's cells, the removal of waste and waste gases, and the activation of the body's immune system. The quantity of blood in the lungs is not evenly distributed. Moreover, it is gravity-dependent. When we are upright, more blood is in the lower portion of our lungs than in the middle and upper parts. Conversely, the flow of gases is at its peak in the upper portions of the lungs. Thus, gas transfer is not as efficient as one would assume.

To provide gas to the lower third of the lungs and to their rich vascular network, **slow, deep diaphragmatic breathing is essential.** If the alveoli are injured due to a physical accident, they become inefficient. Tobacco smokers (or smokers of other substances) will eventually lose pulmonary efficiency. This loss is called **emphysema**. Smoke produces a breakdown in the lining of the lungs, resulting in a "visible hole". This hole reduces the amount of surface area available for oxygen to come into contact with blood across the alveoli. This reduces the amount of gas exchanged across the alveoli.

BLOOD DISTRIBUTION The darker the area, the greater the concentration of blood available for gas exchange.	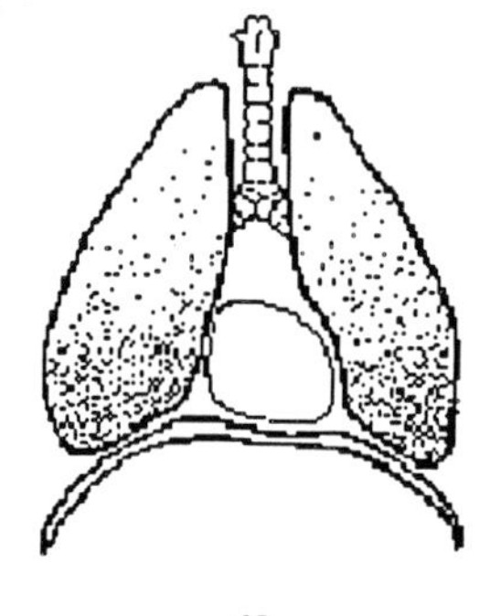
CHEST BREATHING **(INCORRECT)** Chest wall expands, pulling outward, creating a partial vacuum.	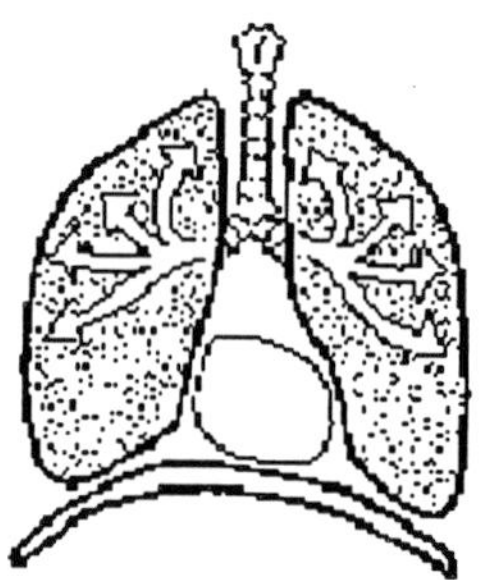
DIAPHRAGMATIC BREATHING **(CORRECT)** Diaphragm contracts pulling down (flat) creating a more complete vacuum that pulls air down into lowest lobes.	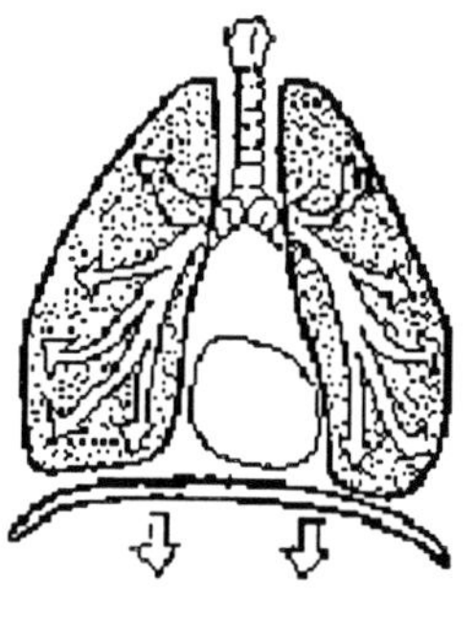
EXHALATION Diaphragm relaxes flexing back into a dome-shape forcing air out of the lungs.	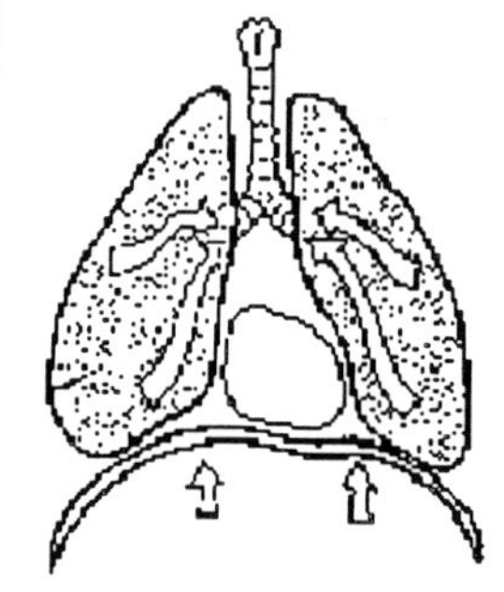

The diffusion of gases across the alveoli results from a difference in hydrostatic pressures. Upon inhalation, the gas in our lungs has a higher oxygen level than does the blood in the alveoli, causing a pressure difference that is equalized through gas exchange.

Once in the alveoli, oxygen is diffused into the pulmonary capillaries. At this point, we have low oxygen pressure. Upon exhaling, the blood in our capillaries contains a reduced volume of oxygen. The carbon dioxide bonded to our hemoglobin is high. This pressure forces the carbon dioxide in our blood into our alveoli where it is exhaled.

Red blood cells (*erythrocytes*) carry the majority of the oxygen required by the body's tissues. Red blood cells transport oxygen via hemoglobin, a protein capable of easily bonding and unbonding with oxygen.

Once oxygen has been diffused into the pulmonary system, it is transported by two mechanisms. Some will remain in simple solution in *blood plasma*, but most of it will bond to hemoglobin. Hemoglobin is composed of four protein chains attached to one atom of iron. It is the iron in hemoglobin that attracts oxygen. This enables the circulatory system to transport oxygen.

Blood turns bright red when hemoglobin becomes oxygenated. People who have low hemoglobin levels are called *anemic*. People who suffer from severe anemia should be very cautious when diving. They should be especially careful when making deep dives. The increased partial pressures of oxygen and carbon dioxide may complicate the anemic condition. Hemoglobin also transports carbon dioxide from the body's cells. This CO_2-enriched hemoglobin turns the blood a bluish color.

With proper gas supplies, the only gases that will combine with hemoglobin are oxygen and carbon dioxide. However, if the gas supply contains carbon monoxide (CO), it will combine with hemoglobin **210 times** more readily than oxygen. In diving, carbon monoxide poisoning generally originates from a contaminated air supply. It is colorless, odorless, and tasteless.

Carbon monoxide will not support life and renders one anemic and hypoxic quite rapidly. If unchecked, high levels of CO may lead to unconsciousness and possible death. Smokers can have 5% to 15% of their hemoglobin combined with CO. As depth increases, so do the partial pressures of **all** gases in the breathing medium. This compounds the effects of carbon monoxide.

As inhaled gas diffuses across the alveoli, it travels from the capillaries in the lungs and enters the heart via the pulmonary arteries. The heart pumps this oxygen-enriched blood via the arteries where it then enters the capillaries and nourishes all the cells in the body. The body eliminates CO_2 by transporting it back to the lungs where it diffuses across the alveoli and is exhaled.

In addition to oxygen, blood transports nourishment absorbed from the body's digestive system. When the body's cells receive oxygen and nourishment, a chemical reaction occurs. Oxygen "burns" this fuel and produces energy. The fuel comes from carbohydrates and fats we consume. This reaction (**metabolism**) takes place within our cells in an area known collectively as **mitochondria.** Mitochondria contain specialized protein molecules, or *enzymes,* referred to as *cytochrome oxidase.* They take energy released from the oxidation of food (fuel) and transfer it to an energy storage molecule called **Adenosine Triphosphate** *(***ATP***).* ATP stores energy within our cells.

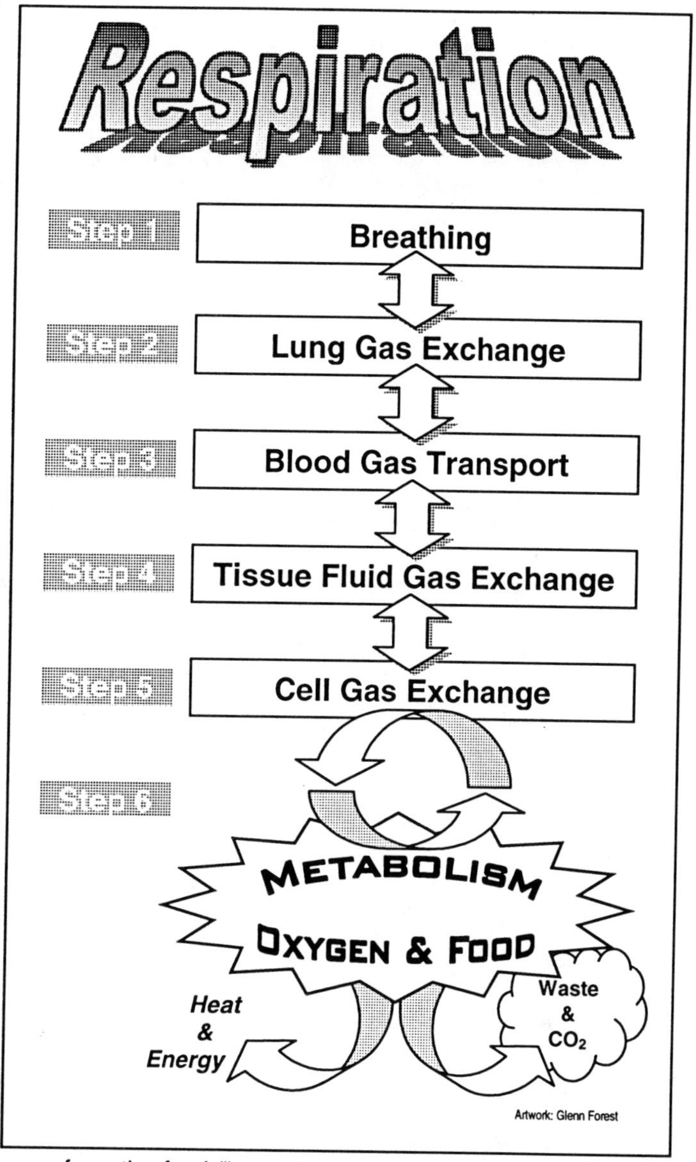

As energy is produced, wastes are generated and carbon dioxide (another waste) is produced. Carbon comes from the food "burned" at the cell level in an oxygen-rich environment. The result is carbon dioxide. The pressure of CO_2 rises as a result of oxidation. CO_2 is forced into the venous capillaries. It is transported by larger and larger veins until it is returned to the heart and the cycle begins again. If the body retains CO_2, or has a reduced capacity to eliminate it, it has an adverse physiological effect on the human mechanism.

Respiration at Depth

Divers must compensate for density in their breathing habits as they dive deeper. The ANS reflex to increasing gas density is to breathe faster - a reaction that increases turbulence in the airways, which in turn leads to reduced breathing efficiency. As the water depth or workload is increased, it becomes important to discipline yourself to maintain slow, deep breathing.

While swimming, experiment with a swim pace that balances workload with your ability to maintain a slow, deep breathing pattern. Swimming faster than this pace is inefficient. It alters your breathing pattern, which could cause increased turbulence in your airway and an inadequate gas supply to the alveoli.

Frequently, divers will accelerate their pace under stress. This may lead to a loss of breathing control. Conversely, divers in an air-sharing situation will drastically slow their pace. This could leave them with insufficient gas to reach the surface. Therefore, the aware diver's conscious reaction to a gas sharing situation should be to maintain a normal pace that allows a balanced swimming pace in harmony with safe breathing patterns.

Surface breathing is usually done through the nose. It takes up to 150% more effort to pull gas through the nose than the mouth. We do it because it provides more than 30 functions benefiting our health and quality of breathing. Nasal breathing filters, moisturizes, directs gas flow, warms and conditions the gas, produces the sense of smell, brings in oxygen, creates mucus, provides drainage for the sinuses and affects the nervous system.

Smoking and Respiratory Health

The lungs, which are made up by the alveoli, are divided into five lobes. The right lung contains three lobes and the left lung has two lobes. If all of the alveoli that compose the lungs were laid out on land, they would cover more than half of a tennis court. The airways connecting the lungs to the nasal passage and mouth are lined with ciliated columnar epithelial cells. These cilia prevent pollutants and dirt laden particles from entering the lungs.

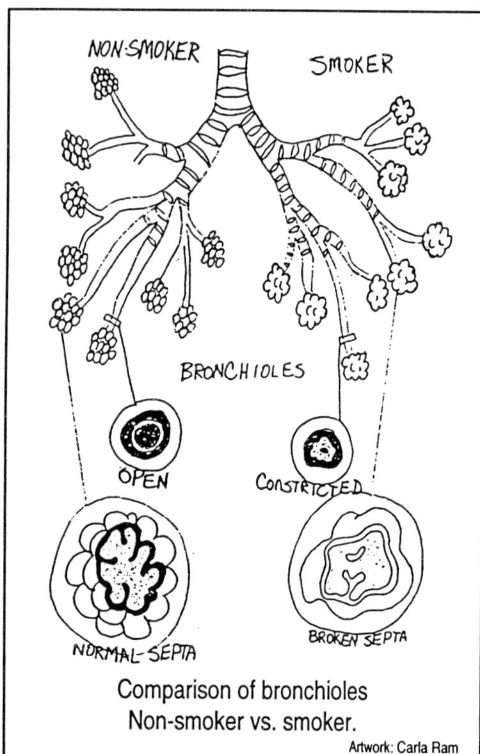

Comparison of bronchioles
Non-smoker vs. smoker.
Artwork: Carla Ram

When a person smokes, there is an immediate effect on the nervous, circulatory and respiratory systems. One early effect is to paralyze the action of cilia. A single cigarette will stop cilia action for 20 minutes. Smoking causes an immediate increase in mucus production and interferes with oxygen uptake. Smoking creates a faster respiratory rate. This increased respiratory rate combined with density at depth leads to turbulent airflow. It increases the work of breathing and, as stated before, causes carbon monoxide to be carried by the blood. The CO displaces oxygen in the hemoglobin. Carbon monoxide combines with hemoglobin 210 times more readily than oxygen.

Smoking causes the heart to work harder, producing a higher pulse rate and an increase in blood pressure. At the same time, blood flow is decreased due to the constriction of blood vessels reacting to tobacco smoke. This eventually predisposes one to heart disease, but more immediately, increases a diver's susceptibility to decompression sickness, as it reduces circulatory efficiency. Smoking also creates a reaction that causes us to experience a drop in body temperature.

One additional risk that divers who smoke face is the possibility of mucus plugs behaving just like a gas bubble. In addition, these plugs will form a base for bubble attachment and will prevent filtering by the lungs. With congestion in the lungs, which is characteristic of smokers, combined with the damaged alveoli, there is a marked probability of gas trapping and a higher risk of pulmonary barotrauma.

A Prescription for Diving Health

As stated at the outset, this chapter contains information from two worlds - Western science and Eastern metaphysical doctrines. Keeping an open mind, digesting all that is essential to your personal needs, learning how to breathe correctly, and continuing to practice correct breathing techniques **will** help you become a better diver and quite possibly improve your health. We're certain you'll be amazed at the overall results.

If we eat correctly, avoid smoking cigarettes (and other substances), keep alcohol consumption to no more than one to two ounces a day, and exercise daily, we will enjoy both a safer dive and better overall health. Many common diseases are caused by a failure to take the basic steps of prevention. It is our choice to be fit or unhealthy. The more fit we are, the safer our dives will be. Choose to smoke that cigarette, eat that donut, and drown it with a six-pack, and you will eventually discover the ills such behaviors bring to your body.

Conversely, you can be moderate in your habits avoid the cigarettes, exercise regularly, limit alcohol intake and enjoy a healthier lifestyle. It isn't just the benefit of feeling good day to day, it is also the increased resistance to diving related injuries that being fit and smoke free will award you with.

References:

Dr. Duarte's Health Alternatives, Alex Duarte, O.D. Ph.D., 10175 Joerschke Drive #335 Grass Valley, Ca. 95945
Health Rider
Enter The Zone, Barry Sears Ph.D., Harper and Collins 10 East 53rd St NY, NY 10022
Power Protein Plan, The Drs. Eades, Colorado Center for Metabolic Medicine, 7490 Clubhouse Rd., Co.
Freedom from Stress, Phil Nuernberger Ph.D., Himalayan International Institute of Yoga RD 1 box 88 Honesdale Pa. 18431
Science of Breath: Swami Rama, Rudolph Ballentine MD, and Alan Hymes MD, International Institute of Yoga, RD 1 Box 88 Honesdale, Pa. 18431
Practical Diving, Tom Mount, University of Miami Press - out of print
The New Practical Diving Tom Mount, University of Miami Press - out of print
Mixed Gas Diving Tom Mount et al., Watersports Publishing - out of print
Cell Physiology
The Lung
Wheels of Life

CHAPTER 6
The Effects Of Drugs On Diving

Bruce V. Voss, M.D.

This chapter deals with the singular issue of drugs and the diver. Drugs can be defined as "...**any substance, synthetic or extracted from plant or animal tissue... which is used as a medicant to prevent or cure disease.**" Consider drugs to be either prescription or non-prescription medications; the latter further divided into illicit or legal medications. I would venture to say that most physical conditions that are being treated by a physician are managed with prescription medications versus nonprescription.

Miria Denlay inspecting the gun mounted just aft of the periscope shears on the submarine USS *Apogon*, Bikini Atoll.

Photo: Kevin Denlay

The former include those medications for chronic condition; i.e., high blood pressure, heart rhythm problems, respiratory problems such as asthma, chronic obstructive pulmonary disease, bronchitis, etc. The non-prescription medications include the legal (or non-controlled) meds; i.e., alcohol, sinus medications, motion sickness pills, headache prescriptions, pain pills, etc. In the illicit category would be hallucinogens, stimulants such as cocaine and amphetamines, euphorics like marijuana, etc., which stimulate the nervous system.

An important distinction needs to be made here. That is, that the autonomic nervous system - the part of the nervous system that responds automatically to the environment (internal or external) - can be subdivided into two components. The sympathetic nervous system is the "flight or fight" system and is opposed by the parasympathetic system. These two control body functions and are involuntary and don't require conscious input. The sympathetic nervous system involves increases in sweating, heart rate, blood sugar and temperature in response to stimuli. The parasympathetic nervous system acts in the opposite direction and opposes sympathetic nervous system input (one exception is the increase in gastrointestinal secretion in response to parasympathetic input).

Activation of the sympathetic system is by way of epinephrine (adrenaline) and norepinephrine (noradrenaline). Drugs such as cocaine and amphetamines that activate the sympathetic system do so because they are chemically similar to epinephrine/norepinephrine or because they can cause a release of those two mediators.

Another mechanism for activation would be a drug that blocks the parasympathetic system (i.e. anticholinergic agent) and so have unopposed sympathetic activity (adrenergic). In essence, the balance between parasympathetic and sympathetic stimulation dictates the physiologic response that the diver shows, i.e. sympathetic or parasympathetic response.

Psychotropics

Many people take medications to control their mood, enhance their sense of well being or to enhance some personal experience. While the schizophrenics and manic-depressives probably aren't highly represented in the technical diving community, I would guess that some divers out there take their daily Valium or Prozac - or even amphetamine. Remember the hyperactive child in your neighborhood? Well, that child, diagnosed as having Attention Deficit Disorder (ADD), has grown up and may still be treated with amphetamines.

Beyond the obvious problems of diving at depth and being on medications that alter mood and/or perception, **the real unknown is the effect of depth on the medications' physiological effect**. In the case of drugs known as psychotropics, one medication that has been used at depth in a hyperbaric chamber - a controlled environment and that lends itself to intervention easier than at say 200 fsw (60 msw) in open water - is Diazepam, more commonly know as Valium.

WARNING!
The late Jefferson Davis, M.D. in his *Medical Examination of Sports Scuba Divers* categorically excluded candidates for diving if they were on psychotropics.

Alcohol

Of the nonprescription legitimate drugs that are used for mood altering or enhancing effects, alcohol is probably at the top of the list. We are all aware that alcohol intoxicates and decreases performance, but there are some other effects that this "drug" has associated with it. First, it dilates - opens up - the blood vessels, which allows more blood to be brought to the skin and, therefore, more heat is lost. It is associated with increased risk of vomiting and, therefore, aspiration (inhaling stomach contents, etc., into the lungs.) It, like tea and coffee, is a diuretic, which means it causes you to urinate more, which means your circulating blood volume decreases (less free water is available to dilute the blood volume). This predisposes divers to decompression sickness (DCS). Also, it will act in a manner that is more than additive (that is, one plus one is greater than two) when you couple it with nitrogen narcosis.

Caffeine

Not to be excluded, caffeine (coffee, tea, colas, etc.) has come under attack in the last few years. There is data to show that coffee will raise blood pressure, which, in the right individuals and diving at depth could give an unwanted hypertensive response. Also it can cause ectopy (extra beats) in the heart. This could lead to a fatal dysrrhythmia (malignant and erratic heart beat). While on the topic of caffeine and mood altering drugs, some of us do use caffeine preparations to combat fatigue. Getting "wired" from a caffeine-type agent and then diving, while it may enhance your attentiveness, it will also increase heart rate, metabolic rate, respiratory rate, and oxygen consumption rate, in and of itself, a recipe for disaster.

Respiratory Tract Medications (Meds)

While we probably won't see the "Blue Bloaters" and "Pink Puffers" (chronic bronchitis and emphysematous patients, respectively), we probably will see the diver who enjoys cigarettes after a dive, or the diver who says he/she gets a little tight in the chest during a certain season or climate change. And what of the diver who has a yearly bout of bronchitis, lays off the cigarettes and gets antibiotics for 10 days? Does that diver have an increased risk for barotrauma? Many would say yes. But with cyclical changes and a paucity of findings, these individuals will continue to dive.

There are a variety of medications that can be prescribed with respect to the respiratory tract. The majority of patients with respiratory meds in all likelihood will probably be using bronchodialators; i.e., Ventolin, Proventil; or a theophylline mixture; i.e., Theodur. While the drugs themselves don't have a track record of causing problems at depth, the underlying condition that would cause one to use these meds do. If the pulmonary condition is bad enough to require bronchodilators, then few would disagree that the patient shouldn't be diving.

Some patients with respiratory problems may be using a prescription antihistamine. Usually these have the side effect of sedation and, needless to say, sedation and diving is a bad combination. There are a class of nonprescription "cold" meds, like the ephedrine or pseudoephedrine (Sudafed, Actifed) based meds that will cause an increase in heart rate, blood pressure and will make you rather jittery or nervous. These effects come about because the drug is being used systemically, that is, in an oral form that circulates in the whole body. If the diver instead uses a locally applied - topical - agent like neosynephrine nose drops, the systemic effect will be less. Neosynephrine is an agent that acts as a vaso constrictor; it makes blood vessels, especially in the mucus membranes, shrink in size temporarily. This gives relief from the feeling of "congestion" in the sinuses/nose.

Gastrointestinal and Genito-urinary Systems Meds

There are a few meds used in both the gastrointestinal (GI) and genito-urinary systems that while used there, the effects show up elsewhere. Patients with spastic colitis or irritable bowel syndrome may be taking anti-cholinergic agents. These slow down the natural "parasympathetic nervous system." The end result can be decreased sweating, light insensitivity, blurring of the vision, dry mouth, etc. There also may be an increase in the heart rate. The decrease in sweating can increase the risk of heat stroke in hot climates, etc.

Some divers have been taking medications for ulcers, acid reflux or a hiatal hernia. A popular class of agents for these mild maladies is the histamine type two (H-2) blockers or antagonists. Cimetidine (Tagamet) or Ranitidine (Zantac) are in vogue. These may cause sedation/drowsiness or headaches, with Zantac causing less side effects than Tagamet. Some patients may use a drug called Reglan (metoclopramide) for acid reflux. This drug can cause sedation and extra pyramidal reactions - musculo-skeletal reactions like spasms or contractions.

For those patients suffering Montezuma's revenge and taking Lomotil, there is also a word of caution. Lomotil is a combination of atropine (an anti-cholinergic) and diphenoxylate, a relative of meperidine (Demerol). Demerol is a narcotic and as such can and does cause sedation and respiratory depression. The effects could be additive or synergistic when coupled with nitrogen narcosis. As an aside, antibiotics by themselves, seem to be okay, but the havoc they can cause in the GI tract can be unpleasant. First of all, they can cause nausea and vomiting. Also, many of them can cause a "colitis" picture with a resultant diarrhea that can not only be profuse, but can cause an acid-based imbalance in the blood.

The logical question would be, "Why would anyone with diarrhea want to dive?" Well, after paying a sizable amount of money for a dive trip and equipment, and while being self-medicated from the local drugstore, it is really a question of not what's probable, but what's possible. And as far as human nature goes, anything is possible.

A quick word about nausea and vomiting, since there are a wide variety of agents for nausea, ranging from pills to patches. Most of these meds like Atarax, Antivert, Benadryl, Compazine, Phenergan, Thorazine and Tigan, can cause sedation and when combined with nitrogen narcosis or DCS, the results may be very unpredictable. Some of these agents have as side-effects neurological ramifications besides just sedation. Those neurological effects can range from muscle spasms and seizures to coma and death. Obviously, a diver exhibiting those effects will be a liability to himself/herself as well as to others.

Similar to antibiotics are the anti-viral agents. Most of these are injected, but there are a couple that are used in pill form and may be around in the diving population. It is not likely that an HIV positive patient under active anti-viral therapy would be diving, but it is likely that a patient with a history of herpes (genital/oral or shingles) may be. As a professor in medical school once said "The difference between love and herpes is that herpes is forever." Therefore, a drug that may be used long term in a diving individual is acyclivir (Zovirax). This agent does have a history of causing nausea, vomiting and headaches. Divers using this agent should be aware of those side effects. Another agent used to decrease the symptoms of a viral complaint - the common cold - is a drug called amantidine (Symetrel). You should know that this agent could also cause nausea, dizziness and insomnia.

Moving on to the urinary tract, a major class of medications used here are the antispasmotics (the anti-cholinergic class) which, as stated before, can cause a dry mouth, blurred vision, increased heart rate and light sensitivity of the eyes. Decreased sweating can also occur. Some of the agents in this class are Cystospaz, Ditarpan, Luvsin, Urised. Some of these, if used in excess (or possibly coupled with DCS, nitrogen narcosis, etc.), have the propensity to proceed to a full-blown cholinergic crisis (hypercholinergic state). That would entail restlessness, irritability, tremors, convulsions and respiratory failure.

There is another class of drugs that are used for stimulation of the male urinary tract, specifically for male sexual dysfunction (objective dysfunction, not just a feeling of inadequacy). This class is an adrenergic antagonist or blocker, specifically alpha. Daytohimbin is one of those drugs (Yohimbine is the generic name) and it allows unopposed stimulation of the cholinergic system. The patient can exhibit decreased urine output, agitation/irritability, increased blood pressure/heart rate, tremors, nervousness, headache and dizziness. Obviously, this is not a good thing to have happen while diving. In some patients, the physician may prescribe the drug Benemid (probenecid) to increase blood levels of penicillin and other antibiotics. What has also been found, though, is that this drug may increase the blood levels of lorazepam (a Valium type of drug), oral sulfonylureas (pills used to decrease blood sugar in diabetics) and the anti-inflammatory drugs like Tylenol, Ibuprofen (Motrin, Advil), etc.

Cardiovascular Meds

The next area of medical management that is disproportionately represented in most people, and probably in more than a few divers, is the cardiovascular system. The intervention in this area runs the gamut from management of high blood pressure and heart rate control, to control of angina (chest pain). There are a multitude of agents used in cardiovascular conditions, but the most popular classes are the beta and calcium channel blockers, alpha blockers, ACE (Angiotension Converting Enzyme) inhibitors, diuretics, anti arrhythmics, vasodilators and vasopressors. Taken as a whole, any patient taking these medications should think seriously about not diving while under the influence of them.

Miria and Kevin Denlay loaded down with cameras and all the trappings of "technical diving" just prior to a dive at Bikini Atoll.
Photo courtesy of Alternate Diving Services.

Their collective side effects can range from low blood pressure and fast heart rate to bronchoconstriction (narrowing of the breathing passages) and severe, even fatal, aberrant heart rhythms. We also must keep in mind that we, as individuals, use medications and drugs that are not only not prescribed, but in some cases outlawed by current federal regulations. Marijuana, cocaine and alcohol are popular agents that affect the cardiovascular system as well as other systems. While used primarily for their euphoric and stimulating properties, these three alone can be unpredictable. In combination they can be lethal. If you then add a hyperbaric situation, you have gone from an unpredictable situation to a potentially lethal combination of events that also threatens the other divers present. In an interesting recent medical report, it was found that while both alcohol and cocaine individually can cause cardiac damage, together their effect was more than either substance alone. Needless to say, with the complexity of the individual drugs and their interactions with each other, any diver undertaking their use while diving would be well served in seeking professional advice. The potential scenario of the respective drug and its unknown contribution to a hyperbaric scenario cannot be underestimated nor predicted accurately.

Muscular/Skeletal

Another area of medical intervention that seems to be popular is the muscular/skeletal area. It seems that the drug companies aren't satisfied with battling against each other over physician recognition and keeping that conflict in the office/hospital realm. Now they have resorted to recruiting the lay public in their fight. So, what you may see in the daily newspapers in this country is company "X" advertising their prescription drugs. Is this healthy? I doubt that having the patient act as an agent of the company and beginning to doctor "shop" until they find a physician who will give them the drug they *think* they want is healthy. It seems that a lot of money is spent on curing the muscle aches and pains we all are subject to. Unfortunately for the drug companies, the OTC (over-the-counter, i.e., non-prescription) crowd has empowered competitors to mass-produce the popular non-steroidal anti-inflammatory drugs (NSAIDS) Ibuprofen and all of its pharmacological look alikes. When you add to the NSAIDS the other available analgesics, you end up with quite a laundry list of drugs. These medications are given for general aches and pains, spasms, strains, sprains and almost any other muscular malady. Continued in the list are the aspirin and acetaminophen (Tylenol) type of agents, with and without codeine; the whole series of NSAIDS, i.e. ibuprofen, naproxen, ketrolac, etc.; the narcotics (synthetic) and narcotics in combination with salicylates (aspirin); and the non narcotic and anxiolytic (anxiety relief) agents, i.e. Darvocet, Fiorinal (barbiturate-based) and Parafon Forte.

To this list, you also need to add muscle relaxants like Robaxin, Flexoril, and Soma. Not uncommonly, some patients will also receive a benzodiazepine (anxiolytic), like Valium, to help with their muscle spasms and anxiety. Not to be neglected, a very potent class of medications called steroids is sometimes prescribed. These can be in combination with many of the above listed agents or they can be used alone. Again, because this list is so extensive and the combinations so varied almost any type of side effect and reaction can be found. You need to check with your physician or pharmacist about the wisdom of diving with the above mentioned drugs. In particular, the class of drugs called steroids can have some nasty side effects - including fluid retention, electrolyte loss and avascular necrosis of the femoral head (cellular death of the head of the upper leg where it joins the hip socket). Some studies showed rates of dysparic osteonecrosis (avascular necrosis) from 2.7 percent to 80 percent. The higher rates were with saturation divers, deep helium greater than 500 fsw (150 msw) divers, and divers with numerous DCS events. Steroids can also lead to increased susceptibility to hyperbaric oxygen toxicity and infections.

Endocrine/Metabolic System

Another large area of medical management that may impact on divers are the endocrine/metabolic systems. This runs the gamut from diabetes to thyroid dysfunction. This can also encompass fertility agents, cholesterol lowering agents, hormonal manipulation (i.e. antibiotic steroids), oral contraceptives and thyroid preparations. Out of this laundry list of conditions, nothing has probably prompted more debate and research than diabetes.

The issue really is should a person who has to artificially control blood sugar be diving? In that vein, should that person be sport diving or partaking in technical diving if not fully aware of the ramifications of low blood sugar (hypoglycemia) or high blood sugar (hyperglycemia). The stress response and its effect on blood sugar and the implications for the diver's partners/friends are paramount.

To start with, DAN (Divers Alert Network) recently launched a research project to delve into the problem of diabetes mellitus (DM) and the sport diver (6). In *Alert Diver* magazine, the Undersea and Hyperbaric Medicine Society (UHMS) is quoted as being supportive of divers with diabetes mellitus. **However,**

UHMS specified that there were exceptions that would exclude some diabetic divers from diving.

These diabetic patient exceptions are:

1. Patients with a history of severe hypoglycemia (loss of consciousness, seizures or requiring assistance of others) in the last 12 months.
2. Patients with advanced secondary complications (i.e., disease of the eyes, nervous system or heart disease).
3. Patients who are unaware of hypoglycemia (lacking stress symptoms).
4. Patients who do not have adequate control of their diabetes or do not understand the relationship between exercise and diabetes.

Clearly, there are divers who dive regularly with diabetes and have enjoyable dives. Should they be diving deep greater than 110-130 fsw (33-39 msw)? Since we as individuals still have the free-will to risk our lives pursuing our dreams and adventures, there will undoubtedly be someone who says he/she can dive with diabetes. But does that same diver also have the right to put a partner at risk? If you're aware that a partner has diabetes, you must assume the risk of diving with him/her. (If you wish to participate in the DAN study or have questions about diving and diabetes, call DAN at Duke University at **919-684-2948**.

Note! DAN's telephone number does change through time. If you expect to use this service then please make certain that you do have the current number **before** you need it.

With respect to the cholesterol lowering drugs, one side effect they may have is neurologic. This can present itself as dizziness or fatigue, and even numbness in the extremities can occur. This is not unlike thyroid dysfunction and, in fact, as with thyroid replacement, if the patient receives too much, he/she can become hypermetabolic. That is not the way to have an enjoyable dive at 200 fsw (60 msw). In the past, some physicians have prescribed thyroid replacement hormone to increase the metabolic rate and help the patients to lose weight. So if the hormone isn't being used for actual hormonal replacement, it might be advisable to dive when not under the influence or effects of the exogenous (supplemental) hormone. If it is for replacement, then the prudent diver should check with his/her physician about the actual drug levels (which should be done on a regular basis) and then the scenario of superimposing a hyperbaric situation on top of that. It has been shown that oxygen toxicity is enhanced with increased thyroid hormone and when that causes the patient to be hypermetabolic, this scenario could spell disaster.

In terms of **oral contraceptives**, these should cause some concern. Theoretically they can cause an increase in blood coagulation (clotting) in the veins, and if combined with smoking, they greatly enhance the risk of heart attack in women over 35 years of age. But as far as the hypercoagulation ability goes, its effect would also manifest as an increased risk of decompression sickness, though this has not yet been supported by well designed clinical trials.

The above listed agents and drugs should not be construed as an all-inclusive or all encompassing list[7]. There are some that are not mentioned for obvious reasons, i.e. anti seizure medications. Some aren't listed also because of the data being so minuscule or the disease itself being a contraindication to diving, i.e. ophthalmologic agents for glaucoma, etc. Also, an area not touched on at all is the medications/drugs that can be purchased at health food stores. Massive doses of certain vitamins, i.e. vitamin A, can mimic some pathologic states and large doses of certain amino acids have in the past caused syndromes of muscle aches and sleep disorders, as well as severe metabolic disorders and acid base imbalances. So, health food supplements can cause a lot of problems if taken in an unwise or uninformed fashion.

In essence, the bottom line is that you as the diver should understand the effects of the medications you are taking and have an appreciation for those effects *at depth,* as well as an appreciation for the risk you assume and *you* impose on others. Therefore, you are obligated to be informed about the drugs you are taking and that can be done through your prescribing physician or a knowledgeable pharmacist. Remember, God protects fools and drunks, and once I've been informed, I am no longer a fool.

References and Works Cited

1. Stress and Performance in Diving: Drs. Bachrach and Egstrom, 1987.
2. Diving and Subaquatic Medicine: Drs. Pennefather, et al., 1992.
3. Medical Examination of Sport Scuba Divers: Dr. J. Davis, M.D., 2nd Edition, 1986.
4. Cardiopulmonary Critical Care: Dr. Dantsker, 2nd Edition, 1991.
5. Critical Care Medicine, December 1994, Volume 22, No. 12, page 1896.
6. Alert Diver (DAN), Jan-Feb 1995.
7. Physician's Desk Reference, 1995.

CHAPTER 7
Oxygen And It's Effect On The Diver

Bruce Voss, M.D.

Oxygen, an important life-giving/saving element in our environment, was identified by Joseph Priestley in 1774 (1). It is approximately 21% of air and, while it isn't flammable, it is necessary to support combustion. In terms of its physical being, it is usually found as a diatomic molecule comprised of two atoms of oxygen. Although the absolute percentage of oxygen in the air today is slightly more than 20%, there is speculation that in the past (i.e., during the eras of the dinosaurs) this percentage was much lower. If this is so, then the best percent of oxygen for diving may not necessarily be the percent on which humans evolved.

Lamar Hires on a sidemount dive in a Florida Cave.
Photo: Bill Dooley

In fact, it may not be that percentage of oxygen that is best for us on land. To quote Dr. Morgan Wells of NOAA (National Oceanic and Atmospheric Administration), "... 21% oxygen may not be the ideal percent of oxygen while scuba diving..." (2).

There is an abundance of data, literature and studies that have analyzed oxygen and its impact/interaction with the human body. Considering a few of the protocols, oxygen has been looked at in terms of percent, partial pressure and concentration in alveolar air, blood, extra vascular fluid, as well as in cells. Oxygen has also been analyzed in terms of its affect when there is a deficit or surfeit of it. If it is accepted that barometric pressure is 760mmHg and water vapor pressure is subtracted from 760mmHg and this difference is multiplied by the percent of oxygen, you get approximately 150mmHg oxygen pressure in the air (Dalton's Law of Partial Pressures). The partial pressure of oxygen (PO_2) is what we "work" with when we respire. Partial pressure, however, is not what our individual cells "see" when the oxygen is finally delivered to them.

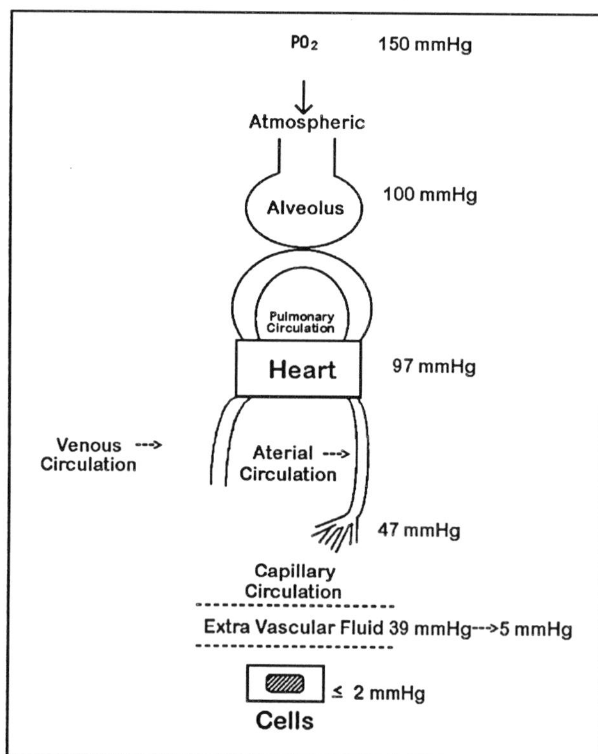

As the oxygen moves into our lungs, it mixes with carbon dioxide and water vapor, and the oxygen is now about 100mmHg in the alveoli or the breathing sacs. The next step for oxygen is to pass into the blood stream on its way to the heart. In a healthy, non-smoking, non-pulmonary diseased individual, the PO_2 in arterialized blood is, after passing to the heart, approximately 97mmHg. As the arteries lead to the capillaries, the oxygen now drops to approximately 47mmHg. For oxygen to cross into individual cells, it must make its way across the extra vascular fluid compartment. Here the PO_2 goes from approximately 39mmHg to approximately 5mmHg. Once in the cells, the PO_2 is approximately 2mmHg (3).

A concept that needs to be developed is percentage versus partial pressure. We are aware that as we dive using air, our PO_2 increases but the percent of O_2 remains at 21%. The proviso is, of course, that we are using an open circuit with air with no recirculation or shunting. Through arithmetic calculations and countless headaches, formulae have been developed to measure O_2 content:

- **O_2 content = (1.39 X Hemoglobin (Hgb) X percent saturation),**
- **O_2 capacity = (1.39 x Hgb)**
- **O_2 dissolved in blood = (.003 x P arterial O_2)**
- **Percent of Hgb saturated with O_2 = (100 x [O_2 content - O_2 dissolved] ÷ 1.39 x Hgb)**
- **O_2 delivery to the peripheral tissues = (O_2 content x cardiac output x 10)**
- **O_2 consumption = (arterial - venous O_2 content x cardiac output x 10)**

These and other calculations are based on a few premises. One premise is that 1 gram of Hgb can carry 1.34 to 1.39 ml or cc of O_2 when fully saturated. Yet, that is **bound** oxygen, not dissolved oxygen that is of interest when we talk about hyperbaric oxygenation (HBO). If the normal Hgb is 15g (100 cc) of blood, then 15 x 1.34 = 20.1 cc of O_2 per 100 cc of blood is bound and carried by the red blood cells (RBCs). For completeness, we can carry 0.003 cc of oxygen per 100 cc of blood. So, the total O_2 carried (bound to RBCs and non-bound) equals 20.4 cc per 100 cc of blood. Hemoglobin is the protein that carries oxygen and is comprised of 4 polypeptide chains (2 alpha and 2 beta) bound to form biochemical rings with a central iron molecule in it. (*Heme* means "iron bearing".)

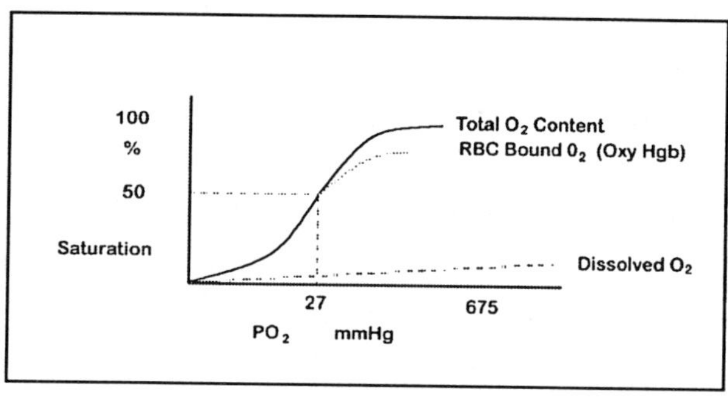

As one can see, even though the blood can be 100 percent saturated with O_2, the partial pressure of O_2 can continue to increase at that 100 percent saturation up to greater than 675mmHg (4). Note that the 50 percent saturation level corresponds with the PO_2 of 27mmHg. Unfortunately, this is not constant. The 50 percent saturation point can change from 27 mmHg up or down, depending on the circumstances.

If the sigmoid-shaped saturation curve shifts left, this is an increase in Hemoglobin-Oxygen (Hgb-O_2) affinity such as a 50 percent saturation at a PO_2 of 20mmHg so, at a lower PO_2, one is still 50 percent saturated. It can also be viewed as being at a higher saturation at a PO_2 of 27mmHg. A left shift occurs with alkalosis (pH increases when one hyperventilates and blows off CO_2) and a decrease in core temperature (i.e. hypothermia). The curve will shift right with increased hydrogen ion concentration (pH decreases, i.e. acidosis), increased temperature (hyperthermia) and increased CO_2 (decreased respiration, i.e. hypercapnea). This is the "Bohr effect".

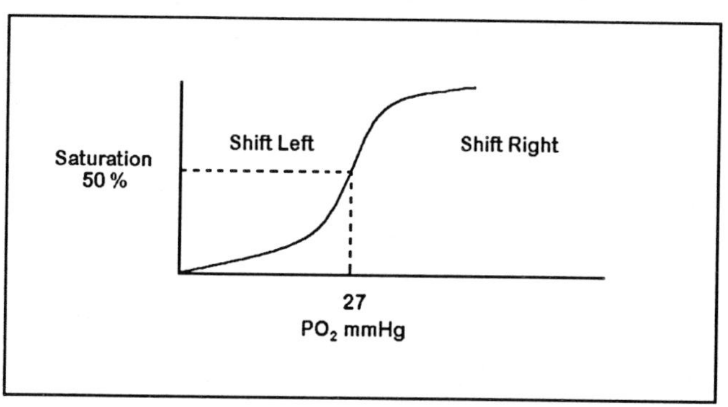

The real essence of the above sigmoid curve shifting is that if the curve shifts left, the Hgb is less inclined to release its hold on oxygen. Cellular respiration suffers, and the cellular environment becomes acidic. As a point of interest, each red blood cell has about 280 million (2.8×10^8) molecules of hemoglobin! If that is not complicated enough, a chronic smoker has an altered form of hemoglobin and, consequently, less oxygen is delivered to the tissues.

Not only can the oxygen curve be manipulated-shifted-to modulate O_2 delivery and release, but certain organs (brain, kidneys and lungs) can modulate their blood flow (autoregulation). This is done in response to either blood pressure (i.e. kidneys) or O_2 and CO_2 levels (i.e. brain). Autoregulation enables optimum O_2 delivery and enhanced organ blood flow and/or O_2 extraction efficiency. Whether this mechanism is altered at depth is open to debate. Yet, it has been shown that at greater pressures there is an increase in urine formation (diuresis) and concentration of the blood volume as well as adrenal gland hypertrophy, growth (5).

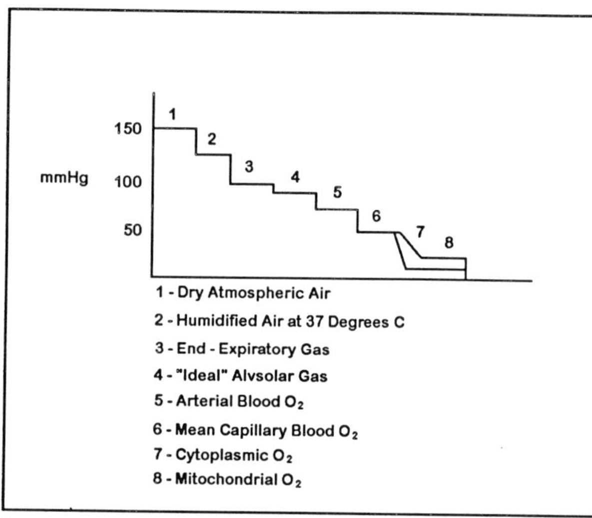

As probably appreciated now, there is a differential O_2 gradient from the alveoli to the end-organ user of O_2 which is the mitochondria, the "cellular powerhouse," in the cells. As the blood carries O_2 from the alveoli to the end-organ user, the mitochondria, there is a progressive decrease in the PO_2. The decrease is secondary to many factors including, but not limited to, faulty transport across the alveoli, inadequate blood perfusion of the alveoli, shunting (adding poorly oxygenated blood to fully oxygenated blood) and Hgb concentration. If the Hgb is fully saturated (100 percent) with oxygen and there is a steady state of O_2 consumption, some interesting things can occur. As stated earlier, blood is 100 percent saturated at about 90mmHg of O_2. Yet, if we increase the percent of inspired O_2 (i.e., 21 percent to 100 percent, such as going from air to pure oxygen) then the amount of the barometric pressure at sea level (760mmHg) that is represented by O_2 increases from about 150mmHg to 680mmHg in arterial blood.

A simple way to look at this is: If there is a non-interest bearing checking account that contains $100, and there is an automatic withdrawal of $100 every month, after one month there will be zero dollars in the account. If $100 is added every month, every month's balance would go from zero to $100 to zero and so forth (there is no reserve to draw from). If every month $1,000 is added to the account, the $100 monthly withdrawal will soon become less and less of a factor since the account is filling up monthly. Now, if $1 million is added to the account every month, the $100 withdrawal will be so minuscule in relation to the total, the account will appear not to have any withdrawals.

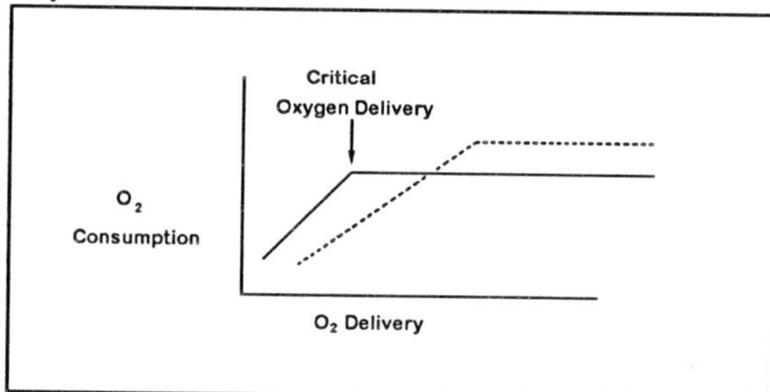

It is almost the same concept with oxygen delivery and consumption, although the total amount of oxygen "deposited" in the body is limited by what is available. If consumption is constant and at a basal metabolic resting rate, the oxygen delivery can overwhelm the consumption and, in fact, consumption will have little impact on delivery. If consumption increases due to increased utilization of oxygen, i.e. working at depth or severe infection, or decreases delivery because of a low Hgb (anemia, bleeding), decreased O_2 in the gas being breathed, then one must slide to the left on the graph and the consumption becomes O_2 delivery dependent (to the left of the "critical O_2 delivery point"). If sick patient, represented by the light line on the graph is septic, (an overwhelming infection) is compared to the healthy patient (heavy line), the healthy patient has a higher O_2 delivery if both have the same rate of consumption. Put another way, the sick patient has a higher critical O_2 point to reach before O_2 consumption is *not* limited by O_2 delivery.

Arterial PO_2	Changes in the Brain
50 mmHg	Neurotransmitter production falls, cerebral blood flow increases
35 mmHg	Acidosis in brain tissue is pronounced, EEG clearly abnormal
20 mmHg	High energy phosphate bond production falls dramatically, coma present
<5 mmHg	Mitochondria cease to function, death ensues

So, a corollary to this model is this: As less and less money is put into an account, the constant withdrawal becomes more of a significant portion of the total. In essence, one goes from an aerobic to anaerobic state because he/she is now limited by the amount of available oxygen. Some physicians also feel that once a deficit is reached, a supra-normal amount of oxygen delivery is needed to diminish the deficit (6). An appreciation can be gleamed from the following chart that deals with brain tissue. See chart at left.

These events reflect the dependence on O_2 of the brain cells. For some organs or tissues, there is a higher demand for oxygen than with others during an oxygen deficiency. The ensuing acidosis, cellular degeneration and cellular death occur concurrently in all the tissues and present differing signs of pulmonary distress, increasing heart failure, progressive renal (kidney) failure, and brain dysfunction such as lethargy, obtundation, coma, and death. Before this global, all encompassing demise occurs, other cellular/biochemical events happen. One event is oxygen free-radical formation. As may be recalled, molecules are "happiest" when all electrons are paired up and the molecules' positive charges equal its negative charges. With free radicals, the molecule has an unpaired electron and, as such, is "reactive or unstable".

A diver enjoying the scenic caves of Akumel Mexico.

Photo: Steve Gerrard

With oxygen, the free radicals that are generated include the Super-oxide anion (O_2^-), Hydroxyl anion (OH^-), and Piroxy radicals (ROO^-) (7). Most of the toxic O_2 metabolites in biological systems come from the super-oxide anion (O_2^-). One site this reaction occurs in is the mitochondria. The effects are far-reaching and profound. Cellular membranes (of RBCs for example) become more rigid and lose their flexibility. So, the RBCs ability to carry oxygen and to negotiate the channels in the spleen, etc., is severely impaired. Not only does this impact on the ability to being O_2 to the cells, but the free-radicals can cause other free-radicals to be formed from lipids (fat) and, in fact, can set up free-radical chain reactions. That is not to say that all free-radical formation is detrimental (8) because the ability of the neutrophils (WBC or white blood cell type) to do their job is dependent on the formation of hypochlorous acid (HOCL) from super-oxide anion.

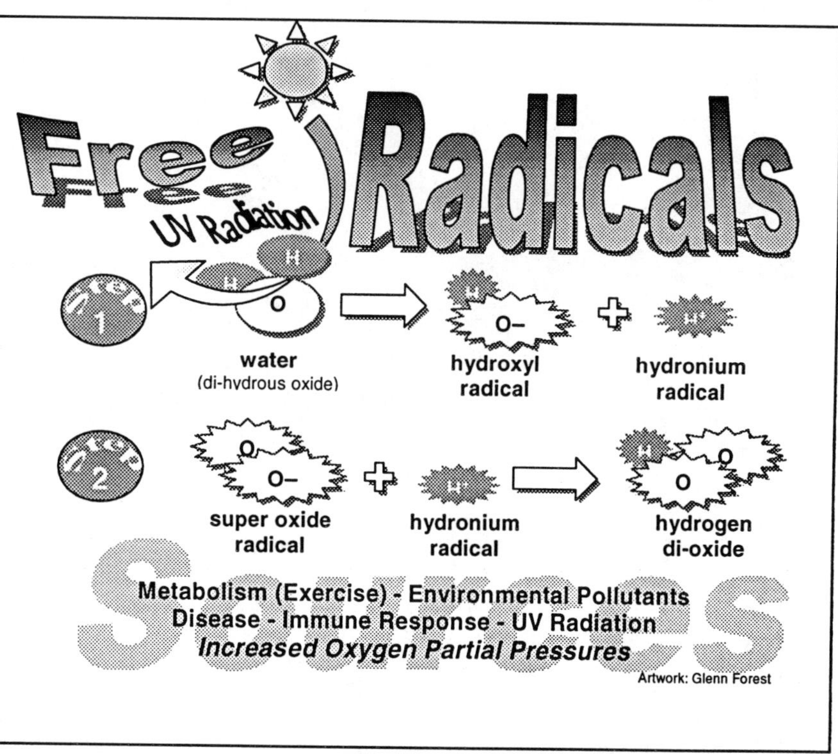

Artwork: Glenn Forest

A logical question would be, if the free-radicals are so destructive, how could we prevent or attenuate them? Should we? Well, the body does have mechanisms to "scavenge" the free-radicals, and there are free-radical scavengers that we ingest everyday, either wittingly or unwittingly. In terms of endogenous scavengers, there are quite a few. These include catalas, urate, super-oxide dismutase and glutathione. While these are not familiar names to most, the exogenous class of compounds probably is familiar. This class includes, but is not limited to, vitamins E and C, beta-carotene, and ethanol. In fact, some hyperbaric chamber medical directors advocate using Vitamin E in their practice (9,10,13). Additionally, a number of anti-oxidant formulations can be purchased at a local health food store. **Note:** Only the "natural" beta-carotene, not the "synthetic" form, exerts anti-oxidant activity (11).

So far, this whole discussion has centered on oxygen transport from the atmosphere to the cells. With this transport, we have come to find that oxygen is bound to hemoglobin and some is dissolved (albeit a small amount) in the liquid phase of the blood. So far, we have said nothing about what *happens* to the oxygen at the cellular level.

Well, what happens is cellular respiration. Somehow, oxygen is utilized and somehow it is called oxidative phosphorylation. Oxidative phosphorylation is a fancy way of saying that high-energy phosphate bonds are formed using oxygen. As humans digest proteins, carbohydrates and fats (lipids), their by-products, can enter the Krebs Cycle. In this cycle (either the Krebs or the Citric Acid Cycle), carbon dioxide and electrons are produced and released from intermediary compounds. These electrons travel down the "electron-transport" chain (also called the cytochrome transport system). The final step in the system is the "reduction" of O_2 to water (addition of electrons).

Adenosine Tri-Phosphate (ATP) is the cell's energy source.

With the stepwise reduction of oxygen comes the production of high energy phosphate bonds called ATP (adenosine tri-phosphate).

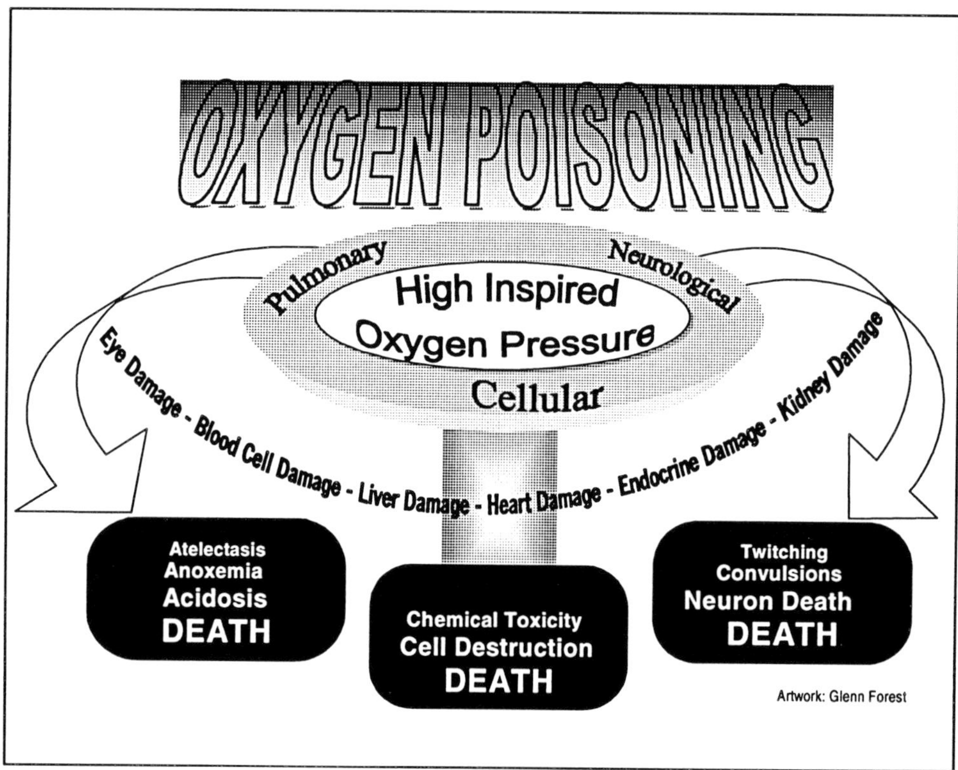

Adding a phosphate bond to adenosine di-phosphate (ADP) makes ATP. Part of the stepwise production of ATP can be done without oxygen (anaerobic) but is very inefficient and the cellular environment becomes acidic. If you look at the ratio of ATP to ADP *x* Pi (inorganic phosphate), that is equal to ATP/ADP *x* Pi, this is the phosphorylation potential (12). This relation is believed to control the oxidative phosphorylation and, therefore, the cellular consumption of oxygen. If the partial pressure increases (that is, ATP either increases or ADP *x* Pi decreases), aerobic metabolism decreases. So, if there is a relative abundance of high energy compounds, the cells slow down the production of ATP. If the partial pressure decreases, the cells increase the ATP production. During exercise, the ATP is used up, decreasing the phosphorylation potential and increasing the ADP *x* Pi levels (ADP is regenerated from ATP). This is accompanied by increased tissue blood flow and O_2 consumption. Also during hypoxia, low O_2 levels, the ADP *x* Pi increase, secondary to decreased ATP, but there is limited O_2 available to make ATP; therefore, O_2 consumption decreases. For the interested reader, further discussion can be found in almost any text on biochemistry.

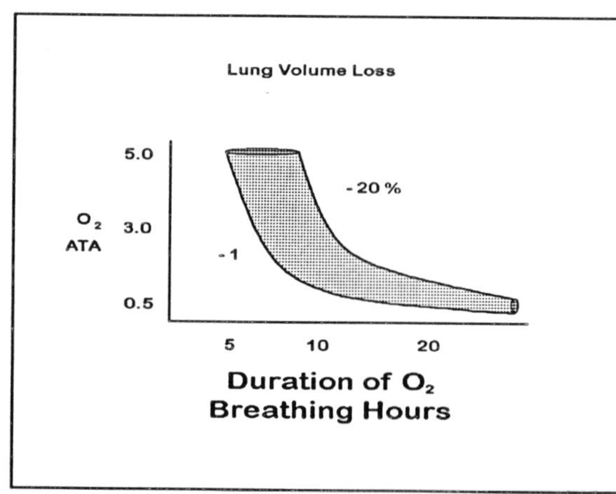

Our last area of concern with oxygen has to do with increased partial pressure. Previously, we dealt with hypoxic and normoxic levels of oxygen. The following will deal with hyperoxic levels. Such luminaries as Ken Donald, C.J. Lambertsen, A.R. Behnke, J.C. Davis, R.G. Eckenhoff, E.M. Camporesi and E.H. Lanphier, to name a few, have documented the toxic effect of increased oxygen. Despite this list of investigators, there are some that doubt not only the toxicity of oxygen but its lethality as well. This is probably due to the "...variation between and within individuals..." to the susceptibility of oxygen (14). All the areas of oxygen utilization and transport mentioned earlier, from the nose to the toes (cells, that is) is affected by hyperoxia. Areas that have been studied and found affected include: pulmonary tissue, retinal (eye) tissue, RBCs, liver, heart muscle, kidneys, central nervous tissue (brain), thyroid tissue and adrenal glands (15). The documentation of pulmonary toxicity with increased oxygen is not only in the diving literature, but it can be found in medical emergency, critical care, internal and hyperbaric literature. The toxicity runs the gamut from loss of lung volumes to actual alveoli damage and dysfunctional transpulmonary oxygen transport. The pulmonary effects can be manifested at different PO_2, i.e. 5ata (atmospheres) of oxygen and with differing lengths of time of exposure.

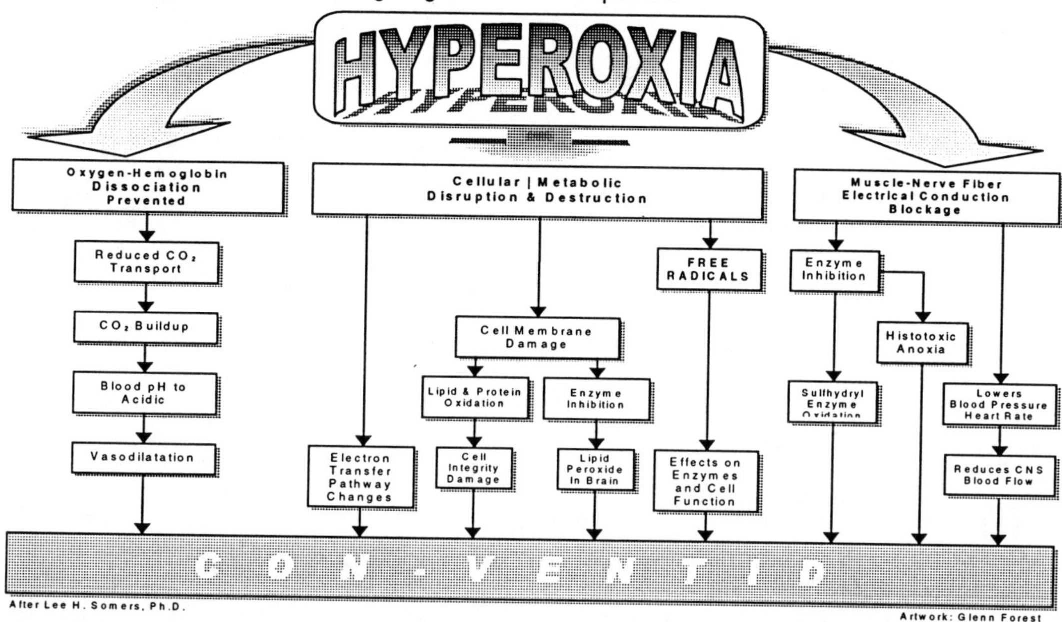

After Lee H. Somers, Ph.D.

Artwork: Glenn Forest

Retinal tissues are very susceptible to the vaso-constrictive effect of oxygen in the newborn. With adults and prolonged oxygen breathing, the visual fields will narrow. Behnke described this effect as early as 1935. The resulting tunnel vision can cause almost total blindness (15). Anderson (11) described changed in the lens of the eye, but most were temporary when resulting from 2ata of oxygen. The effects on RBCs by increased oxygen has been shown to be membrane changes secondary to oxygen free-radicals with the now rigid RBC unable to conform or negotiate the narrow channels of the spleen. This membrane inflexibility is detected as a hallmark of an aged RBC and is taken out of circulation by the spleen. In fact, a decreased circulating red cell mass (RBC element of blood) has been documented to occur. Other organs such as the endocrine (adrenal and thyroid), the hepatic and the renal systems show varying effects with increased oxygen. In at least one reference, mention is made of increased damage to the organs if adrenal hormones are given during hyperoxia (i.e. cortisone) (5).

Despite the above mentioned tissue/organs being affected, there is basically one organ system that can be so rapidly and dramatically affected by oxygen that the manifestations strike fear in all who see them. If one witnesses a central nervous system (CNS) toxicity reaction (seizure) on land, it won't be forgotten. If one has a seizure under water, chances are very good that he/she will not live to remember it. A seizure under water is a very unforgiving event.

As a side note, the reason I believe some divers do not fear the occurrence of an oxygen seizure is not because of its effects, but, as

The acronym for the 7 symptoms of **Oxygen Toxicity** is

CON-VENTID:

- **CON**vulsions
- **V**isual Changes
- **E**uphoria
- **N**ausea
- **T**witching
- **I**rritability
- **D**izziness

stated earlier, because of its variable onset. We all probably know stories where a diver "pushed the envelope" on air, EAN, or O_2, and exceeded the "supposed" O_2 CNS limits and did not have a problem. Well, anecdotally, that is fine, but, because of individual variability, what may be a safe dive profile today may not be the case tomorrow. In fact, the diver pushing the O_2 "envelope" may be fine *right up to the sudden appearance of the seizure.* When an epileptic seizure occurs, there is a massive electrical discharge in the brain and the EEG (electroencephalograph) will document that electrical discharge. In early O_2 studies (17), researchers found that gross or global EEG activity was not consistently altered prior to a hyperoxic seizure. Torbati, et al. (18) found if you measure the energy content of the individual EEG frequency bands, as well as the combined total energy content of the bands, there was a significant change in the energy (total and individual) up to 60 minutes prior to the seizure. Also, Ken Donald in 1947 showed that using the same diver on O_2 at 70 feet for twenty dives over a period of ninety days, the time of onset of CNS symptoms in minutes varied from a low of less than 10 minutes to a high of about 150 minutes! The symptoms included facial pallor, sweating, depression/euphoria, apprehension, visual changes, nausea, vomiting, lip/cheek twitching, dizziness, and other constitutional systems.

Another study reported by Ken Donald in 1947 looked at oxygen toxicity variability between individuals. Thirty-six divers were exposed to O_2 at about 3.5ata from 6 to 96 minutes per period. As each one developed symptoms of CNS O_2 toxicity (**CON-VENTID**, etc.), he stopped their participation in the dive. What he did not find was a clustering of symptom onset at any particular time, but rather that most divers were eliminated from their dive before 25 minutes had elapsed. He graphically captured the intra and inter-individual variability to oxygen toxicity in terms of CNS symptoms. This CNS reaction to increased oxygen, the "Paul Bert" effect, is named in deference to this pioneer's work in the physiologic responses to oxygen. Incidentally, Dr. Bert reported his work in 1878! (19)

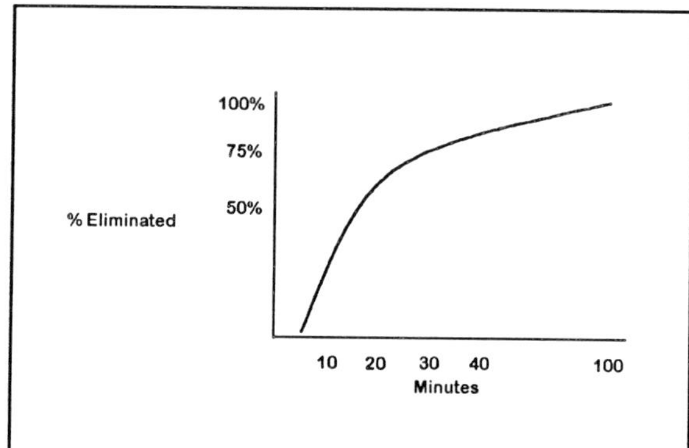

A question to which I have alluded but have not stated is, "Why do the seizures occur?" Of note, with increased oxygen two things have been documented to occur in the cells of the brains of rats. The first event is the enzyme that transports sodium (Na) and potassium (K) across cell membranes will have decreased activity (15). Also, if the arterial carbon dioxide (CO_2) is increased, the onset of oxygen seizures is hastened along with a greater de-activation of the Na-K transport enzyme. Some feel this seizure augmentation could be secondary to increased extracellular levels of K and glutamate, since both cause neuronal excitability. The second event noted with increased oxygen is decreased GABA (gamma-aminobutyric acid) (20). Some studies in rats, mice, rabbits, and guinea pigs have shown that the rate of decrease in brain GABA levels is correlated with the increased susceptibility to oxygen seizures in these animals. What is interesting is that a drug called Valium (a member of the class of drugs benzodiazepines) in a way acts at GABA receptors as if it was GABA (GABA-mimetic) (21). Paradoxically, if GABA has been depleted, then the benzodiazepines do not work!

One theory is that benzodiazepines block or "antagonize" a specific brain protein that blocks the binding of GABA to its receptors. Therefore, if this protein is blocked, then GABA is free to bind to the GABA receptors and inhibit seizures. It is also interesting that some hyperbaric chamber directors have noticed that very few, if any, patients have had an oxygen seizure if the patient is on increased oxygen and had been pretreated with Valium (22). Another drug known to increase GABA levels is Lithium (used with bipolar disorders). It also decreases seizure likelihood with increased oxygen partial pressures. In hyperbaric medicine, research interest continues with GABA, and its ability to modulate seizure likelihood with increased oxygen. Of course, the side effects of Valium and most other drugs prohibit their use in diving and is only of value in hyperbaric research.

This leads to our last area of discussion, hyperbaric oxygen and its effect on free-radical formation from oxygen. There is some anecdotal data as well as some research to support the contention that as the partial pressure of oxygen (PO_2) increases, so does the formation of oxygen free-radicals (9,15,23,24). As stated earlier, some researchers and directors of hyperbaric oxygenation (HBO) recommend anti-oxidants be used by their patients. A corollary here is: do divers who increase their PO_2 greater than 0.21 atmospheres generate more oxygen free radicals? I think that question may have part of its answer in terms of HBO findings. I am not aware of a rigid scientific study in divers at depth that confirms what has been found in chamber HBO research. Unfortunately, what appears to be logically appealing is not necessarily always the case. Regardless, I think the benign and salutary effects of most anti-oxidants alone should mitigate any concern if taking them routinely. Also, because of the typical fat-ladened American diet and lack of a consistent exercise program, I think most divers would be well served to supplement their diet. A very readable and in-depth discussion of free-radicals and anti-oxidants can be found in the IANTD Journal *Nitrox Diver*, published as a two-part series in 1995-1996.

This chapter was meant as a brief overview of oxygen, a look at its journey from the environment to the cells, the hypo/hyper and normoxic states of oxygen and some lucid comments about oxygen in light of the diving community. Some areas of oxygen impact have been dealt with in some depth, some areas rather briefly and some not at all, i.e., platelet aggregation and white blood cell adherence. The references that I have cited are complete and should satiate your curiosity about any topic we have covered in this chapter. Lastly, I am indebted to Dr. Morgan Wells, Mr. Dick Rutkowski, and Mr. Tom Mount for showing me how diving is contained within the envelope of medicine. More importantly, they showed me how that envelope can be bent, manipulated and stretched in a safe fashion.

Works Cited

1. Oxygen Transport, Principles and Practice. Shoemaker, W., et al., 1993.
2. Personal Communication with M. Wells. Diving Medical Officer Course XX, 1994
3. Clinical Application of Blood Gases, 5th Edition. Shapiro, B., et al., 1994
4. ibid
5. Diving and Subaquatic Medicine, 3rd Edition. Edmonds, Carl, et al., 1992
6. ibid
7. Multiple Organ System Failure. Fry, 1992
8. ibid
9. R. Barlett, M.D., Richland Memorial Hospital, Hyperbaric Medical Director, March, 1996
10. Archives Surgery 9/94, 129(9): 982-7, Yamaguchi, K., et al.
11. J. Appl. Physiol., 3/94, 76 (3): 1073-6, Bitterman, N., et al.
12. Cardiopulmonary Critical Care, Dantzker et al., 1991
13. *Nitrox Diver* IANTD, Vol 96-1, February-April
14. Oxygen and the Diver, 1992, Donald, K.
15. The Physiology and Medicine of Diving. Bennett, P., 1993
16. Trans. Am. Ophth. Soc. 1978, 76 (116-124), Anderson, et al.
17. Journal of Neurophysiology. 1945 (8), 155-160
18. Aviat. Space Environ. Med. 1981 (52) 598-603. Torbati,et al.
19. La Pression Barometrique, 1878. Bert, P. (Reprinted 1943, Researches in Experimental Physiology)
20. Can. J. Biochem. Physiol. 41(1907-13)1963, Wood, et al.
21. Goodman and Gillman Pharmacological Basis of Therapeutics, 1980
22. Hyperbaric Medicine Practice. Kindwall, et al., 1995
23. Brain Research. 1982: 248 (355-360) Dirks et al.
24. Ann. Int. Med. 1978: 89 (122-127) McCord, et al.

CHAPTER 8

Inert Gas Narcosis

David J. Doolette, Ph.D.

Introduction

The narcotic effects of breathing compressed air at depths greater than 100 fsw (30 msw)[1] are probably familiar to most divers. The collection of neurological effects from breathing air at high pressure, including intoxication, slowing of mental processes and reduced manual dexterity are generally referred to as nitrogen narcosis. Such effects can be produced by breathing many other inert gases[2] in addition to nitrogen, so the condition is more generally known as inert gas narcosis. After describing the signs and symptoms of inert gas narcosis, this chapter will show that such narcosis can be interpreted as the effects of anaesthesia prior to unconsciousness. Although the underlying mechanisms of narcosis and anaesthesia are not completely understood, a number of features of both theoretical and practical interest will be presented, including features other than inert gas partial pressure which modify narcosis.

Historical Descriptions

Intoxication of caisson workers and divers was noted by the middle of the 19th century when engineering advances allowed work at sufficiently elevated pressure. The seminal work describes the narcotic effect of deep air diving dates from the 1930s. Narcosis was encountered during the first Royal Navy deep air diving trials to 300 fsw (91 msw) and was appropriately described as a "slowing of cerebration" or "as if ... under an anaesthetic", but was at that time attributed to "mental instability" in some deep diving candidates (Hill and Phillips, 1932). The role of raised inspired partial pressure of nitrogen in producing narcosis was suspected by 1935 and the use of an alternative breathing gas mixture to eliminate narcosis was proposed[3] (Behnke *et al.*, 1935). Since then, the threshold pressure for air diving that consistently produces a decrement in diver performance has been considered to be 4ata [100 fsw (30 msw)]. Confirmation of the role of nitrogen in narcosis came with the report of Max Nohl's 410 ffw (128 mfw) fresh water dive using a Heliox Rebreather of his own design (End, 1938).

Signs and Symptoms of Inert Gas Narcosis & Behavioral Modification

Classification of Signs and Symptoms

Inert gas narcosis is an alteration of function of the nervous system that produces behavioral modifications that may impair a diver's ability to work effectively or even survive. In order to recognize all the potential performance impairments resulting from inert gas narcosis and to help understand the causes of narcosis, it is useful to classify the various effects. Behnke originally divided the effects of narcosis into three categories: emotional reactions, impairment of higher mental processes and impairment of neuromuscular control (Behnke *et al.*, 1935). A similar classification is used here: subjective sensations, impaired cognitive function, slowed mental activity and impaired neuromuscular coordination.

Subjective Sensations

Subjective sensations are the sensations that any diver would associate with inert gas narcosis. These include euphoria, intoxication hyper-confidence, recklessness and various altered states of consciousness and attention. Subjective sensations of inert gas narcosis can be assessed using questionnaires asking for a global estimate of the magnitude of narcosis and responses to adjectives, checklists describing work capability (for instance, ability to work, alertness, concentration) and body/mental sensations (for instance, intoxicated, reckless, dreamy, uninhibited). (Hamilton *et al.*, 1992; Hamilton *et al.*, 1995).

---

[1] Depths quoted as meters sea water gauge (mswg) imply the information results from open-water dives whereas pressures quoted as atmospheres absolute (ata) imply chamber tests. Approximate conversions to feet sea water gauge (fswg) are included.

[2] Inert gases exert biological effects without change in their own chemical structure. In terms of respiration, inert gases exclude oxygen, carbon dioxide and water vapor.

[3] Helium had been proposed as a breathing gas diluent that might accelerate decompression but the cost of helium required for standard dress had prevented human dives.

Impaired Cognitive Function

Cognitive functions are higher brain processes including perception, thinking, understanding and remembering.

The effects of inert gas narcosis on cognitive function includes:

- Difficulty assimilating facts
- Slowed and inaccurate thought processes
- Memory loss

In the laboratory, inert gas narcosis can be measured by tests for impaired cognitive function including:

- Conceptual reasoning
- Sentence comprehension
- Mental arithmetic ability
- Short-term memory

Slowed Mental Activity

In addition to increased errors in cognitive function tests, narcosis significantly reduces the speed at which such problems are solved. Apparently information processing in the central nervous system is slowed, and this can be measured in two ways: the rate at which test problems are attempted, or by testing reaction time. Reaction time measures the time between receiving a sensory signal and reacting with the appropriate response and represents the speed of higher mental processes, particularly decision making. Inert gas narcosis slows the reaction time. In a typical laboratory reaction time test one of a series of LEDs is illuminated and the time until it is extinguished by pushing its matched microswitch is measured.

Reduced Neuromuscular Coordination

Neuromuscular coordination (manual dexterity)[4] is impaired by inert gas narcosis, but usually only at greater depths than the intellectual impairments described above. Neuromuscular coordination is often assessed by peg board and screw board tests that involve assembly and disassembly of patterns of nuts, bolts and pegs.

Diver exploring a wreck's anchor off Sweden in the Baltic Sea.
Photo: Anders Jallai

Inert Gas Narcosis at Extreme Depth on Air

Air breathing at depths greater than 300 fsw (91 msw) produces altered states of consciousness including manic or depressive states, hallucinations, time disorganization and lapses of consciousness[5].

Thermoregulation

In addition to the obvious actions of narcosis on brain activity, other body activities are affected as a result of changes in the nervous system. Of particular importance to divers, but less widely known, is the distortion caused by inert gas narcosis of the physiological and behavioral control of body core temperature (thermoregulation). Narcosis reduces shivering and therefore the production of body heat (shivering thermogenesis), the main defense

---

[4] Neuromuscular coordination, also called manual dexterity, is a consequence of not only muscle contraction, but the nervous system control of muscle contraction and the neuromotor (movement) programs in the central nervous system.

[5] Reports by divers of lapses of consciousness might actually be memory lapses.

against body cooling. As a result, narcosis allows a more rapid drop in body core temperature than expected during cold water. (Mekjavic *et al.,* 1995.) Additionally, despite body core cooling, perceived thermal comfort is greater with narcosis than otherwise expected. (Mekjavic *et al.,* 1994.) As a result, the diver may neglect to take action to reduce heat loss (behavioral thermoregulation).

Mechanism of Inert Gas Narcosis

Anaesthesia

It is apparent that the signs and symptoms of inert gas narcosis result from an alteration of the function of the nervous system. It was noted prior that breathing air at depths greater than 300 fsw (91 msw) produces lapses of consciousness. At much greater depths, air will cause complete unconsciousness (anaesthesia)[6]. Indeed, many of the inert gases will produce anaesthesia, each such gas having a characteristic anaesthetic potency. For instance, the approximate inspired partial pressure required to produce anaesthesia for nitrogen is 33ata, for argon is 15ata, for nitrous oxide is 1.5ata and for halothane[7] is 0.008ata. (Smith, 1986.) Some inert gases, notably helium and neon, have no practical anaesthetic potency. Owing to its similarity with anaesthesia, inert gas narcosis is now generally accepted to be a manifestation of the effects of anaesthetic gases at sub-anaesthetic doses (incipient anaesthesia). The severity of narcosis increases as the inspired partial pressure of the inert gas approaches the anaesthetic level.

Narcosis is an incipient anaesthesia.

Different Inert Gases and Anaesthetics Produce Identical Narcosis

The narcotic effects of the inert gases and other anaesthetics are identical. In specific test of narcosis in either monkeys or humans, argon, nitrogen, nitrous oxide and other general anaesthetics have identical effects (although at different partial pressures). Nitrous oxide, which is sufficiently potent to produce narcosis at the surface, has been used extensively in laboratory tests to simulate nitrogen narcosis.

Mechanism of Anaesthesia

The mechanism by which any anaesthetics, including the inert gases, produce anaesthesia is not entirely understood. However, it is widely accepted that the site of anaesthesia and narcosis are the synapses in the central nervous system[8]. The majority of drugs which act on the nervous system work by modifying chemical synaptic transmission (see figure right). Anaesthetics enhance the action of a variety of the inhibitory neurotransmitters (particularly GABA) at their specific post-synaptic receptors[9], resulting in a reduced frequency of action potentials. Such depression of central nervous system activity ultimately produces anaesthesia.

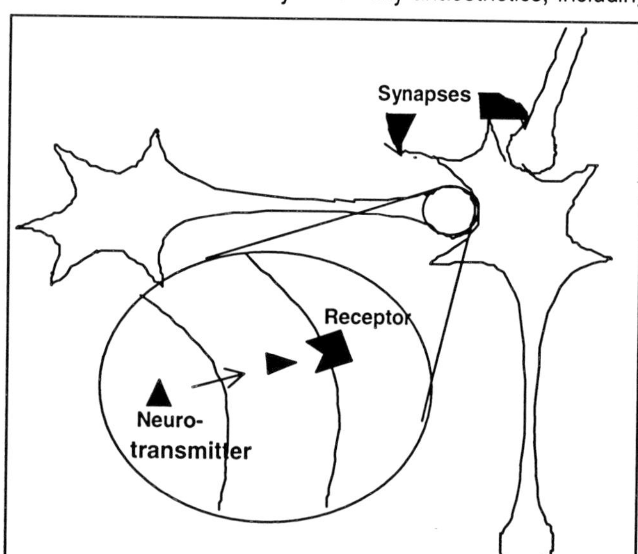

Synapses (*enlarged in inset at left*) between neurons. Signals in the brain are carried along neurons in the form of an electrical potential called an action potential.

Signals are transmitted across the synapse between neurons by chemicals called neurotransmitters, released in response to an action potential. Neurotransmitters combine with specific receptor proteins on the post-synaptic (target) neuron. Some

---

6 Anaesthesia can be defined as an unconscious state that eliminates response to surgical pain.

7 Halothane is used for clinical anaesthesia.

8 Neurons are the cells that carry the electrical signals in the nervous system, synapses are a type of junction between neurons.

9 Many drugs alter synaptic transmission owing to a chemical similarity with particular neurotransmitters; however, anaesthetics do not resemble neurotransmitters. How such a variety of chemically different anaesthetics exert similar effects on the nervous system is an area of ongoing research. Some evidence suggests that the mechanism by which inert gases produce their anaesthetic actions may be slightly different to other general anaesthetics.

neurons release inhibitory neurotransmitters which make the target neuron less likely to fire an action potential while other neurons release excitatory transmitter which make the target neurons more likely to fire an action potential.

Errol Kalayci preparing for a dive on the Halcyon Rebreather.

Meyer-Overton Correlation and the Critical Volume Hypothesis

Early hypotheses of anaesthetic mechanisms pre-date the discovery of chemical synaptic transmission. The most famous of these is the Meyer-Overton correlation, which originated at the turn of this century. Meyer (1899) and later Overton (1902) noticed that there exists a remarkably strong correlation between an anaesthetic's potency and its solubility in olive oil. The Meyer-Overton hypothesis states that anaesthesia occurs with certain molar concentration of a compound in the lipid (fat) of a cell[10]. An elaboration of this hypothesis was proposed by Mullins[11] (1954), and states that narcosis occurs as the volume of some hydrophobic site[12] (probably lipid) expands due to uptake of inert substance (Smith, 1986). It is implied in both these hypotheses that the lipid site is the neuronal cell membrane and that anaesthetics work by dissolving in the cell membrane and disrupting the voltage-gated ion channels which allow the neuron to conduct electrical impulses[13].

It is no longer widely believed that the membrane voltage-gated ion channels are the site of anaesthesia because evidence has accumulated that any effects of anaesthetics on neuronal membranes are physiologically insignificant. Anaesthetics may act by occupying hydrophobic pockets inside the neurotransmitter receptor proteins[14] and it is not altogether surprising that a strong correlation exists between anaesthetic potency and hydrophobicity. Also, the receptors are embedded in the cell membrane and lipophilic compounds will diffuse rapidly through the membrane and reach high concentration surrounding the receptors. Additionally, lipid soluble compounds readily cross the blood-brain-barrier. So, rather than explaining anaesthesia, the Meyer-Overton hypothesis is a useful, incidental relationship. Indeed, it was the low lipid solubility of helium that originally suggested it be tested as a non-narcotic breathing gas diluent. (Behnke, *et al.,* 1935.)

---

[10] According to Henry's Law, molar concentration = partial pressure x solubility. According to the Meyer-Overton correlation the potency of an anaesthetic should be determined by its solubility in lipid.

[11] Miller (1971) later expounded Mullins idea in the form of the critical volume hypothesis to explain the opposing actions of narcosis and high pressure nervous syndrome.

[12] Solubility in water and lipid are often inversely related. Non-polar compounds typically have a low solubility in water (hydrophobic) and a high solubility in lipid (lipophilic).

[13] There is an electrical potential difference across a neuronal cell membrane (inside negative) that is maintained by an unequal distribution of small charged particles called ions. There are channels in the membrane through which ions can flow, but these are closed in the resting state. Opening of these channels causes a brief, localized reversal of the membrane potential called an action potential. These channels open in response to small voltage changes (voltage-gated ion channels) and thus are triggered by electrical activity in an adjacent area of the membrane, propagating the action potential. Neurotransmitter receptors produce smaller, decaying electrical potentials by opening different ion channels (receptor-gated ion channels).

[14] In support of a protein site for anaesthesia is another strong correlation, that between anaesthetic potency in mammals and luciferase (firefly light emitting protein) activity depression over 100,000 range of potency.

Narcosis Produces Slowed Mental Processing

Many of the actions of narcosis can be attributed to slowed information processing in the central nervous system. The slowed processing model is a useful tool to understand and investigate narcosis (Fowler *et al.*, 1985). The slowed processing model suggests that decreased arousal due to the anaesthetic properties of inert gases slows the processing of information in the central nervous system and results in the some of the behavioral modifications typical of inert gas narcosis. In order to understand this model one must consider the underlying model of information processing and then how it is affected by narcosis.

Information Processing Model

Information processing occurs in a series of stages. For instance, a simple information processing task such as a reaction time involves a perceptual and evaluation stage, a decision making stage and an effector stage. An example of a reaction time is the delay between seeing a red stop light while driving and applying the brakes. Recognizing a red stop light amongst the thousands of other stimuli occurs in the perceptual and evaluation stage. The decision whether or not to brake, involving calculating speed, distance and chance of a collision, occurs in the decision making stage. Activating the neuromotor programs to operate the leg muscles occurs in the effector stage. There are three aspects of such a system that could be influenced by narcosis. Firstly, is the **structure** of the system. Each information processing stage occurs in a different brain area and narcosis could disturb those areas. Secondly, the **functional aspect** of this model is the overall performance of the system due to the speed of information processing at each stage. Within limits, decreasing the speed of information handling at any stage impairs performance. Thirdly, the **strategy** for information handling includes distribution of attention, decision criteria, rehearsal strategies, and speed-accuracy trade-offs.

Inert gas narcosis probably affects the functional and strategic aspects but not structural components of information processing.

Functional Component

Slowed processing of information due to inert gas narcosis is evident in laboratory tests of cognitive function where the number of problems attempted is reduced (Hesser, *et al.*, 1978; Fothergill, *et al.*, 1991) and in increased reaction time. (Hamilton, *et al.*, 1995; Fowler, *et al.*, 1986; Fowler *et al.*, 1993.) Considerable experimental data indicates that narcosis produces a general functional deficit rather than distorting the structural components[15]. (Fowler, *et al.*, 1986; Fowler, *et al.*, 1985.) This functional deficit can be explained as slowed processing at any of the stages owing to decreased arousal (decreased general level of brain activity) or reduced activation (reduced readiness for activity). It is now thought that narcosis may influence multiple processing stages. Reaction time tests in combination with recording of brain electrical events indicate that slowed processing by narcosis seems to involve both slowing of the perceptual evaluation stage and also reduction of motor readiness at a later effector stage. (Fowler, *et al.*, 1993.) The notion of narcosis resulting from slowed processing is supported by the effects of amphetamine which increase arousal and reduce the effects of narcosis and by the effects of alcohol which reduce arousal and increase the effects of narcosis. (Hamilton, *et al.*, 1989; Fowler, *et al.*, 1986.)

Strategic Component

Decreased accuracy on cognitive function tests with narcosis (Moeller, *et al.*, 1981; Hesser, *et al.*, 1978; Fothergill, *et al.*, 1991) may be due to strategic changes in information handling attempting to compensate for slowed processing. One strategic variable is the speed-accuracy trade-off and a shift in this variable can mean that accuracy is sacrificed in an attempt to maintain the speed of responses. (Fowler, *et al.*, 1985; Hesser, *et al.*, 1978.) Curiously, such a rapid guessing technique has been found to be typical of one population of occupational divers at the surface. (Williamson, *et al.*, 1987.)

Modification

Dive Profile

Since inert gas narcosis is dependent on the partial pressure of the narcotic gas, it is depth dependent. As already noted some effects are more apparent at shallower depths, with other effects becoming evident deeper.

---

[15] Using the additive factor method where stimulus intensity is varied under control and narcotic conditions, a parallel shift, rather than a change in slope, of the stimulus intensity/response relationship indicates that narcosis produces a general functional deficit rather than interfering with structural stages.

The onset of narcosis upon breathing a narcotic partial pressure of gas is rapid but not instantaneous. The time to onset of narcosis should represent the time for a narcotic tension of inert gas to be achieved in the brain, and thus can be characterized by the half-time of the brain[16] and on the depth of the dive. For typical descent rates, narcosis will onset during compression past 100 fsw (30 msw) or soon after arriving at depths. Rapid compression can temporarily raise alveolar carbon dioxide levels that can exacerbate narcosis causing a temporary higher peak level of narcosis.

Oxygen

Theoretical and experimental evidence suggests that oxygen is also narcotic, producing performance deficits similar to inert gases. Although central nervous system oxygen toxicity prevents pure oxygen breathing at sufficiently high partial pressure to cause subjective sensations of narcosis, it can produce cognitive function impairment alone or in gas mixtures containing another narcotic gas. Lipid solubility predicts oxygen could be two times as narcotic as nitrogen and cognitive function tests indicate oxygen may be three to four times as narcotic as nitrogen. (Hesser, *et al.,* 1978.) It is therefore prudent to include oxygen in any calculations of equinarcotic depths in mixed gas dive planning.

Carbon Dioxide

Carbon dioxide produces a form of narcosis that is somewhat different to inert gas narcosis, and probably involves a different mechanism. (Hesser, *et al.,* 1978; Fothergill, *et al.,* 1991.) Whereas inert gas narcosis decreases both speed and accuracy in cognitive function tests, carbon dioxide tends to decrease the speed only without influencing accuracy. Carbon dioxide is relatively more potent than inert gases at reducing neuromuscular coordination. Carbon dioxide is narcotic at extremely small alveolar partial pressure and can be debilitating alone or can act additively with inert gas narcosis. An increase in alveolar carbon dioxide from its normal level of 5.6 - 6.1 kPa to 7 - 8 kPa causes significant narcosis. Alveolar carbon dioxide can easily rise to this level due to respiratory resistance from poor equipment or the high breathing gas density of nitrogen mixtures at depth, breathing equipment dead space or inadequate pulmonary ventilation. For instance, a diver swimming at a fast sustainable pace breathing less than 15 litres/min (BTPS) may be at risk of alveolar carbon dioxide reaching narcotic levels due to inadequate alveolar ventilation.

Anxiety

Anecdotal evidence suggests that anxiety can enhance narcosis. There is some experimental evidence, mostly arising from greater test score decrements under open-sea conditions suggested to produce anxiety in comparison to chamber tests. In one study describing the effects of narcosis in a cold open-water test at 100 fsw (30 msw), urine adrenaline and noradrenaline was elevated (a sign of stress) in those subjects showing the worst narcosis on cognitive function and dexterity tests (Davis, *et al.,* 1972).

Arousal: Fatigue, Drugs and Alcohol

According to the slowed processing model of inert gas narcosis, any condition that influences the level of arousal will modify narcosis. Fatigue would be expected to enhance narcosis and this is in fact the case. As previously described for amphetamine and alcohol, any drugs which produce increased or decreased arousal are likely to interact with narcosis.

Tolerance or Adaptation

Tolerance

Drug tolerance is the phenomena of reduced effect of a drug due to repeated exposure. In the context of narcosis, development of tolerance would imply a reduced narcotic potency of inert gas with repeated diving exposure, but this is apparently not the case since repeated diving exposure does not reduce the objective behavioral measures of inert gas narcosis. Five successive daily chamber air dives to 7ata each produce the same deterioration compared to 1.3ata in cognitive tests, reaction time and dexterity tests (Moeller *et al.,* 1981). Body sway (a measure of intoxication) is similarly increased by narcosis at 5.5ata compared to 1.3ata over 12 successive daily air dives. (Rogers and Moeller, 1989.) Clearly, tolerance to the narcotic actions of inert gases does not develop; repetitive diving exposures do not reduce the anaesthetic potency of inert gases.

---

[16] Unpublished experiments in my laboratory indicate that the half-time of the brain after a step change in arterial nitrogen partial pressure should be approximately 1 minute.

Subjective Adaptation

Adaptation is the adjustment by an organism to its environment; in the case of narcosis, adaptation would be a rearrangement of behavior that allows a performance enhancement[17]. Repeated diving produces a dissociation of behavioral and subjective components of narcosis. It is unclear whether this represents a true tolerance[18] or an adaptation. During five consecutive daily dives to 6.46ata on air, reaction time does not improve relative to 1ata, but subjective evaluation of narcosis does change. Global estimates of the magnitude of narcosis begin to decline by the third daily dive as does identification of body/mental sensations associated with intoxication; however, subjects continue to describe their ability to work as being equally impaired. (Hamilton, *et al.*, 1995.) It is evident that it is inappropriate to use the intensity of sensations of intoxication sensation as a gauge for underwater efficiency.

Specific Adaptation and Individual Variability

It is deeply entrenched in the diving community that some individuals can work effectively at depth and that diving experience improves performance during deep dives. Indeed, as with any biological phenomena, there is some individual variability in susceptibility to narcosis, but whether adaptation specific to the narcotic situation occurs with repeated exposures is speculative. For instance, reduction in subjective sensations of intoxication may allow better focus of the task at hand. Also, some individuals may adopt more appropriate adaptive strategies to cope with narcosis and experience may also help identify such strategies. For instance, it is possible to control accuracy on tests for narcosis, allowing only speed to decline (Fowler, *et al.*, 1993), so a potential strategic adaptation could be to choose an appropriate speed-accuracy trade-off. Indeed, one of the earliest observations of narcosis is that using deliberately slow movements can lessen neuromuscular impairment. (Behnke, *et al.*, 1935.)

Summary and Practical Strategies

Some inert gases possess anaesthetic properties, narcosis results from breathing these gases at sub-anaesthetic doses and is an unavoidable consequence of air diving beyond 100 fsw (30 msw). A possible explanation of the effects of narcosis on behavior is a slowing of information processing in the central nervous system, often combined with a shift in the speed-accuracy trade-off making the diver more prone to errors. The subjective sensations of inert gas narcosis include intoxication and repeated diving may reduce these sensations. Objective laboratory tests of narcosis show slow and inaccurate cognitive function, slowed reaction time, and decreased neuromuscular coordination. Performance on such objective tests does not improve with repeated dives. A less well appreciated action of inert gas narcosis is impaired thermoregulation which can result in greater heat loss during water immersion. Since narcosis is enhanced by factors such as carbon dioxide retention, anxiety and fatigue, narcosis can increase during a dive without further change in depth.

Strategies to enhance performance with narcosis might exist. Although the nature of such strategies is unknown, some issues are worthy of consideration. First, it is important to recognize that narcosis will reduce overall efficiency during air dives deeper than 100 fsw (30 msw). Also, owing to subjective adaptation, it is inappropriate to use the intensity of intoxication as a gauge for underwater safety and efficiency. Secondly, over-learned skills are less likely to be influenced by impaired information processing. Furthermore, subjective adaptation may be of some value particularly for performing over-learned tasks. On the other hand, subjective adaptation will be of no value to novel situations or situations that require cognitive information processing or memory (for instance gas management or decompression calculations). Thirdly, if some of the performance decrement is due to an inappropriate shift in speed-accuracy trade-off, training may allow more appropriate information processing strategies to be implemented. Finally, it must be recognized that such strategies may improve performance with moderate levels of narcosis but are unlikely to protect against the debilitating effects of extreme narcosis.

By far the best choice is to avoid narcosis where feasible and in particular where safety may be reduced. The level of narcosis is primarily influenced by inspired partial pressures of nitrogen and oxygen and therefore the depth of a dive and the breathing gas mixture. The use of helium as a partial or complete replacement for nitrogen as a breathing gas diluent reduces or eliminates inert gas narcosis and owing to lower breathing gas density reduces the level of narcosis due to carbon dioxide build-up.

---

[17] Adaptation also has a meaning similar to tolerance but is a reduced nervous system response to *continual* stimulation, this is not implied here.

[18] Development of tolerance would imply that narcosis produces these subjective effects by a different mechanism to the other behavioral effects that are not altered by repeated exposures.

References

Behnke A.R., Thomson R.M., Motley E.P. (1935). The psychological effects from breathing at 4 atmospheres pressure. American Journal of Physiology; 112:554-558.

Cheung S.S., Mekjavic I.B. (1995). Human temperature regulation during subanesthetic levels of nitrous oxide-induced narcosis. Journal of Applied Physiology; 78:2301-2308.

Davis F.M., Osborne J.P., Baddeley A.D., Graham I.M.F. (1972). Diver performance: nitrogen narcosis and anxiety. Aerospace Medicine; 43:1079-1082.

End E. (1938) The use of new equipment and helium gas in a world record dive. J. Ind. Hyg. Toxicol.; 20:511-520

Fothergill D.M., Hedges D., Morrison J.B. (1991). Effects of CO_2 and N_2 partial pressures on cognitive and psychomotor performance. Undersea Biomedical Research; 18:1-19.

Fowler B., Ackles K.N., Portlier G. (1985). Effects of inert gas narcosis on behavior - a critical review. Undersea Biomedical Research; 12:369-402.

Fowler B., Hamilton K., Portlier G. (1986). Effects of ethanol and amphetamine on inert gas narcosis in humans. Undersea Biomedical Research; 13:345-354.

Fowler B., Hamel R., Lindeis A.E. (1993). Relationship between the event-related brain potential P300 and inert gas narcosis. Undersea Hyperbaric Medicine; 20:49-62.

Hamilton K., Fowler B., Porlier G. (1989). The effects of hyperbaric air in combination with ethyl alcohol and dextroamphetamine on serial choice-reaction time. Ergonomics 32:409-422.

Hamilton K., LaLiberté M.F., Heslegrave M.A. (1992) Subjective and behavioural effects associated with repeated exposure to narcosis. Aviation Space Environmental Medicine; 63:865-869.

Hamilton K., Laliberte M.F., Fowler B. (1995). Dissociation of the behavioral and subjective components of nitrogen narcosis and diver adaptation. Undersea Hyperbaric Medicine; 22:41-49.

Hesser C.M., Fagraeus L., Adolfson J. (1978). Roles of nitrogen, oxygen, and carbon dioxide in compressed-air narcosis. Undersea Biomedical Research; 5:391-400.

Hill L., Phillips A.E. (1932). Deep sea diving. Journal of the Royal Naval Medical Service; 18:157-183.

Mekjavic I.B., Passias T., Sundberg C.J. and Eiken O. (1994). Perception of thermal comfort during narcosis. Undersea Hyperbaric Medicine; 21:9-19.

Mekjavic I.B., Savic S.A., Eiken O. (1995). Nitrogen narcosis attenuates shivering thermogenesis. Journal of Applied Physiology; 78:2241-2244.

Moeller G., Chattin C., Rogers W., Laxar K., Ryack B. (1981). Performance effects with repeated exposure to the diving environment. Journal of Applied Physiology; 66:502-510.

Rogers W.H., Moeller G. (1989). Effect of brief, repeated hyperbaric exposures on susceptibility to nitrogen narcosis. Undersea Biomedical Research; 16:227-232.

Smith E.B. (1986). On the science of deep-sea diving-observations on the respiration of different kinds of air. Undersea Biomedical Research; 14:347-369.

Williamson A.M., Clarke B., Edmonds C. (1987). Neurobehavioural effects of professional abalone diving. Br. J. Ind. Med. 44:459-466.

CHAPTER 9
Carbon Dioxide Retention

Jolie Bookspan, Ph.D.

In a US Navy experimental facility, testing for new decompression schedules was underway using Nitrox mixtures with a higher concentration of oxygen than the 21 percent in air. The Navy investigators first used 100 percent O_2 at various pressures to work out tolerance limits for oxygen itself. They established a tentative "limit curve" based upon presumably reliable data. The actual tests were carried to 25 percent longer times than on the limit curve. No serious toxicity was observed inside the limit curve, so this was accepted as safe.

A diver on the *Hirokawa Maru* in the Solomon Islands.

Photo: Kevin & Miria Denaly

It seemed rational to assume that PO_2 was the only crucial variable to derive limits for mixtures. Simply translating the limits for 100 percent O_2 into curves for different Nitrox mixtures on the basis of oxygen partial pressures, meant the mixtures should have been all right. But in the first experiment that they tested Nitrox mixtures, the diver convulsed. After that there were problems suggesting early oxygen poisoning and other strange effects where no difficulties were expected.

What's Going On With Mixed Gas?

The year was 1952. The U.S. Navy Experimental Diving Unit (EDU), then located in Washington, D.C., was ordered to work out a system utilizing "mixed gas" to reduce decompression requirements for practical applications like clearing mines from a harbor. Project Officer Lieutenant Commander J.V. Dwyer and Assistant Medical Officer Lieutenant E.H. Lanphier (MC) took major responsibility for this work.

Dives with Nitrox mixtures appeared to produce an unusual number of problems compared to previously worked-out oxygen limits. Furthermore, these problems did not occur when using helium-oxygen mixtures with the same oxygen pressure. The only plausible explanation involved carbon dioxide (CO_2). There was no CO_2 in the mixes, and dead space in the breathing apparatus was minimal; but data from an earlier study (1) indicated that, at depth, some divers breathed less than others during similar exertion. Divers who breathed much less probably did not eliminate CO_2 adequately. This was of particular concern from the standpoint of susceptibility to oxygen convulsions. CO_2 excess increases brain blood flow, and that increases the "dose" of oxygen to the brain. Lanphier and Dwyer experimentally verified that some EDU divers breathed less than others during equivalent work. They sampled end-tidal gas (the last gas breathed out in a normal expiration, ideally consisting only of alveolar gas) for an estimate of levels of CO_2 in arterial blood. At depth, end-tidal CO_2 was definitely high in certain individuals, particularly when N_2O_2 mixtures were used (2). (**Note:** it is sometimes possible for end-tidal CO_2 samples to overestimate arterial levels with certain breathing patterns, most notably slow, deep breathing. For this reason, studies using end-tidal gas readings should cross-verify against arterial samples, as was done in this study.)

An independent study in 1995 repeated the EDU conditions and confirmed the results. Investigators looked at CO_2 retention during hyperbaric exercise while breathing EAN 40. They determined that CO_2 retention, "Is not expected to be globally aggravated by breathing Nitrox down to 100 fsw (30 msw), but that some individuals could be so affected."(3)

Startling Results With Helium-Oxygen (HeO_2) Mixtures

From continued work it became clear that while breathing N_2O_2 mixtures at depth CO_2 retention occurred, whereas with HeO_2, ventilation was essentially unimpaired and CO_2 levels stayed close to normal.

Conclusions reached following the 1956 and 1957 studies (4) included the following:

(1) Retention of CO_2 during working dives at moderate depth is a definite reality.

(2) Only when the breathing medium is a HeO_2 mixture is an increase in body CO_2 tension absent or small.

(3) Although increased breathing resistance and dead space both favor CO_2 retention, keeping these factors to a practical minimum does not eliminate the problem.

(4) Some individuals are much more likely to develop high CO_2 tensions than others, but all individuals show a tendency in this direction especially when breathing an N_2O_2 mixture. There is no sharp dividing line between "retainers" and "normals".

(5) The most effective method of minimizing the complications caused by CO_2 retention is to use HeO_2 mixtures for "mixed gas" dives.

The recommendations of Research Report 7-58 can be reproduced verbatim: "It is recommended that:

(1) Attempts to use high-oxygen nitrogen-oxygen mixtures be abandoned as a means of reducing the requirements of decompression.

(2) Studies leading to the use of HeO_2 mixtures for "mixed gas" diving be carried forward as rapidly as possible."

Why is CO_2 Retention a Problem?

As early as 1878, physiologist Paul Bert demonstrated "auto-intoxication" of animals by their own CO_2 in a super-oxygenated environment. He was also aware of the possible connection between CO_2 and O_2 toxicity (5). CO_2 retention at depth was once suggested as the sole cause of nitrogen narcosis (6, 7). Another, less prominent idea, was that only CO_2 retainers might suffer O_2 toxicity during exertion more readily than others (8). CO_2 retention is now viewed as a contributor to O_2 toxicity and nitrogen narcosis, suspected as a contributor to decompression sickness, and implicated in incidents of underwater confusion and loss of consciousness.

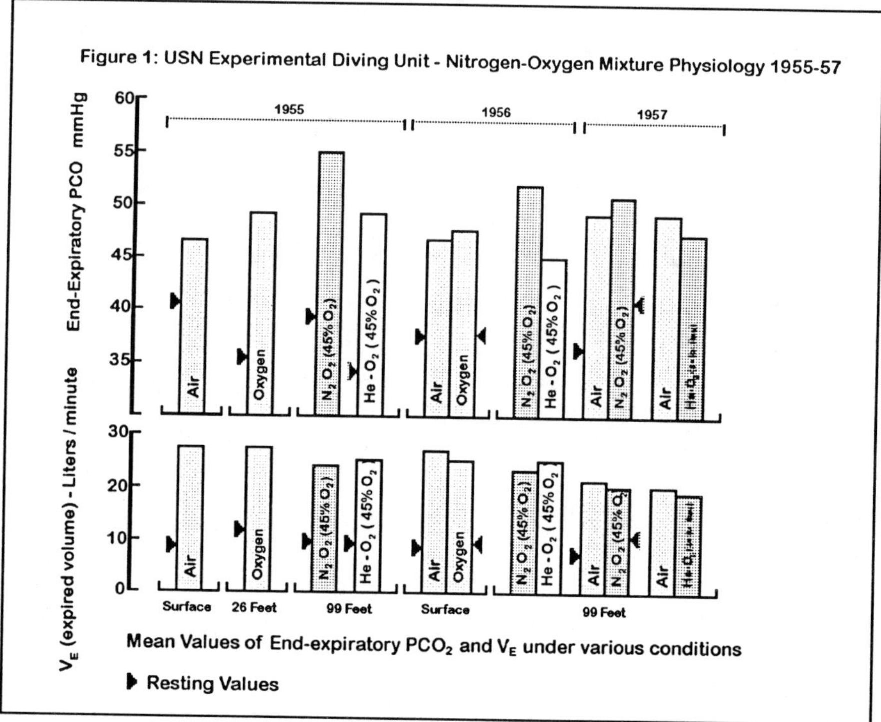

Oxygen Toxicity

During World War II, British Royal Navy torpedo divers using oxygen rebreathers were passing out without warning. The term "shallow water blackout" was used in 1944 by Barlow and MacIntosh for blackout suspected, and later confirmed, from too high CO_2 levels (hypercapnia) (9). It was termed "shallow water" because oxygen rebreathers could not be used in deep water because of the high oxygen content. Most of the cases weren't deep enough to have been O_2 toxicity, which had previously been the prime suspect. The problem subsided after improving CO_2 absorption canisters. Although the term "shallow water blackout" had the established meaning of

CO_2 retention-induced blackout, it was later applied to unconsciousness from too low oxygen (hypoxia) in breath-hold diving, especially following excessive hyperventilation. The mix-up has continued into common use.

Inert Gas Narcosis

When CO_2 retention occurs during exposure to a narcotic partial pressure of inert gas, it seems to accentuate the resulting narcosis. Case and Haldane described this accentuation in 1941 (10) Hesser et al., (11) analyzed narcosis into its 'CO_2' and 'N_2' components. They concluded that high N_2 and CO_2 pressures are additive in their effects on human performance. Fothergill, Hedges & Morrison described similar findings (12).

Sterba reported a study of underwater bicycle ergometry with US Navy divers in a pressure chamber (13). The subjects developed high end-tidal levels of CO_2 when breathing air at 190 feet (57 meters) and HeO_2 at 300 and 1000 ft. (91. and 305.8 meters). Above 65mmHg, dizziness and headache occurred, while above 70mm, severe confusion and amnesia developed. Some subjects had to be rescued due to severe CO_2 narcosis.

Bennett and Blenkarn (14) studied 4 resting subjects at 6.7 and 9.6 atm abs, alternating between air and HeO_2. Mental performance was decidedly impaired when the subjects breathed air, but there was no evidence of problems or CO_2 retention under any of the experimental conditions.

Does Narcosis Depress Ventilation?

Lanphier (15) brought up the interesting possibility that a vicious cycle would develop if inert gas narcosis decreased a diver's drive to breathe, and if the resulting rising CO_2 levels in turn, enhanced narcosis. Lanphier's own experience indicated that severe narcosis does not abolish the respiratory drive or the experience of dyspnea (16, 17), but the possibility of some depression of ventilation by narcosis is difficult to rule out. For example, density and narcotic effects are pretty much inseparable - if helium is substituted for nitrogen to avoid narcosis, the density is also greatly decreased. There is some evidence, e.g., Giry, et al., that hydrogen narcosis decreases ventilation (18).

Schaefer reviewed earlier evidence that narcosis does not alter the basic CO_2 response (19). Gelfand and colleagues analyzed the ventilatory responses of two male subjects over a wide range of pressure and gas density (20). The reduction of ventilatory response to CO_2 correlated with increased gas density but not with narcosis. Other work to distinguish the effects of increased gas density from the central nervous system effects of increased nitrogen pressure include was reported by Linnarsson and Hesser (21) and Hesser and Lind (22).

It seems very unlikely that narcosis, except perhaps with hydrogen, is responsible for CO_2 retention at depth. Whether pressure itself may have such an effect is unclear. Saltzman and colleagues reported that resting $PaCO_2$ increased about 0.5mmHg per atmosphere of increasing pressure (23). Researchers Tarasiuk and Grossman supported the idea of a direct effect of pressure on the respiratory center (24).

Observations with Nitrous Oxide

With little change in density, nitrous oxide in relatively low concentration (e.g. 30 percent at 1 atm abs) produces a narcotic effect subjectively indistinguishable from narcosis at considerable depth. But is it the same phenomenon? Bradley and Dickson (25) found that inhaling nitrous oxide increased 'expired total ventilation' (V_E) and respiratory frequency with decreases in tidal volume and arterial carbon dioxide levels during both rest and work. These changes are the opposite of those seen with air at depth, and were thought to reflect nitrous oxide sensitization of the pulmonary stretch receptors. Webber also reported an increase in frequency, but his calculations indicated no net change in alveolar ventilation (26). Apparently, nitrous oxide narcosis differs in significant ways from inert gas narcosis at depth.

Altered Consciousness

Warkander, et al., (27) described severe impairment of consciousness in two subjects experimentally exposed to high breathing resistance during wet chamber dives. The divers did not experience exceptional dyspnea (difficulty in breathing). The authors concluded, "These incidents indicate that severe hypercapnia does not necessarily correlate with dyspnea and that severe disturbances in mental function due to hypercapnia can develop suddenly when high breathing resistance is encountered in diving." Based in part on such experience, in further work Warkander, et al., proposed "physiologically acceptable" standards for breathing apparatus (28).

Lanphier described an experience where he and a student assistant tested a newly constructed bicycle ergometer in a dry chamber at 7.8 atm abs (16, 17). He writes in the third person, "They breathed air from a demand breathing circuit that included a recording gas meter and had been used successfully at lesser pressures. The test was to consist of 5 min. of moderate work on the new ergometer. It soon became obvious that the breathing circuit did not provide sufficient air, but both were determined to complete the test. They both became

Altered consciousness in diving was the main topic of an Undersea Medical Society workshop (29). Participants considered CO_2 retention and related abnormalities to be important among causes of impairment.

comatose in a few minutes. Subsequent measurements indicated that they had achieved only about half of the alveolar ventilation needed to maintain normal $PaCO_2$. Dyspnea was extreme before loss of consciousness, and it became a terrifying sensation when consciousness started to return after exertion ceased. Lanphier and the student were not CO_2 retainers, but it seems likely that the retention tendency would favor loss or impairment of consciousness under less arduous circumstances and might involve less warning of impending danger. Even non-retainers would presumably experience similar effects if narcosis were present along with failure or inadequacy of CO_2 absorption in closed- or semi-closed circuit scuba. As has been noted elsewhere, consciousness is at risk when CO_2 absorption is inadequate in rebreathing scuba."

Inspired CO_2

Technical divers would not ordinarily be subjected to high levels of inspired CO_2. In other words, they would not inhale higher than normal levels of CO_2 from their breathing mixtures. Still, response to inspired CO_2 deserves mention. Here is an interesting story from Case Histories of Diving and Hyperbaric Accidents (16):

"In 1948, I was a medical student and also working on a master's degree in pharmacology at the University of Illinois College of Medicine in Chicago. My duties as an assistant instructor in pharmacology included a student laboratory session called Gas Pharmacology that I had designed myself.

At that same time, Dr. Meduna, who had done much to promote electroshock therapy (EST) for mental illness, was very much interested in "CO_2 convulsions" as a relatively benign potential substitute for EST or as a treatment in its own right. My research concerned anticonvulsant drugs, so my combined interests made curiosity about "the CO_2 treatment" inevitable.

One day, several of us, including our chairman, visited a state mental hospital where a young physician was applying Meduna's new modality. The treatment involved administration of 30 percent CO_2 in oxygen by inhalation. The patients lost consciousness very promptly and went into a motor phenomenon much more like decerebrate rigidity than the tonic-clonic seizures that I was accustomed to seeing after electroshock in my animals. The aftereffects appeared to be minimal.

Dr. Meduna's young associate graciously offered the experience to any of us, and I accepted. Inhaling the high concentration of CO_2 felt like aspirating a bottle of club soda; but the sensation was brief, as was the tremendous drive to breathe. I recall some mental activity similar to what I'd experienced on various anesthetic gases; but that, too, was brief. I was told that the expected muscular activity occurred and that the mask was removed when it did. Consciousness returned rather rapidly, and I do not recall any sequelae." - Rev. Dr. Ed Lanphier.

Normal CO_2 Production and Removal

"One Saturday morning in Buffalo some years ago, I was working on my camper in the driveway when my attention was suddenly captured by a voice coming from the open window of my next-door neighbor's bedroom.

It was a very familiar voice but clearly not that of Ernie Reid or his wife. I shortly became convinced that the speaker was an old friend, Joe MacInnis. It seemed highly improbable that Joe would be in the Reids' bedroom, but I investigated anyway. The voice was emanating from Ernie's new bedside FM radio; and it did indeed belong to Joe MacInnis, the renowned Canadian diver-physician, underwater explorer, and arctic authority. Dr. MacInnis was being interviewed in his underwater habitat at Tobermory in Georgian Bay.

I listened at first with interest and then with fascination. The interview seemed to be growing more and more spirited; then positively breathless. The questions and answers became shorter and shorter. They were almost down to gasps and monosyllables when Joe said something about CO_2 and getting back to the surface. I assume that he and his companions surfaced safely." - Rev. Dr. Ed Lanphier, in a 1960's account (16).

Normally, arterial CO_2 is held, almost without exception, within 3mmHg during both rest and exercise, a very tight range. How does your body do this?

How much, and how deeply you breathe, is regulated by your arterial oxygen pressure, CO_2 tension, pH, by reflexes in your lung and chest wall, and through control by your brain.

Not enough oxygen in your breathing mixture enhances the ventilatory drive; there is a hypoxic drive to breathe. CO_2 is an even more profound respiratory stimulant. Of all the various inputs, your arterial CO_2 is the most influential. That means that rising production of CO_2 with exercise increases how much and how fast you breathe, regulating your CO_2, so that CO_2 does not normally rise at all, even during heavy exercise.

In the normal population, CO_2 is also constant at rest, only rising a bit during sleep. An important exception sometimes involves the condition of sleep-apnea. Sleep apnea is a sleep disorder involving snoring, where the snorer stops breathing during sleep because of upper airway obstruction, resulting in repeated shortage of oxygen to the brain. CO_2 levels rise, due to absence of ventilation for varying periods, sometimes hundreds of times per night. Sleep apnea sufferers are often overweight, heavy necked males. For long-term treatment, losing weight is often very effective.

Mechanisms of CO_2 Retention

Normally, no great rise in your CO_2 levels occurs during rest or exercise. Sometimes it does rise, however. Why is this?

Several variables seem to impair the CO_2 response during underwater work. From Lanphier three main contributors emerged: Breathing high partial pressures of oxygen (elevated PIO_2), inadequate ventilatory response during exertion, and increased work of breathing (30).

High PO_2 decreases ventilation in some situations. Lanphier found that increased inspiratory oxygen pressure accounts for about 25 percent of the elevation in end tidal CO_2. Lambertsen, et al. (31) demonstrated that exercise while breathing hyperbaric oxygen decreases ventilation significantly. Other authors find that at a given work rate below the anaerobic threshold, (steady-state exercise) ventilation is not appreciably different between 100 percent O_2 breathing, and air breathing (32, 33, 34). Your respiratory center responds to CO_2 to the extent that it keeps things level whether working or at rest, with some modifications. Working hard enough to produce lactic acid will change that to compensate for the metabolic acidosis, but high inspired oxygen levels knock out the chemoreceptor response to lactic acid, which helps explain CO_2 retention in working divers who at least are verging on the anaerobic threshold.

Most of the elevations of $PaCO_2$ were accounted for by the increased work of breathing at depth. Work of breathing is made more difficult by the higher gas density at depth. Your body compensates by reducing ventilation - easily demonstrated by trying to breathe through a narrow tube. In a 1977 study of tolerance to various gases at extreme densities, Lambertsen et al., found a "prominent reduction of total and alveolar ventilation (35). Response was unrelated to any narcotic properties of the gases in questions, demonstrating that ventilatory suppression was not a function of narcotic depression. It was the gas density and work of breathing that limited pulmonary function. The early work at EDU seemed to show that the critical factor in the CO_2 problems was the higher gas density of the nitrogen mixtures compared to helium mixtures.

Why CO_2 Acclimatization?

Ordinarily, rising levels of CO_2 produce an increasingly uncomfortable desire to breathe more. However, there is a great range of response. Some people have a normal response, others are remarkable in retaining CO_2 to a large extent - they just don't have much response to CO_2. The question behind carbon dioxide retention is, why do some subjects not increase ventilation to regulate their rising CO_2 levels?

Some evidence suggests that the tendency to retain CO_2 increases with chronic exposure to high CO_2 environments, such as those encountered during specific diving situations. The body gets used to higher levels, allowing them to occur without the usual autoregulation that would correct the situation.

In the first EDU studies, almost all of the subjects had been experienced "hard hat" divers. The volumes of air needed for adequate ventilation of a helmet are very great, particularly at significant depth. Adequate ventilation of a helmet is unlikely, so acclimatization to CO_2 may have been an occupational necessity.

Divers often had other reasons for repeated elevation of their arterial PCO_2 such as repeated deep breath-hold diving in submarine escape training. Schaefer (36) found that submarine escape tank instructors retained more CO_2 than the average untrained man. He suggested a possible adaptation effect. Kerem and colleagues (37) found that both diver and non-diver subjects exhibited similar resting CO_2 arterial levels, but when exercising, arterial CO_2 was higher in divers. They confirmed this in a later study of CO_2 retention during Nitrox breathing (3). MacDonald and Pilmanis (38) found a moderate, consistent elevated CO_2 level and characteristic hypoventilation in 10 of 10 male divers they tested on open circuit scuba during open water dives.

There may be some sort of selection, where those who tolerated high CO_2 levels via a blunted chemoreceptor or other adaptive response, self-select to continue with their diving career. That situation must be less prevalent today, so the number of CO_2-tolerant divers from that source may be considerably smaller. Perhaps, a number of the carbon-dioxide retaining divers are sleep-apneics, who routinely experience high CO_2 levels during sleep. The large, heavy, body types of many divers suggests this.

In some cases, CO_2 retention occurs in subjects with no experience with high-CO_2 environments, but who may be exposed in other ways, most notably a learned adaptation from breathing patterns that regularly produce elevated internal CO_2 levels. When scuba diving first became prevalent, "skip breathing" was often taught or popularized as a means of conserving the air supply in open circuit scuba. Educational efforts to discourage skip breathing have had some effect, so fewer individuals have probably become CO_2-tolerant in this way.

Some CO_2 retainers lack any history of probable acclimatization. There are a few individuals (we don't know just how few) who retain CO_2 with no suggestion that this is an adaptive response. A 1995 study by Clark, et al., (39) found increased levels of arterial CO_2 with increasing exertion in normal subjects exposed to 2 atm of oxygen on dry land.

Still, CO_2 acclimatization is not as cut-and-dried as it may sound. A recent book on the control of respiration (40) contains this statement: "... significant, sustained CO_2 retention is extremely rare in health, even under the most extreme conditions of exercise intensity and flow limitation." One of the editors, Jerome Dempsey, acknowledges that this statement does not necessarily apply to individuals who have had some reason for adaptation to CO_2. Dempsey (41) says that in a career of exercise-related research, he has encountered only one or two individuals who would be classified as "CO_2 retainers" in terms of our definition.

Identification of Retainers

Many attempts have been made to identify carbon dioxide retainers. Such people could be at unexpected risk of CO_2 blackout, unusual degrees of nitrogen narcosis, or susceptibility to oxygen toxicity. Identification, for that reason, would be a helpful screening.

The main hope at EDU originally was that outstanding CO_2 retainers could be identified and kept from

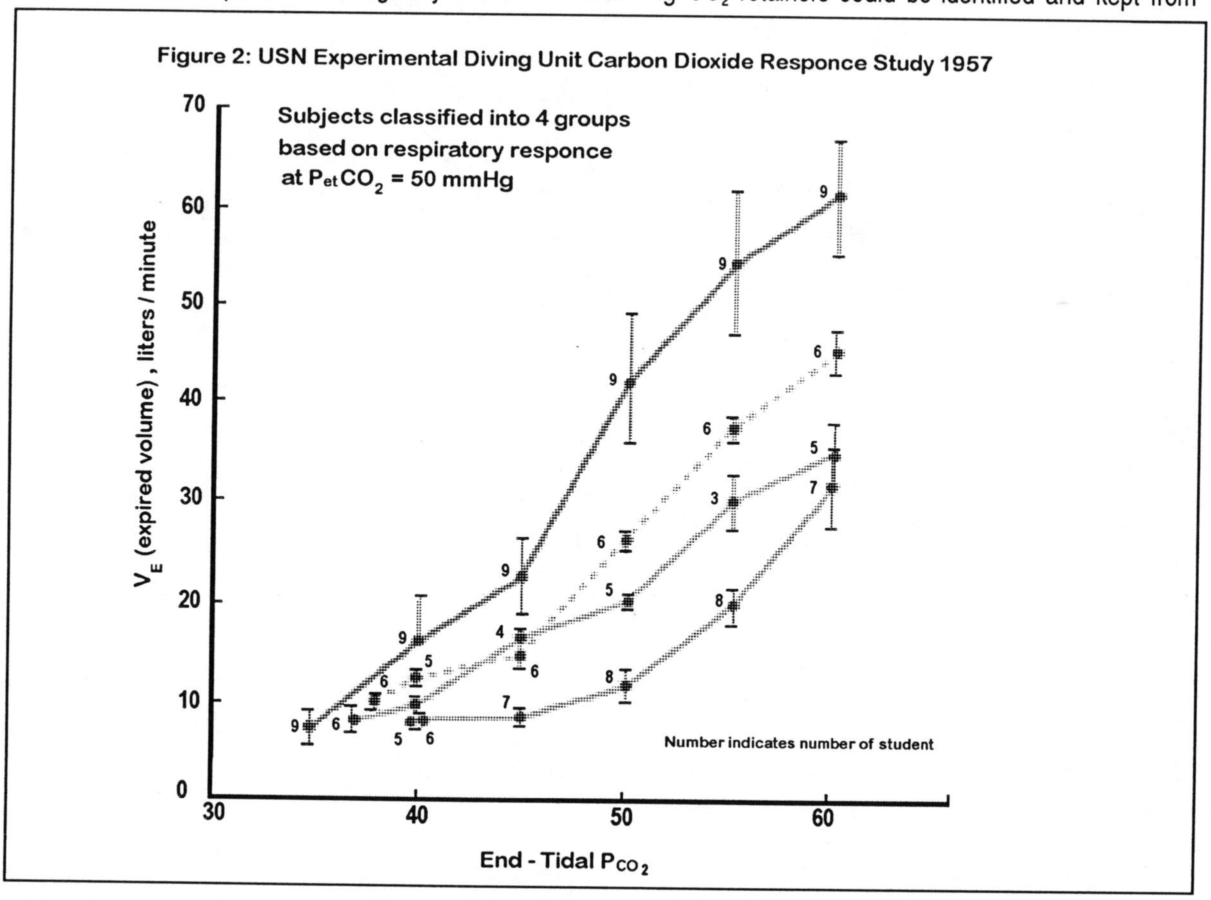

hazardous exposures. If so, others could take advantage of the benefits of Nitrox diving. A dry-land test of ventilatory response to various levels of inspired CO_2 was set up (3). There was a great spread of results **(Figure 2)**, and these were compared with the CO_2 levels that the divers developed spontaneously at depth. In about 60 percent of cases, high CO_2 at depth corresponded to low response to inspired CO_2; but in the other 40 percent, such a relationship was not seen. The correlation was not good enough for a fair, reliable selection test.

Ventilatory Response to CO2

In other work involving tethered swimming at submaximal work rate, 11 of 19 subjects developed elevated CO_2 levels. A CO_2 rebreathing test did not clearly pre-identify these people, leading to the conclusion that identification of CO_2 retainers may require a test with exercise (42). A tethered fin-swimming test is an example.

David Elliott recommends screening tests be developed for compressed air divers by working divers doing heavy work deeper than 120 feet (36 meters) who might be at risk of unconsciousness (43). However, it seems there is no easy, reliable method of identifying retainers in advance. However, unusually low air-use rates would arouse our suspicions. The need for better and more accurate tests is evident.

Questions Remain

CO_2 retention has been demonstrated to result from conditions including increased gas density at depth, but this leaves unexplained the tendency of some individuals to retain CO_2 during exertion under seemingly optimal conditions.

Also, not all investigators agree with the findings and conclusions of U.S. Navy Experimental Diving Unit studies described in this chapter. In his book Oxygen and the Diver (44), the late Professor Kenneth Donald noted his opposition to most of the observations and conclusions of the EDU studies. Donald concluded that CO_2 retention and its alleged consequences remain unproven. He also questioned any need to restrict oxygen exposure as depth increases. Donald particularly distrusted end-tidal (end-expiratory) gas sampling and analysis as an index of CO_2 levels in the body.

Dr. Lanphier writes, "Some of Donald's criticisms are admittedly well-taken, and many of his contentions are difficult if not impossible to refute at this point in time. Overall, however, the only point on which we can agree with Donald is on the need for further study. Whether such investigations will ever be possible, only time will tell."

Avoiding CO_2 Retention

If the solution of the CO_2 retention problem does not lie in personnel selection, what other avenues are open?

Avoiding "skip breathing" and any other attempt to conserve air seems obvious, but it may be easier to recommend than to accomplish. Providing ventilatory assistance to divers may deserve investigation.

Another solution would be to promote helium-oxygen and Trimix as breathing media for mixed-gas diving, at least for demonstrated or suspected CO_2 retainers. There is work supporting that CO_2 retention is minimal or non-existent when the breathing medium is a HeO_2 mixture (2, 4). In the probable range of depths and times, helium should not be much less desirable than N_2O_2 from the standpoint of decompression. Some advantages of Nitrox would be lost if Heliox were to be adopted, but for certain divers, a tendency to retention may be considered a deciding factor. Meanwhile, divers who use Nitrox mixtures should exercise caution with depth/time limits, reduce PO_2 depth/time limits, particularly if CO_2 retention is suspected.

Author's note: Gratitude and thanks are due to the Rev. Dr. Ed Lanphier, M.D., without whom this chapter would not be written, and very likely, not any other chapter on CO_2 retention.

Works Cited

1. Report of the Cooperative Underwater Swimmer Project (CUSP). Jan 1953 National Research Council Committee on Amphibious Operations Report NRC:CAO:0033,
2. Lanphier EH. 1955. Nitrogen-Oxygen Mixture Physiology, Phases I and 2. Formal Report 7-55, Washington: Navy Experimental Diving Unit.
3. Kerem D., Daskalovic Y.I., Arieli R., Shupak A. 1995. CO_2 Retention During Hyperbaric Exercise While Breathing 40/60 Nitrox. Undersea & Hyperbaric Medicine 22(4): 339-346.
4. Lanphier E.H. June 1958. Nitrogen-Oxygen Mixture Physiology, Phases 4 and 6. Research Report 7-58. Navy Experimental Diving Unit. Panama City Florida 32407.
5. Bert P. 1878. La Pression Manometrique. G. Masson, Paris.
6. Bean J.W. 1950. Tensional Changes Of Alveolar Gas In Reactions To Rapid Compression And Decompression And Question Of Nitrogen Narcosis. Am J Physiol 16, 417-425.
7. Seusing J. and Drube H.C. 1960. The Significance Of Hypercapnia For The Occurrence Of Depth Intoxication. Klin Wschr 38, 1088-1090.
8. Lambertsen C.J., Owen S.G., Wendel H., Stroud M.W., Lurie A.A., Lochner W., and Clark G.F. (1959). Respiratory Cerebral Circulatory Control During Exercise At 0.21 And 2.0 Atmospheres Inspired PO2. J Applied Physiol 14, 966-982.
9. Barlow H.B., MacIntosh F.C. (1944). Shallow Water Black-Out. Royal Navy Physiological Laboratory Report R.N.P. 44/125 UPS 48a.
10. Case E.M., Haldane J.B.S. (1941). Human Physiology Under High Pressure. I. Effects of nitrogen, carbon dioxide and cold. J. Hygiene, Camb. 41:225-249.
11. Hesser C.M., Adolfson J., Fagraeus L. (1971). Role of CO_2 In Compressed-Air Narcosis. Aerospace Med 42: 162-168.

12 Fothergill D.M., Hedges D., Morrison J.B.. (1991). Effects Of CO_2 And N_2 Partial Pressures On Cognitive And Psychomotor Performance. Undersea Biomed Res 18:1-19.

13. Sterba J.A..(1990). Hypercapnia During Deep Air and Mixed Gas Diving, Report No.12-90. Panama City, FL: Navy Experimental Diving Unit (NEDU), 22pp.
14. Bennett P.B., Blenkarn G.D. (1974). Arterial Blood Gases In Man During Gas Narcosis. J Appl Physiol 36: 45-48.
15. Lanphier E.H. (1975). Pulmonary Function, In: Bennett PB, Elliott DE. The Physiology and Medicine of Diving and Compressed Air Work. 2d ed. London: Bailliere Tindall, 102-154.

16 Lanphier E.H. (1988). Carbon Dioxide Poisoning. In: Waite C.L., ed. Case Histories of Diving and Hyperbaric Accidents. Bethesda: Undersea and Hyperbaric Medical Society, 199-213.

17. Lanphier E.H. (1963). Influence Of Increased Ambient Pressure Upon Alveolar Ventilation. In: Lambertsen C.J, Greenbaum L.J. Jr, eds. 2d Symp Underwater Physiol. Washington, DC: Nat'l Acad Sci - Nat'l Res Council, 124-133.
18. Giry P., Battesti A., Hyacinthe R., Burnet H. (1987). Ventilatory Tolerance To Exercise During A Hydrogen-Helium-Oxygen Saturation Dive (Hydra V). In: Brauer RW, ed. Hydrogen as a Diving Gas. Bethesda: Undersea and Hyperbaric Medical Society, 179-196.
19. Schaefer K.E. (1969). Carbon Dioxide Effects Under Conditions Of Raised Environmental Pressure. In: Bennett PB, Elliott DE , eds. The Physiology and Medicine of Diving and Compressed Air Work. Baltimore: Williams & Wilkins, 144-154.
20. Gelfand R., Lambertsen C.J., Peterson R.E. (1980). Human Respiratory Control At High Ambient Pressures And Inspired Gas Densities. J Appl Physiol, 48:528-539.
21. Linnarsson D., Hesser C.M. (1978). Dissociated Ventilatory And Central Respiratory Responses To CO_2 At Raised N_2 Pressure. J Appl Physiol, 45:756-761.
22. Hesser C.M., Lind F. (1981). Effects Of Exercise And Hyperbaric Air On Ventilation And Central Inspiratory activity. In: Bachrach A.J., Matzen M.M., eds. Proc 7th Symp Underwater Physiology. Bethesda, Md: Undersea Medical Society, 173-180.
23. Saltzman H.A., Salzano J.V., Blenkarn G.D., Kylstra J.A. (1971). Effects Of Pressure On Ventilation And Gas Exchange In Man. J Appl Physiol 30:443-449.
24. Tarasiuk A., Grossman Y. (1990). Respiratory-Center Activity Under High Pressure Conditions. Proc 2d International Meeting on High Pressure Biology, Paper No. 25, Toulon.

25. Bradley M.E., Dickson J.G., Jr. (1975). The Effects Of Nitrous Oxide Narcosis On The Physiologic And Psychologic Performance Of Man At Rest And During Exercise. In: Lambertsen CJ, ed. Vth Symp Underwater Physiology. Bethesda: Fedn. Am. Soc. Exp. Biol. 617-626.
26. Webber J.T. (1969). Respiratory Effects Of Nitrous Oxide Narcosis. M.A. thesis, State University of New York at Buffalo.
27. Warkander D.E., Norfleet W.T., Nagasawa G.K. & Lundgren C.E.G. (1990). CO_2 Retention With Minimal Symptoms But Severe Dysfunction During Wet Simulated Dives To 6.8 Atm Abs. Undersea Biomed Res. 17:515-523.
28. Warkander D.E., Nagasawa G.K., Norfleet W.T., Lundgren C.E.G. (1991). Physiologically Acceptable Breathing Resistance In Divers' Gear And External Work Of Breathing (Abstr). Undersea Biomed Res 18(suppl):99.
29. Lanphier E.H., ed. (1982). The Unconscious Diver: Respiratory Control And Other Contributing Factors. 25th Undersea Medical Society Workshop, Madison Wisconsin 18-20 held September 1980. Bethesda: Undersea Medical Society.
30. Lanphier, E.H., Lambertsen C.J., Funderbunk L.R.. (1956). Nitrogen-Oxygen Mixture Physiology Phase 3. End Tidal Gas Sampling System Carbon Dioxide Regulation In Divers Carbon Dioxide Sensitivity Tests. Research report 2-56. Dept of the Navy. Navy Experimental Diving Unit. Panama City, FL 32407.
31. Lambertsen C.J. (1955). Respiratory And Circulatory Action Of High Oxygen Pressure. Proc. Underwater Physiol. Symposium. Pubn. 377, Nat. Ac Sc & Nat Res C. Washington, DC.
32. Asmussen E., Nielsen M. (1946). Studies on the regulation of respiration in heavy work Acta Physiol Scand. 12, 171-178;
33. Wasserman K. (1976). Testing regulation of ventilation with exercise. Chest, 70, 173S-178S
34. Welch, Mullin, Wilson and Lewis. (1974). Effects of breathing O_2-enriched mixtures on metabolic rate during exercise. Med Sci Sports, 6, 26-32
35. Lambertsen C.J., Gelfand R., Peterson R., Strauss R., Wright W.B., Dickson J.G., Puglia C., and Hamilton R.W. (1977). Human tolerance to He, Ne, and N_2 at respiratory gas densities equivalent to He-O_2 breathing at depths to 1200, 2000, 3000, 4000, and 5000 feet of sea water (predictive studies III). Aviat, Space and Env Med. 48 (9): 843-855.
36. Schaefer K.E. (1965). Adaptation to breath-hold diving. In Physiology of breath-hold diving and the Ama of Japan. Pub 1342, p 237-251, NRC-NAS, Washington, DC.
37. Kerem D., Melamed Y, and Moran A. (1980). Alveolar PCO_2 during rest and exercise in divers and non-divers breathing O_2 at 1ata. Undersea Biomed Res 7, 17-26.
38. MacDonald J.W., Pilmanis A.A. (1980). Carbon Dioxide retention with underwater work in the open ocean. In The Unconscious Diver. 25th Undersea Medical Society Workshop Madison Wisconsin 18-20 September 1980. E.H. Lanphier (ed). UMS Bethesda, MD.
39. Clark J.M., Gelfand R., Lambertsen C.J., Stevens W.C., Beck, G. Jr., Fisher D.G. (1995). Human tolerance and physiological responses to exercise while breathing oxygen at 2.0ata. Aviat. Space, Environ. Med. 66: 336-345.
40. Dempsey J, Pack A. Editors. (1995). Regulation of Breathing. Second Edition. Marcel Deckker, Inc. NY, Basel, Hong Kong.
41. Dempsey, J. Personal communication to Dr. Ed Lanphier, August 1995.
42. Hashimoto A., Daskalovic L., Reddan W.G., Lanphier E.H. (1981). Detection and modification of CO_2 retention in divers. Undersea Biomed Res (Suppl.) 8, 47 (abstract 68).
43 Elliott D. (1990) Loss of consciousness underwater. In Diving Accident Management: Proc. Forty-first Undersea and Hyperbaric Medical Society Workshop, pp 301-310, Durham, NC.
44. Donald, K. Oxygen and the Diver. Flagstaff, AZ: Best Publishing, 1992.

CHAPTER 10
Carbon Monoxide - The Black Gas

Martin Shamlian, Ph.D.

Introduction

There is a true "black gas" for divers and it can remain with you for the entire life of your oxygen-carrying red blood cells. Cigarette smoking is the most common way to do this type mixed-gas diving and is therefore preventable. And unless you regularly hang around burning buildings or try to blow up cars by placing your mouth on exhaust pipes, it's probably preventable via that means as well. As the diving population ages and new divers getting into the sport also raise the average age, former habits can become dangerous even though they were tolerable at a younger age.

Over a decade ago while a Master Diver Trainer-Special Operations US Army, I stopped training divers who were cigarette smokers due to an adverse outcome on a military mission. A cargo ship preparing to go to a Central American port had a cargo of cocaine onboard (how unusual). The captain of the ship decided that blowing it up was the best course of action to avoid being boarded, inspected and jailed. The ship lay on the bottom in only 62 fsw (18 msw) and our SCUBA team was deployed for practice and national goodwill. The wreckage was dangerous because the steel was so twisted and the bags of cocaine, were they to rupture, could "melt" our wet suits and be absorbed through our skin. A third danger, "blackout by a diver", was one for which I had not calculated.

"Zak" was a serious cigarette smoker in his early 30s, and in tactical operations my first pick for any ground, airborne or SCUBA mission. It was a strenuous dive due to the wreckage and the sled on each trip was fully rigged and hard to manage through the wreckage. Then without warning Zak became short of breath and looked like he was going to pass out, yet had 1300 PSI in doubles and we had 7 minutes before reaching 1.6ata O_2 saturation before going into our next protocol. Since we lost three upper-30-year olds to heart attacks in the previous three months, I could only imagine that Zak was experiencing a heart attack.

Later after being Medevac'd, the hospital checked blood gases, electrolytes and other chemistries which presented a clinical picture of near drowning and hypoxia with abnormal Carbxy, oxy, and methemoglobin. Additionally both Zak and I knew that lungs and blood saturated by years of smoking and resultant residual damage caused the episode in a normally healthy, combat-ready soldier. Since then Zak immediately gave up smoking; and I have refused to teach smokers above the entry level of diving.

General Pulmonary Mechanics

Inspiration

Inspiration is the active process of bulk mechanical movement of air or other gases into the breathing passages and alveoli. Inspiration is not a religious experience but rather that which is triggered by an automatic or voluntary contraction of the skeletal muscles of the chest wall and diaphragm. Normally only the diaphragm contracts, with minimal activity of the external rib cage muscles (external intercostal muscles). As the volume of the inspired air or gases increase in the chest, the pressure inside the airways and alveolar air sacs of the lungs fall, as does the interpleural pressure and air flows into the lungs.

The pressure drop on average falls from approximately -2.5mmHg to -6mmHg. Therefore inspiration and inspiratory ventilation of the lungs is a negative pressure ventilation mode similar to placing a straw into a glass of water. The negative pressure inside the straw compared to the ambient pressure drives the water up into the straw.

Hypoxemia (insufficient oxygenation of the blood) and hypercarbia (elevated carbon dioxide in the blood) and decreased pH normally drive or stimulate inspiration. This is accomplished by receptors in the aortic arch and in the respiratory center of the medulla, which is mostly automatic, but is also under some degree of voluntary control, e.g. the child holding it's breath due to a temper tantrum then passing out, or breath hold divers hyperventilating which can result in shallow water blackout. The end of inspiration occurs when the stretch receptors of the airways are stimulated by lung inflation, (distention) causing a relaxation of the inspiratory muscles and cessation of inspiration.

Expiration

Expiration is normally a passive process. The chest wall and rib cage have a tendency to prevent complete inward motion of the chest, tending to keep the lungs expanded since the lungs themselves are characterized by an elastic tendency to collapse inwardly at all times. The pleural space (which we are attentive to in barotraumas like pneumothorax, air embolisms and pulmonary edemas), due to its being a potential cavity (potential since normally only a small amount of lubricating pleural fluid occupies the space) between the lungs and the chest wall, normally has a negative interpleural pressure (with respect to the barometric pressure), keeping the lungs and the chest wall closely approximated to one another.

Divers explore a wreck in Sweden.

Photo: Anders Jallai

It is this negative interpleural pressure which creates the tendency of the lungs to move inward, and the tendency of the chest wall to remain expanded (or move outward).

At the end of inspiration when the intrapleural pressure is most negative, the elastic recoil properties of healthy lungs causes the lungs to collapse inward, and the intrapleural pressure goes back to approximately -2mmHg and the air moves out of the lungs. Control of these two functions is paramount to all diving and requires normal healthy lungs. In technical diving and particularly deep and/or mixed gas diving these mechanics, if understood and visualized, can relax the diver and effect proper breathing techniques.

Mechanisms Governing Increased Ventilation

Breathing Passages

The larger airways, including the trachea and a large portion of the bronchial tree serve a conducting and humidifying function for gases coming into the lungs. These airways have more cartilage than smooth muscle and remain open despite wide changes in intrathoracic pressure. The smaller airways, including the bronchioles, also serve conducting and humidifying functions, but they contain relatively more smooth muscle than cartilage as they become smaller in diameter. The rate of flow, or velocity of a gas, is inversely proportional to the overall diameter of similar airways; e.g., in a like manner electric cords or water pipes are subject to flow rate differentials by similar gauge wires or pipe diameters. Smoking can irritate and variably constrict these diameters to critically dysfunctional calibers.

Alveoli

Alveoli are composed of single epithelial cells abutting adjacent capillary networks normally consisting of Type I cells, thicker Type H cells and miscellaneous other cells which are present at all levels of the tracheobronchial tree. The Type H cells secrete surfactant which decreases the surface tension of the completely water saturated alveoli (of normal healthy non-smokers). This allows the alveoli to remain open even at low lung volumes as seen at the end of a forced expiration, breath hold dive, emergency swimming ascent or other out-of-air situation. Without sufficient surfactant the lungs can collapse.

Control of the Tracheobroncial Tree

Generally the smaller the airway, except for alveoli, the more smooth muscle control available to control the distribution of air flow. Proper breathing and control of the distribution of breathing gases in the respiratory system is of such importance that it is the first module I teach in mixed gas diving.

Cooling the airway by rapid movement of large volumes of air or mixed gases, especially those containing Helium can also cause bronchoconstriction. Again the smoker is at a disadvantage especially on long and/or very deep Helium content dives since their entire respiratory system is under-used (in relation to the size of the respiratory system) yet over-taxed (as to the usable volume). The amount or degree of contraction in the smooth muscles of the bronchi controls the internal diameter of these smaller airways. However, during expiration, as the degree of intrapleural pressure becomes positive, small airways which are constricted can be collapsed leading to air trapping in the alveoli even in non-smokers This can be aggravated by the presence of tar mixed with cellular secretions in the airways. Several clinical problems, to include air embolisms, pneumothorax, etc., are then probable depending on the given profile, as well as the diver.

Surfactant

Spherical structures like the alveoli have a tendency to collapse when their volume is small. Laplace's Law states that the pressure distending alveoli is directly proportional to the surface tension, and inversely proportional to the radius; P=2T/r. Therefore, if the surface tension does not go down as the radius of the alveoli decreases during expiration due, for example, to congestion, the surface tension will eventually exceed the distending pressure and the alveolus will collapse.

Normally surfactant produced by healthy type H alveolar epithelial cells reduces the tension within the alveoli during expiration when the alveoli become small. Reduced quantities of surfactant found in hyaline membrane disease in infants and in adult respiratory distress syndrome predisposes the alveoli to collapse. Smoking causes these same states, moving towards or ending in COPD "Chronic Obstructive Pulmonary Disease", which involves other clinical physiological pathologies we do not have a need to go into.

While following the rule taught by the sport diving community "don't smoke prior to diving" is certainly better than nothing, it is a false sense of security. Accidentally prolonged smoking will make the Type II epithelial cells inadequate or incapable of manufacturing adequate amounts of surfactant. Since the surface tension favors the movement of fluid from the blood into the alveoli, smoking-induced respiratory distress syndromes can be labeled capillary leak syndromes or non-cardiogenic pulmonary edema. Think on these things before you light up again.

The pressure of a gas in a system is directly proportional to the amount of gas present and to the temperature of the gas, and is inversely proportional to the volume in which the gas is dispersed. In a mixture of gases, the pressure of each gas is called its partial pressure;

$$P = \frac{Amount\ of\ \text{gas x Temperature}}{Volume} \quad P_{gas} = \%_{\text{gas}} \text{ x } \text{P}_{\text{total}}$$

The total pressure of dry air at sea level is 760mmHg or 14.7 psi or 1 atmosphere. Air is approximately 21% oxygen, which is usable gas and approximately 79% inert (non-physiologically useful) gases to include helium, hydrogen, argon, neon, etc. When air or any other combination of mixed gases is not dry, or is humidified, then the amount of water in the mixture must be accounted for. The partial pressure of water vapor in humidified air, as is the case in the air reaching the lower respiratory tract is 47mmHg. Therefore, the partial pressure of oxygen at sea level is;

$PO_2 = 0.\ 21 \times (760mmHg - 47mmHg) = 149mmHg$

Not the chemistry model of $PO_2 = 0.21 \times 760mmHg = 160mmHg$

Hemoglobin and Myoglobin

Energy generated is largely dependent on oxygen supply to tissues. As was mentioned before, normally oxygen uptake (U O_2) by cells in tissues is independent of oxygen delivery (D O_2) to those cells, except at low oxygen delivery or in hyperbaric pressures.

Hemoglobin

Hemoglobin is a red pigmentary protein consisting of four peptide units each of which is associated with a Heme molecule. Without going into depth, Heme is an organic chemical which contains iron in the ferrous state, or iron having two positive charges. This is important, since if the iron is oxidated (like rust) rather than oxygenated, the iron will have three positive charges and will be unable to bind with oxygen. At this time it is only theoretical which of the 19 poisonous compounds found in cigarette smoke may oxidize iron from the ferrous to the ferric state resulting in methemogloinemia (dusky skin discoloration, mimicking cyanosis) in varying degrees. The carbon monoxide (CO) in cigarette smoke is the most serious competitor for Heme. CO has a much higher affinity for Heme than does oxygen in the gas competitive process but high concentrations of oxygen can help displace CO from the Heme, allowing for normalization of the oxygenation of Heme. Some of the most outstanding military, technical and sport divers known, therefore advocate that smoking is O.K. just as long as you don't smoke before the dive. They would be correct if cigarette smoke was only composed of CO which can and will be treated with hyperbaric oxygen (HBO) on the dive.

Myoglobin

Myoglobin behaves like hemoglobin. Myoglobin is found within the muscle cells but binds only one O_2 molecule instead of the four bound by hemoglobin. Therefore a non-stressed physical (streamlined, properly weighted and paced) and mental state is necessary for optimal diving in sport as well as technical diving.

CO is a colorless, odorless, tasteless gas most often formed during the combustion of carbon-containing materials. It binds to the same part of the hemoglobin molecule as does molecular oxygen but is approximately 250 times more avidly bound to the hemoglobin than is the molecular oxygen. A concentration of 0.4% CO in gas inhaled can be fatal. Treatment of CO poisoning involves increasing the amount of available oxygen in the mixture of inspired gas. Typically 100% oxygen is provided. Oxygen at higher partial pressure is able to compete with CO for binding to the hemoglobin molecule. However, treatment for toxic poisoning by the 19 other cigarette poisonous inhalants, and the effects noted previously, in the overall respiratory system still leave much room for research and speculation.

Furfurol, one of the aromatic compounds in cigarettes for instance is *50x stronger than alcohol in causing muscle tremors and convulsion in animals.* Nicontinism is a "poisoning by nicotine characterized by stimulation and subsequent depression of the central and autonomic nervous systems, with death due to respiratory paralysis" - *Dorland's Illustrated Medical Dictionary.*

In summary, there are two things we do know about the respiratory system. One, hemoglobin provides an efficient mechanism for oxygen transport to the tissues and two, there is much more research which needs to be done to explore the physiobiochemistry of cigarette smoking and diving. You decide; is CO the black gas of diving or are the total of accumulated poisons in cigarette smoke in general the Black Gas?

CHAPTER 11
High Pressure Nervous Syndrome

John Zumrick, MD

History of HPNS and Deep Diving Research

The late 60's and early 70's saw a major expansion in the search for oil into deeper waters in the Gulf of Mexico and elsewhere. Fueled by this enterprise, investigations in the use of helium gas mixtures (Heliox) for diving in deeper water expanded greatly. These experiments led to the description of the signs and symptoms of High Pressure Nervous Syndrome (HPNS).

In 1965, Bennett first described the presence of tremors in divers during experiments conducted at the Royal Naval Physiologic Laboratory (RNPL) using rapid compression to 600 to 800 fsw (183.5 to 244.6 msw). Divers experienced dizziness, nausea and vomiting in addition to tremors. In 1968 during experiments as deep as 1,189 fsw (363.6 msw), Brauer noted periods of somnolence termed microsleep and changes in the brains electrical activity as recorded on the electroencephalogram (EEG). By comparing these EEG changes together with the appearance of tremors, and a correlative similar change in animals, he predicted the appearance of seizures at a depth of about 1,200 fsw (367 msw). Later, he coined the term HPNS to describe the combination of tremor, dizziness, nausea, vomiting, microsleep and EEG changes.

Billy Deans on a DPV dive to the Wilkes Barre in Key West, FL.
Photo: Dan Burton

In 1970, using compression rates significantly slower than those used in the above experiments, Comex, a French diving firm, successfully exceeded the proposed 1,200 fsw (367 msw) barrier. Divers in this study experienced the effects of HPNS with prominent tremors and EEG changes, but were able to function at depth although at a lower level of performance.

In 1974 Duke University and Tarreytown Labs conducted the first experiments using Trimix - the combination of oxygen, helium and nitrogen - in an attempt to reduce the effects of HPNS and permit more rapid compression rates. These experiments led to divers successfully reaching 2,250 fsw (688.1 msw) (1981; Duke University). Although these dives allowed divers to reach record depths using faster compression rates than when using Heliox, high gas density led to shortness of breath and limited exercise tolerance.

Manifestations of HPNS?

Syndromes such as HPNS are defined as the occurrence of certain signs and symptoms together, often associated with some external event such as a deep dive. For HPNS these include dizziness, nausea or a sense of disorientation. External signs can appear as tremors, vomiting, tonic-clonic muscle jerks, microsleep, EEG changes and changes in performance tests. Based on the above, HPNS can be described as the syndrome of dizziness, vertigo, nausea, vomiting, tremor, microsleep and EEG changes associated with deep diving. Investigators observe these signs in divers and attempt to quantify them in an effort to objectively evaluate the effects of certain dive procedures on the diver. EEG testing, performance tests and tremor tests are generally used to evaluate the severity of HPNS.

EEG Changes

The electroencephalogram (EEG) was the first apparatus to be used in an attempt to quantify HPNS. The EEG is the recording of the brains electrical activity by means of electrodes applied to the divers scalp. Recordings taken at depth are compared with those taken on the surface to evaluate the changes introduced by depth and to follow their changes throughout the dive.

EEG recordings taken during dives reveal an increase of theta waves, a slow wave component of the EEG (4 to 7 per second), and an associated decrease in alpha waves (8 to 13 per second), a faster wave component of the EEG. These changes are often associated with focal spikes in the EEG. These changes provide an objective measurement of the changes produced by increased depth and changes in the compression rate, as well as recovery from HPNS.

EEG changes begin to appear at about 1,000 fsw (305.8 msw), when slow compressions are used and to appear at progressively shallower depth as compression rates increase. Thus, while a compression to 1189 fsw (363.6 msw) for over 2 hours - such as those conducted by Comex in 1968 - resulted in severe EEG changes and severe HPNS resulted in the dive being aborted. The US Navy Experimental Diving Unit in 1969 during a deep dive conducted at Duke University noted no such changes. This dive used a much slower compression rate of 77 hours to reach 1,000 feet (305.8 m). Rapid compression at the rate of 100 feet (30.58 meters) per minute can be expected to result in severe changes that develop as shallow as 600 fsw (183.5 msw) when breathing Heliox. EEG changes seem to persist and even worsen for a period of about 6 hours after reaching maximum depth. Rapid excursions deeper, after reaching depth, dramatically worsen these changes.

Microsleep

During dives below 1,000 fsw (305.8 msw) researchers commonly noted increasing signs of somnolence (sleepiness) in divers. When divers were unstimulated they readily appeared to fall asleep. However, once stimulated - usually with only a word or light touch they would instantly wake-up. The transition between sleep and wakefulness was almost imperceptible.

This author experienced microsleep during a dive to 1500 fsw (458.7 msw). I was asked as part of the experimental studies to memorize from a list as many words and associated two digit numbers as I could during a one minute period. Later, I was asked to reconstruct this list from a rearranged list of words and numbers. During the one minute memorization period, I noted my vision blurring and had to stimulate myself to continue memorizing the list. This happened at least three times during the one minute memorization period. This is best classified as mild microsleep. Experiences at even shallower depth, but with more rapid compression have resulted in serious microsleep where divers were experiencing microsleep at least 50% of the time at depth.

The appearance of microsleep is different from normal sleep and can be detected by noting associated changes on EEG. Normal sleep consists of two phases: rapid eye movement (REM) sleep, and non-rapid eye movement (NREM) sleep. Microsleep associated with HPNS is associated with a NREM sleep pattern. This EEG pattern did not progress to a REM sleep pattern as would have occurred during normal sleep.

Performance Testing

Knowledge of the effects on diver performance of deep diving procedures is central to safe diving practice. Tests such as placing small pegs in holes using pickups, and solving math problems are practiced at the surface until peak proficiency is obtained to eliminate the effects of learning from disturbing test results. These results are then compared to those taken at depth.

Tests such as moving small pegs or ball bearings with pickups are useful in testing manual dexterity. Similarly, tests of mathematical ability evaluate decision making and are useful in evaluating cognitive function. In general HPNS tests evaluating manual dexterity and alertness showed deterioration, while those evaluating cognitive function showed less affectation. However, as we shall see later, this was not the case while breathing Trimix where tremors were decreased, but cognitive function also decreased.

Although these tests are useful in determining the effects of a certain dive on diver performance, they provide little if any information in defining the cause of this decreased performance. Thus, for example, if the nausea of HPNS were relieved by medication would performance improve, or is the decrease in performance due to altered function in other areas of the brain, or both? Moreover, there is no general agreement on how these tests might be used to determine when a diver is not fit to dive.

Tremor is the most prominently noted sign of HPNS. If severe it can greatly affect ones ability to perform fine motor tasks. It can be measured in a variety of ways including tests of dexterity such as lifting and placing a ball bearing with tweezers, but is better quantified by placing an accelerometer on a person's finger and noting the frequency and amplitude of the tremor using power spectral analysis.

Tremor is normally present in all individuals. It is classified as either normal rest tremor, normal postural tremor or normal intention tremor, depending on whether the measurements were taken during a resting posture, while holding the finger outstretched or performing some motion. Normal rest, postural and intention tremors have a prominent frequency component of 8-12 cycles per second which sets it apart from abnormal tremors which have a slower frequency component between 3 and 8 cycles per second.

Johan Candert on the Champagne Wreck in the Baltic Sea.
Photo: Anders Jallai

Tremors associated with HPNS occur in a frequency range of 5-8 cycles per second and tend to be continuous and rhythmic, and predominantly demonstrated in the arms, hands, upper torso and head. Overall, this tremor is similar to that seen in Parkinson's disease. Symptoms of tremor were reported as shallow at 429 fsw (128.72 msw) during rapid compression. The amplitude of HPNS tremor seems dependent on compression rates being much worse with faster compressions.

Other Signs and Symptoms

Symptoms reported by divers consistent with HPNS include dizziness, vertigo, nausea, visual distortions, and altered sleep. Although it is difficult to quantify these, clearly they have effects on diver performance. Taken together with the other previously discussed signs these often result in a divers inability to perform certain essential tasks during the dive. The challenge for researchers is to define dive procedures that minimized the effects of HPNS while allowing as rapid as possible rate of compression to depth.

Causes of HPNS

HPNS is a syndrome primarily of neurologic dysfunction. Its diverse signs and symptoms suggest that its causes are complex. While originally termed helium tremors, it is now clear that hydrostatic pressure rather than helium is the cause of HPNS.

Current theory on the cause of HPNS stems from the work of anesthesiologists investigating the phenomenon of pressure reversal of anesthesia. They noticed that increased pressure tended to reverse the effects of narcotic anesthetics. It holds that the narcotic potency of anesthetics and certain other gases relates to their solubility in lipid-rich membranes such as those in the central nervous system. Such distortions in membrane structure could disrupt sodium and calcium channels and various receptor sites where neurotransmitters that regulate normal function act. The application of pressure has been found to reverse these narcotic properties presumably due to the direct effects of pressure that tend to offset the increased lipid volume. In diving the reverse would occur with hydrostatic pressure causing decreased lipid volume. Helium is very poorly lipid soluble and appears to be inadequate to cause lipid volume increase to offset the increased pressure. Thus, helium itself appears to be related to HPNS only in its ability to help prevent it.

The membrane effects appear to result in biochemical alterations within cells. The precise biochemical alterations that occur with HPNS have not been well defined. Observations in man as well as animal studies suggest that reductions in gamma amino butyric acid (GABA), a neurotransmitter that has an inhibitory effect on the central nervous system (thereby reducing excitability), may play a role in HPNS. Similarly it has been suggested that increases in excitatory neurotransmitters may occur and may also contribute to HPNS symptoms.

However, drugs given in an attempt to alter these agents have not convincingly proven their usefulness. When four drugs known to have GABA enhancing effects were tested in animals only one, sodium valproate (VPA), was shown to have a broad range of effects on HPNS. VPA also reduces the level of aspartic acid, another neurotransmitter that has excitatory effects. Studies have shown that a reduction in aspartic acid also reduces the symptoms of HPNS. Thus, GABA alone does not appear to play an exclusive role in the manifestations of HPNS. It is likely that a reduction of HPNS is dependent on both an enhancement of GABA production and an associated decrease in excitatory neurotransmitters such as aspartic acid.

The actual structures affected by HPNS have been studied in animals. These electrophysiological experiments compared with observations in man indicate that the brain cortex, lower brain centers, the spinal cord and peripheral nervous system all may play a role in the expression of the signs and symptoms of HPNS.

Limitations of HPNS Research

The interpretation of the current literature on HPNS, as an attempt to define safe diving practice, is complicated by a number of variables. Most dive profiles were designed at least in part with the intention of satisfying the interests of the program sponsors. Often this was a navy or a commercial diving firm seeking some competitive advantage. As a consequence diving research was primarily empirical - try it and see what the results are. With this primary purpose in mind a systematic search for the complete delineation of the important factors that affect the severity of HPNS was secondary. As a consequence much of what we know about factors essential in planning very deep dives are empirical in nature. Based on such a limited understanding of HPNS, new and different dive profiles, which differ from those already in use, must be carefully tested to insure their safety.

This empirically driven research often led to an experimental design where compression rates were varied in an attempt to achieve the optimum profile; often conflicting with the desire to systematically explore those important factors that affect HPNS severity. Other limiting factors include the limited number of divers as the test group (due to chamber size), thus limiting the amount of data that could be collected. Often, the amount of testing and the type of quantifiable tests for HPNS varied greatly between studies carried out at the various research centers. Finally, the compression rates and dive profiles differed greatly, complicating greatly any attempt to clearly isolate and quantitate the effects of variables such as absolute depth, rate of compression, and diver variability on the manifestations of HPNS.

Nonetheless, we have learned much about factors that affect the onset and severity of HPNS. Knowledge of these factors has led to the current level of deep diving practice used by various navies and commercial diving companies throughout the world. Unfortunately, our understanding of these effects is still not sufficient to allow the development of new diving procedures without their careful testing - first under rigidly controlled conditions prior to use in the open sea.

Factors Affecting the Onset of HPNS

Four factors affect the depth of onset and severity of HPNS. They are:

1. The absolute hydrostatic pressure (depth)
2. Individual diver susceptibility
3. The rate of compression
4. The composition of the breathing gas.

The studies done at different research centers all used differing compression rates, hydrostatic pressure, gas compositions and divers, often in a non-systematic fashion. This has often resulted in conflicting results in tests conducted at the various research centers.

Individual Susceptibility is a 5 to 1 Effect

One important emerging concept about HPNS is that individuals vary in their susceptibility to it. This inter-individual variability can be large. If EEG changes alone were compared, then the difference can be as great as 5 to 1 between different divers. The effects of severe HPNS and its differing effect on divers is illustrated in a US Navy experience during a dive to 1,800 fsw (550.5 msw) using Heliox. Of six divers, two were severely affected by HPNS and unable to perform useful work. They were essentially confined to their bunks. The second two divers could function only marginally - passing tools, etc. and only for brief periods. The remaining two divers who showed the least effects of HPNS, could function, but only at reduced ability. For example, these two divers were asked to replace a breathing gas heater. This task consisted of removing three threaded hoses, two gas hoses and the hot water supply hose. This took approximately 30 minutes to accomplish, and it was discovered they had inadvertently reattached the heater they were supposed to remove. All divers showed sleep alterations, no appetite, and lost significant weight during 4.5 days at 1,800 fsw (550.5 msw).

Comex conducted a series of experiments in an effort to define a means to select the most HPNS resistant divers to use in their very deep dives. These studies consisted of measuring both EEG changes and a battery of performance tests at 590 fsw (180.4 msw) breathing 10% nitrogen in Trimix, and again using the same divers at 1,500 fsw (458.7 msw). Compression rates were 40 ft/min (12.2 m/min) to 590 fsw (177 msw) and compression to 1,500 fsw (458.7 msw) was in stages taking 38 hours overall. All divers were ranked as to the magnitude of EEG changes noted as well as to performance test results. They found that as a group EEG changes and performance test results decreased with depth. When individuals were compared there was no such correlation. While EEG changes correlated, meaning that those divers most affected shallow were also the most affected deep, the same could not be said for the performance test results. Deeper, some divers actually did better on performance tests than others who had better performance scores at shallower depths.

Thus, one is forced to conclude that there is no easy test to evaluate susceptibility to HPNS. One might be tempted to evaluate deep performance based on performance test results, but because of the relationship of EEG changes to seizures, using performance tests alone as a measure of performance at depth is dangerous. These same investigators also noted a latency of between 30 and 60 minutes in the onset of symptoms; with symptoms appearing sooner in some divers than others did.

Rate of Compression

The depth at which HPNS appears and its severity is influenced by the rate of compression. In early studies of HPNS using Heliox mixtures compression rates as fast as 100 fsw/min (30.6 m/min) were used. These tests uniformly documented severe tremors, along with performance deterioration and EEG changes before reaching 1,000 fsw (305.8 msw). For example Bennett documented test decrements of approximately 25% in arithmetic and manual dexterity at 600 fsw (183.5 msw). These changes doubled at 800 fsw (244.6 msw). In addition the divers report severe nausea, dizziness and increased tremors. Comex found that tremors appeared well before 1,000 fsw (305.8 msw) and that rapid compression to 1,000 fsw (305.8 msw) resulted in complete incapacitation of the divers requiring immediate termination of the dive. Based upon these studies rapid compression deeper than 600 fsw (183.5 msw) was largely abandoned using Heliox mixtures.

Absolute Pressure - Heliox

If divers were to successfully dive at or beyond 1,000 fsw (305.8 msw), slower rates of compression would have to be used. Focus of research efforts turned to defining the optimum compression profile, or at least those where divers can be expected to be productive as soon after reaching working depth.

Further studies in diving to and beyond 1,000 fsw (305.8 msw) focused on using slower compression rates and with holds at various intermediate depths. Experiments by numerous labs indicated that compression to 1,000 fsw (305.8 msw) with minor changes in diver performance could be conducted only if compression was less than 3 fsw/min (0.9 msw/min). Often these were exponential compressions with faster rates being used shallow, gradually slowing as depth increased, but resulting in a rate less than 3 fsw/min (0.9 msw/min).

If more rapid compression rates were used diver performance could not be guaranteed. The following examples illustrate the combined effects of compression rate and diver variability on the manifestations of HPNS. Comex found that a compression rate of 10 fsw/min (3 msw/min) resulted in severe tremors and gross motor difficulty in their divers. On the other hand three divers were able to perform diving tasks after a compression of 16.7 fsw/min (5 msw/min) to 1,000 fsw (305.8 msw) for Bühlmann. Using a linear compression rate of 3.3 fsw/min (1 msw/min) investigators at the Admiralty Marine Technology Establishment, Physiological Laboratory (AMTE/PL) noted severe nausea and impending unconsciousness at 820 fsw (250 msw).

Using these and even slower overall rates of compression dives below 1,000 fsw (305.8 msw) were attempted. Often compression was stopped at intermediate depths prior to reaching the maximum depth. This had the overall effect of reducing the overall compression rate as well as allowing for recovery of the divers from the increasing effects of HPNS. Past 1,000 fsw (305.8 msw) the question is not: was the diver affected by HPNS, rather how much is the diver affected?

In general as depth increases so do the symptoms of HPNS. In shallower dives HPNS was found to have a latency of onset, mentioned previously, along with gradual increase in symptoms over a period of 4 to 6 hours once maximum depth had been reached. Afterwards, symptoms tended to decline, and performance testing results to improve, but with residual EEG changes. As dives progressed deeper toward 1,600 fsw (489.3 msw) performance decrements increased and no longer showed improvement with time at depth.

It was clear that for dives beyond 1,600 fsw (489.3 msw) using very slow compression so as to eliminate any compression rate effect on symptoms, high hydrostatic pressure itself induces severe and incapacitating HPNS. The deepest dive accomplished using Heliox mixture was to 2,001 fsw (610 msw) by Comex in 1972. Bottom time was limited to 80 minutes due to severe HPNS.

Helium, Oxygen, and Nitrogen (Trimix) Research

The above studies using Heliox mixtures clearly demonstrate that by using very slow and largely impractical compression rates divers could function as deep as 1500 fsw (458.7 msw), but that something else must be done to allow faster compression and/or allow deeper dives without severe HPNS. In 1973 Bennett began conducting initial investigations on the use of nitrogen to offset the effects of HPNS. He noted that nitrogen had the opposite effects on a phospolipid monolayer such as those comprising nerve cell membranes, causing them to expand while increased hydrostatic pressure caused them to contract. He concluded that the narcotic potency of nitrogen may be sufficient to offset the pressure changes. Helium on the other hand seemed to have little effect on the monolayer. He reasoned that this might provide protection from HPNS by offsetting the pressure effects on the nerve cell membranes and allow deeper dives and/or faster compression rates.

Tom Mount (r) and Gilberto Menezes (l) at Eagles Nest, Florida.
Photo: Shelley Orlowski

Bennett compressed divers to 720 fsw (220.2 msw) using Trimix with 25% nitrogen at a rate of 26 fsw/min (7.95 msw/min). The same divers also performed dives to 1,000 fsw (305.8 msw) using Trimix and Heliox mixtures with a compression rate of 33 fsw/min (10 msw/min) and an air dive to 200 fsw (61.2 msw). Except for the Heliox dive all three exposures had an equivalent partial pressure of nitrogen of 5.6 atmospheres absolute or an equivalent air depth of 200 fsw (61.2 msw). In these studies Trimix suppressed symptoms of HPNS, but also reduced the intellectual performance of the divers. Subjectively, two divers who were more sensitive to HPNS preferred the Trimix while two other less sensitive divers preferred the Heliox mixture because of reduced euphoria and other symptoms of nitrogen narcosis. These studies showed that nitrogen and other more lipid soluble inert gases than helium might be useful in reducing HPNS.

Based on these experiments, researchers developed a model based on the physiochemical properties of inert gases dissolved in lipids. This model predicted 10% nitrogen, 0.5% nitrous oxide, or 16% hydrogen as the optimum concentrations for these narcotic gases to offset the effects of HPNS. A series of subsequent dives to 1,000 fsw (305.8 msw) using compression rates from 33 fsw/min (10 msw/min) to 100 fsw/min (30.6 msw/min) confirmed the ability to offset the effects of HPNS. Although the nitrogen markedly reduced the tremors and other symptoms of

HPNS, it also produced euphoria and shortness of breath in the divers.

Comex conducted a dive series to 1,000 fsw (305.8 msw) comparing the efficiency of using 4.5%, and 9% Trimix and compared these results to a similar Heliox exposure. This dive series differed from the previous ones in that a slower average compression rate of 4 fsw/min (1.2 msw/min) was used. They concluded that efficiency was better with 4.5% nitrogen after such compression than with Heliox to 1,300 fsw (397.6 msw) and slow compression, and the efficiency was much worse than with 9% Trimix. Divers demonstrated euphoria and behavioral problems, and were unable to work for at least 4 hours after arrival at depth.

These studies demonstrated two problems with the use of Trimix. First, nitrogen seems to produce narcosis effects that adversely affect diver performance. Second, higher concentrations of nitrogen seem necessary to allow more rapid compressions. While on the one hand, one would want to use higher concentrations of nitrogen to allow rapid compression; such dives invariably produce undesirable narcosis. It would appear that the trick would be to define the optimum dosing of helium to allow rapid compression with minimal narcosis.

In England a dive series was performed comparing Heliox, Trimix and a Nitrox dive where the nitrogen partial pressure and compression rate was the same as the Trimix dive. During the Trimix dive, divers reported symptoms of narcosis, including euphoria, inability to concentrate, amnesia and inability to perform complex tasks. No such effects were seen with Heliox, or on the Nitrox dive. This observation would suggest that the divers were effected both by effects of HPNS unreversed by nitrogen, and narcosis effects unreversed by pressure, and that the combination of these two is worse than can be explained by nitrogen alone. This makes it difficult to establish an appropriate dose for nitrogen based upon equivalent air depth, since clearly other factors than the direct narcotic effects of nitrogen are affecting diver performance. Without knowledge of these effects it is impossible to plan a compression rate and nitrogen concentration that would provide optimum results without individual testing.

For dives to 1,000 fsw (305.8 msw), current studies would suggest that for compression at a rate of 30 fsw/min (9.2 msw/min), 10% nitrogen concentrations are best, but that divers can be expected to demonstrate significant narcosis effects. For faster compression rates the optimum Trimix is unknown. Slowing compression to 3-4 fsw/min (0.9-1.2 msw/min) will permit the use of 5% nitrogen with little narcosis effects. As dives progress deeper to 1500 fsw (458.7 msw), 5% is effective, but with slower compression rates on the order of 38 hours to 1,500 fsw (458.7 msw). More rapid compression, or the use of higher concentrations of nitrogen has produced enough undesirable affects to cause some investigators to prefer slow compression with Heliox over Trimix for dives to 1,500 fsw (458.7 msw).

Deeper than 1,500 fsw (458.7 msw), 5% nitrogen is insufficient to reduce the effects of HPNS. The results of studies using 10% nitrogen are mixed. At Duke University divers on two dives were successfully compressed to 2,250 fsw (688.1 msw) using 10% nitrogen over an approximate 7 day compression period. On these dives divers reported feeling well, and were able to perform complex tasks. However, in a similar dive to 2,250 fsw (688.1 msw) also using 10% nitrogen conducted at AMTE/PL, divers reported feeling good on arrival at depth, but within 4 hours subjects developed nausea and vomiting, fatigue, shortness of breath and became semi-conscious. In this case the compression rate was over 3 days 6 hours, roughly twice as fast as in the Duke dives. These mixed results combined with a similar Norwegian experience where divers actually performed better on Heliox than Trimix at 1,650 fsw (504.6 msw) suggests that further research is needed. During the Norwegian dive Trimix was changed to Heliox with rapid reduction in narcotic symptoms in the divers, but increased tremor.

Hydrox (Hydrogen-Oxygen or Hydrogen-Helium-Oxygen)

A series of experiments were conducted by Comex that investigated the use of Hydrogen-Oxygen mixtures and Hydrogen-Helium-Oxygen mixtures (Hydrox) as a means to facilitate deep diving. Since hydrogen is more soluble in lipid membranes than helium, it follows that hydrogen in the proper proportion would function like nitrogen in reducing HPNS. Although hydrogen reacts violently with oxygen to produce water, when the proportion of either oxygen or hydrogen is sufficiently low this mixture is stable. Hydrogen has the advantage of being the lowest density gas available thereby lowering the work of breathing and, hopefully, eliminating the dyspnea (shortness of breath) seen when breathing Trimix at very deep depths.

Initial experiments were conducted with divers breathing a hydrogen oxygen mixture at various depths to 1,000 fsw (305.8 msw), however, severe narcosis bothered the divers below 700 fsw (214.1 msw). To minimize the narcosis further experiments were conducted using 50% hydrogen in Helium-Oxygen. These studies conducted as deep as 1,500 fsw (458.7 msw) showed EEG changes similar to those seen with Heliox, and performance decrements consistent with narcosis. Furthermore, three divers were noted to paradoxically develop tremors during the dive and have a psychotic episode similar to that seen on one very deep dive with Trimix. Although an open sea dive with Hydrox has been successfully conducted most research using it has ceased.

Summary Of HPNS Research Discussed In Chapter 11

Investigator	Dive Gas	Depth fsw (msw)	Compression Rate fpm (mpm) Overall	Notes
Duke University	Trimix 18%	1,000 (305.8)	37 (11.3) continuous	Narcosis, euphoria, decreased tremors.
Tarrytown Labs	Trimix 13%	1,000 (305.8)	100 (30.5) continuous	Mild tremors, dyspnea, 15% performance deficit.
Duke University	Trimix 10%	1,000 (305.8)	37 (11.3) exponential slowing	No changes noted.
Comex Coraz 1	Trimix 9%	1,000 (305.8)	4 (1.2) exponential slowing with holds	No tremor, euphoria, EEG changes, 15% performance deficit.
Comex Coraz 2	Trimix 4.5%	1,000 (305.8)	4 (1.2) same as Coraz 1	Slight tremor, less euphoria than Coraz 1, EEG changes, 5% performance deficit.
Comex Coraz 3	Trimix 4.5%	1,000 (305.8)	4 (1.2) same as Coraz 1	Diver fatigue. Others same as Coraz 2.
Comex Coraz 4	Heliox	1,000 (305.8)	4 (1.2) same as Coraz 1	EEG changes, marked tremor, 20% performance deficit.
Duke University and AMTE/PL	Trimix 6%	1,312 (401.2)	13.2 (4.0) exponential slowing with short holds	Greater than 25% performance deficit, marked tremor, dizziness, light headed, confusion, moderate HPNS.
Duke University and AMTE/PL	Trimix 5%	1,512 (462.3)	8.6 (2.6) to 1312 (401.2) 6.3 (1.9) to 1512 (462.3)	Fewer effects at 1,312 (401.2) than above dive 1,512 (462.3), unable to keep eyes open, severe HPNS, aborted dive.
AMTE/PL	Heliox	1,000 (305.8)	2.8 (0.86)	60% decrease in performance test, marked tremor, nausea, vertigo
Comex Janus 4A	Trimix 4%	1,312 (401.2)	0.9 (0.28)	Exponential slowing with holds, light tremor, major EEG changes.
Comex Janus 4B	Trimix 4%	1,508 (461.2)	0.8 (0.24), 6 day hold at 1500 fsw (485.7 msw)	Underwater pipe connection made. Used selected divers.
AMTE/PL	Heliox	1,000 (305.8)	3.3 (1.0)	Light headed, imbalance at 686.7 (210), 30-50% decrease in performance tests.
AMTE/PL	Heliox	1,377 (421.1)	0.11 (0.03)	Decreasing rate with holds. No serious symptoms, intention tremor, decreased appetite.
AMTE/PL	Heliox	1,377 (421.1)	0.14 (0.04) decreasing rate with holds	Marked intention tremor. No appetite.
Duke University Atlantis 1	Trimix 5%	1,510 (461.8)	2 (0.61) decreasing rate with 1 hour holds	Dyspnea worse on Heliox, no postural tremor, mild intention tremor, performance decreased, dizziness.
AMTE/PL	Heliox	1,770 (541.3)	0.4 (0.12) decreasing rate with holds	Severe tremor, no appetite, dizziness.
DRET	Trimix 4.8%	1,476 (451.4)	0.65 (0.2) decreasing rate	10% performance decrease, no tremors.
Duke University Atlantis 2	Trimix 10% (1,510) Trimix 7% (2,132)	2,132 (652)	1.8 (0.55) to 1,510 (461.8) 0.19 (0.06) to 2,132 (652)	Performance better than Atlantis 1.
AMTE/PL	Trimix 10%	2,164 (661.8)	0.5 (0.15) exponential slowing with holds	No signs HPNS on arrival later tremor, breathing difficulty and semi-consciousness.
Duke University Atlantis 3	Trimix 10%	2,250 (688.1)	0.21 (0.06) exponential slowing with holds	Subjects well. 15% performance deficit.
Duke University Atlantis 4	Trimix 5%	2,132 (652)	0.21 (0.06) exponential slowing with holds	Two divers well & one diver hyper manic, mild tremors, good performance.
GISMER	Trimix 4.8%	1,476 (451.4)	0.65 (0.2) exponential slowing with holds	Diver drowsiness, no tremor, 10% performance deficit.
NUTEC DEEP EX80	Trimix 10% Heliox	1,000 (305.9)	3.5 (1.1) exponential slowing	Heliox divers severe HPNS, 20% performance deficit. Trimix divers less tremor, 15% performance deficit, euphoria.
NUTEC DEEP EX81	Trimix 10% Heliox	1,640 (501.5)	Heliox 1 (0.31) Trimix 0.7 (0.21)	Both groups ill. Trimix associated with deficit in cognitive performance that cleared on Heliox.
GISMER Entex 9	Heliox	2,000 (611.6)	0.35 (0.11) exponential slowing with holds	20% performance deficit, microsleep, tremor.

Other High Pressure Physiologic Effects

Two other physiologic phenomenon related to deep diving deserve mention: hyperbaric arthralgia and paradoxically induced diver dyspnea. Associated with the first descriptions of HPNS diver reported stiffness and pain in the joints. Most commonly affected in decreasing order were the shoulders, knee, wrist, hip and back. Divers described this as "no joint juice," or a gritty sensation in the joint. These symptoms may begin as shallow as 300 fsw and increase in intensity as depth increases. Once a bottom depth is reached these symptoms tend to decrease with time. Most often these symptoms are uncomfortable, but not incapacitating to the diver.

I have coined the term paradoxically induced diver dyspnea to describe an observation made by Bennet. He noted on a rapid compression Trimix dive that the divers complained of dyspnea shortly after reaching the bottom. Paradoxically, the dyspnea worsened on switching to Heliox even though as a less dense gas it should have eased these symptoms. This paradoxical dyspnea is probably an uninvestigated subtle effect of HPNS. Perhaps HPNS can affect the diver's respiratory control center in the brain that controls the rate of breathing. A side effect could be to increase the divers gas consumption rate. This could explain the larger than expected gas usage in a recent deep dive by Jim Bowden past 900 fsw (275.3 msw) at Zacaton in Mexico.

How Might HPNS Affect Diver Safety?

The table included in this chapter was adapted from Bennett in *The Physiology of Medicine and Diving*, 4th Edition. It lists those dives which best illustrates the principles discussed previously. Most of the experiments referred to in the table and in the proceeding discussion were conducted in dry hyperbaric chambers most often without the diver immersed in water. How might one relate these various tests of diver performance under experimental conditions to actual diving operations? How much a decrement in performance as seen in these dry experiments should be allowed before a diving procedure or guideline is considered unsatisfactory for actual diving operations? There is no easy answer to these questions.

However, one must consider that while diving in open ocean conditions the lack of light, extreme cold and presence of currents is likely to add to the performance deficits one can expect. Furthermore, the amount of time pressure is imposed, especially when conducting dives using open circuit scuba apparatus, should further confound the diver attempting a complex technical dive.

Open Sea Diving to 600 fsw (183.5 msw)

Current information suggests the rapid compression of up to 100 fsw/min (30.6 msw/min) to a depth of about 600 fsw (183.5 msw) on Heliox can be conducted without severe HPNS. There would not appear to be any advantage to using Trimix in this range because HPNS should not be a major problem except for reduced cost and possibly reduced decompression time for short bounce dives. On the other hand using Heliox has the advantage of avoiding any potential narcosis problems associated with Trimix, and offers lower work of breathing because it is less dense than Trimix.

Dives to 600 fsw (183.5 msw) are commonly done in the commercial diving industry with the aid of a chamber and mateable diving bell. With the divers at surface pressure the bell is lowered to the working depth. Once the divers are geared up the pressure inside the bell is increased to the ambient pressure of the work site, the hatch is opened, and the diver exits to complete the task. A tender usually remains inside the bell to tend the diver who is supplied with an umbilical, communications, and a hot water supply to the hot water suit. Once the task is completed the diver re-enters the bell, the hatch is closed maintaining bottom pressure, the bell is raised to the surface, and mated to the surface decompression chamber. While raising and mating the bell to the decompression chamber, the surface diving supervisor begins diver decompression, and decompression is completed in the surface decompression chamber.

In such a diving operation, the various tasks necessary to conduct such a dive are shared among several team members. The divers need only concern themselves with the bottom tasks they need to perform. The divers need not concern themselves with bottom time, decent or ascent rate, or even the gas mix they are breathing since these tasks are handled by others at the surface. Gas supply is from large surface mounted banks being essentially unlimited given the planned course of the dive. The divers have a plentiful and temperature regulated hot water supply to heat the diver and the breathing gases if needed. Contrast this situation to deep technical diving using open-circuit scuba techniques. In this situation, the diver alone must handle all these tasks, and with considerably less backup support. In this type of diving scenario with a high degree of task loading should we tolerate more performance decrement than might be tolerated by the commercial diver?

Open Sea Diving, 600 - 1,000 fsw (183.5 - 305.8 msw)

Most open sea diving in the 600 to 1,000 fsw (183.5 - 305.8 msw) range is done on Heliox using saturation diving techniques with a surface chamber and mateable diving bell. In this method of diving the divers are compressed to bottom depth in the surface chamber. Upon reaching bottom and being declared fit to dive, the divers move to the diving bell, and are lowered to bottom depth and exit the bell to conduct their work. Often divers work 6 hour shifts diving, and are replaced with a second diving crew. This dive, rest, dive procedure is continued for up to 30 days before decompression to the surface is conducted. This approach is very efficient in accomplishing a construction task such as constructing an undersea oil pipeline. After 24 hours on the bottom decompression time becomes fixed at about 1 day per each 100 fsw (30.6 msw) depth plus an additional 24 hours. Thus, for a dive to 1,000 fsw (305.8 msw), decompression is about 11 days regardless of bottom time. When diving in this manner slower compression rates are feasible compared with bounce dive techniques.

Bell diving using bounce techniques from the surface such as that described for 600 fsw (183.5 msw), are less commonly used. Such a procedure requires a fast compression rate that can be expected to cause severe HPNS in nearly all divers especially near 1,000 fsw (305.8 msw). As a consequence, Trimix must be used to prevent expected severe HPNS. However, such short interventional dives were not a major part of commercial deep diving practice. This together with the increased use of remotely operated vehicles (ROV) and one atmosphere diving suits (i.e., the NEWT suit) mean that the necessary empirical research defining a safe rapid compression profile and optimum nitrogen dose has not been established. Thus, any planned profile cannot be guaranteed to allow a diver to function adequately in most dives.

Recently several divers have begun conducting dives with the goal of reaching 1,000 fsw (305.8 msw) using open-circuit scuba. In addition to the problem of preventing HPNS and narcosis, consider for a minute the additional complicating issues of gas planning, the use of equipment designed primarily for recreational use and in the darkness. Together, these problems represent a major risk that cannot be adequately and reliably controlled at our present state of knowledge. The discussion below is based upon an actual planned scenario for a dive to 1,000 fsw (305.8 msw).

Gas Planning: The volume of gas used per minute increases proportionately with depth. At 1,000 fsw (305.8 msw) (31.3 ata) the diver will use 31.3 times the amount of gas than will be used on the surface. Moreover, the amount of gas available from each cylinder will be proportionately reduced due to the high ambient pressure. At 1,000 fsw (305.8 msw) the ambient pressure is 460 psig (31.3 ata). Thus when tank pressure falls to 460 psig (31.3 ata) no additional gas will be available. Since regulators are set for an intermediate pressure of 125 psig (8.5 ata) or greater depending on model, a cylinder is effectively empty at about 600 psig (40.8 ata). If a diver consumes gas at 1 cubic foot (28.32 free liters) per minute, one can expect an 80 cubic foot (2.8 free liter) cylinder to last 2.0 minutes at 1,000 fsw (305.8 msw).

Assume for planning purposes a gas consumption rate of 0.6 cu ft (16.99 free liters) per minute throughout the dive, and that the diver used dual 120s (19 L), and two 80 cu ft (10 L) stage bottles. The diver would be carrying either 522 cu ft (14,783 free liters) of Trimix in the doubles pumped to 3600 psig (244.9 bar), or 559 cu ft (15,830 free liters) if doubles were pumped to 4,000 psig (272.1 bar). This corresponds to an available gas volume of 475 or 513 cu ft (13,452 or 14,528 free liters) of gas respectively with the diver at 350 fsw (107 msw), the location of the first decompression bottle. The table below shows the expected gas requirement to reach 350 fsw (107 msw) at gas consumption rates of 0.6, 0.7 and 0.8 cubic feet (16.99, 19.82, and 22.66 free liter) per minute. The table below also indicates the volume of Trimix need to support the various bottom times including decent from 350 fsw (107 msw) to 1,000 fsw (305.8 msw), and ascent including decompression stop to the first decompression bottle. The diver would have had sufficient gas to support the 10 minute bottom time throughout planned decompression on Trimix, but insufficient gas to reach the 350 fsw (107 msw) stage using the 14 minute schedule. If gas consumption increased to 0.7 cfm (19.82 flpm) then the diver would have had insufficient gas to reach the 350 fsw (107 msw) bottle.

Gas Required to Reach the 350 fsw (107 msw) Stage Bottle in cubic feet (free liters)

Gas Consumption Rate in CFM (FLPM)	Bottom Time (Minutes) 10	12	14
0.6 (16.99)	362 (10,252)	446 (12,631)	526 (14,896)
0.7 (19.82)	423 (11,979)	518 (14,670)	613 (17,360)
0.8 (22.66)	483 (13,679)	592 (16,765)	701 (19,852)

The chart calculations assume that no gas was used to inflate the buoyancy compensator. However, a portion of his bottom mix would have been used to maintain buoyancy during descent. The buoyancy compensator used has an internal volume of at least 1 cubic foot (28.32 free liters) that would require 31 cubic feet (877.6 free liters) to fill at 1,000 fsw (305.8 msw). If only 20 lbs. of lift was needed then only 10 cubic feet (283.2 free liters) of gas would be needed.

As can be seen from this discussion even minor delays in descent, or ascent will increase the gas needed during the dive. This is compounded by the fact that minor difficulties that might be encountered during the dive can easily increase the rate of gas consumption above 0.6 cfm (16.99 flpm) that is a very slow swimming gas consumption rate. Additionally, experience now suggests that divers do consume gas faster deep than at a shallower depth. There clearly is *no* margin for error during such a dive.

Equipment Function: Most diving equipment used by technical divers was never intended for use at these depths. This can present major problems if the component is unable to function adequately at depth. The regulator is probably the most critical component in this regard.

Sheck Exley, a practitioner of deep technical diving, had reported to me that he felt considerable inhalation effort during his deep Mante dives at 800 fsw (244.6 msw). This could have been dyspnea secondary to pressure, or regulator resistance due to breathing very dense gas. At 1,000 fsw (305.8 msw) the gas density on bottom mix (6% oxygen, 22% nitrogen, 72% helium) would be 15.5 grams/liter. The density of air at 200 fsw (61.0 msw) is 9.1 g/l. The density of the bottom mix was equivalent to the density of air at 364 fsw (111.3 msw). These are gas densities well beyond the limit in which conventional regulators are designed to function. High breathing resistance due to the regulator, in addition to increased work of breathing dense gas, may easily result in carbon dioxide retention that would further hamper diver performance. Recognizing these problems, a special second stage regulator commonly used by commercial diving services was designed with performance characteristics compatible with this increased gas density. Even if such a regulator were used with scuba, flow limitations due to the tank valve port size or the first stage regulator may limit available flow over that delivered to an umbilical supplied diver.

Flow limitations secondary to increased gas density may also limit the speed with which a diver can adjust buoyancy. This may mean that the diver becomes overly heavy and may not be able to arrest descent where planned.

Finally, one must consider the effects of environmental factors such as cold and darkness. Imagine a diver descending rapidly to 1,000 fsw (305.8 msw), feeling dizzy and nauseous from HPNS, while rapidly descending a single line without any visual reference points. One would easily expect the feeling of dizziness and nausea to be heightened when no stable reference points aid in maintaining orientation. At Bushmangat, a deep underwater cavern located at a 5,000 foot (1,529.1 meter) elevation in South Africa, Sheck Exley attained a depth of 860 fsw (263 msw) on his depth recorder. Upon reaching 700 fsw (214.1 msw) following a rapid 100 fsw (30.1 msw) per minute descent, Sheck first experienced the effects of HPNS even though he breathed a 22% nitrogen Trimix. In his dive log Sheck reports, "Itching and tingling in the skin (Argon in the suit)," and "Regular spaced sparkles in vision, slight blurring," and "deeper got uncontrolled shivering." He therefore slowed his descent rate to approximately 30 fsw (9.2 msw) per minute eventually attaining the bottom at 860 (263 msw) after a 12 to 13 minute descent. His vision continued to deteriorate on the bottom and the uncontrolled shaking also worsened. Sheck reported that the symptoms disappeared upon reaching 400 fsw (122.3 msw) during the ascent. Had Sheck remained on the bottom longer, one would have expected the symptoms to continue to intensify as is common during dives of rapid descent.

Time pressure due to gas consumption could be reduced if one used closed circuit units whose duration theoretically is independent of depth. However, the time pressure of mounting decompression obligation still remains. Additionally, these rigs present unique planning problems of their own, the details of which could occupy a chapter of their own. Suffice it to say that such diving is ill advised without the availability of a diving bell and mateable diving chamber, an umbilical support diver, and a good surface support team.

Conclusion

Less than 600 fsw (183.5 msw) HPNS is not a significant problem when using Heliox. Since the use of Trimix involves an element of nitrogen narcosis that may be worse than predicted by an equivalent air depth computation, there seems no valid reason to prefer it to Heliox. HPNS is a significant problem when diving Heliox below 600 fsw (183.5 msw). Its effects are greatest after rapid compression and in certain susceptible divers. Utilizing Trimix can reduce the effects of HPNS. While Trimix decreases the tremor and other effects of HPNS, it also induces narcosis in the diver. Trimix can be helpful on dives from 1,000 fsw (305.8 msw) to 1500 fsw (458.7 msw), and is essential for dives deeper than 1,500 fsw (458.7 msw). Optimum concentrations of nitrogen in Trimix have been established by empirical testing for certain compression rates and depths. However, our knowledge is still insufficient to establish the necessary nitrogen concentration for other compression rates.

In open sea diving the negative effects of HPNS on diver performance and safety can be increased by environmental factors. Commercial diving companies have developed procedures using diving bells, and a team approach to diving that minimizes these negative effects on the diver and allow open sea operations to be conducted with reasonable safety. However, without such extensive equipment and personnel support deep technical dives especially those beyond 600 fsw (183.5 msw) must be considered highly hazardous and beyond the scope of the technical scuba diver.

References:

Most of the above material was drawn from *The Physiology and Medicine of Diving and Compressed Air Work* by Bennett and Elliott, 4th Edition, available from Best Publishing Company and from the *Proceedings of the Fifth through Eighth Symposia on Underwater Physiology* available through the Undersea and Hyperbaric Medical Society.

CHAPTER 12
Combining Theories for Decompression Safety

JP Imbert

There is a limit to the number of original ideas in any field of human activity, and decompression modeling is no exception. Haldane had a good idea when he introduced tissue compartments, Dr. Behnke was inspired when he discovered the oxygen window and Dr. Fructus proved intuition when he started treating air decompression accidents with Heliox gas mixtures. But who is next? The problem is that most of us are reasonably gifted for adapting, improving, and modifying existing material but remain pathetic when it comes to generating new concepts. Thinking in terms of tissue compartments, any one with the ability of calculating the exponential function can reach the exaltation of computing a decompression profile. But where does it lead to introduce more tissues and more M-values? To over dimensioned models that just describe and do not explain a field of experience. Since the time people have been fiddling with tissue half times, we have not learned much about the critical issue: what is the risk for my next dive?

Kevin Denlay cutting tables for a deep wreck dive.
Photo: Miria Denlay

What we need are new ideas on decompression safety. During my career in the offshore industry or in my contacts with the scientific world, I must admit I have only retained four. Like any diver, I have a series of experiences that I would like to put into perspective. A sort of puzzle, for which no one has a clue as to the final image, but is fun to put together nonetheless. My four pieces of ideas fit nicely together and I call it the "multi model approach to decompression safety".

It all started in the early 1980s. I was the Safety and Diving Manager of Comex and had designed all kinds of tables; deep Heliox saturation's and fancy excursion procedures. Non linear second-degree differential equations were my cup of tea and I was running programs that would take a night to simulate an hour of decompression. But suddenly a series of problems occurred that none of my programs could solve.

At the time, the diving industry drastically changed its way of operating in the North Sea. There were platforms, pipes, flares, and loading buoys all over the place. The North Sea looked much like an English garden with no room for any additional dwarfs. The time for juicy construction contracts was gone and the only job left was to maintain these installations. This does not mean that there was no more work, because all structures at sea tend to rust, fatigue and crack. Not to mention trawlers that drop anchors on expensive subsea structures or the German submarine that ran into the bracing's of the Oseberg platform. However, wave action, oxygen corrosion, marine life and supply boats tend to act shallow and the whole character of commercial diving changed from sea floor work to near surface activities.

In terms of operations, this meant that the industry had to do less saturation bell runs and more air supplied dives. Saturation diving had been improved over the previous decade and had become a very safe and efficient way of intervention. As a consequence, air diving had been considered as a secondary means of intervention and was put aside without any further consideration. For this reason, when the IRM (inspection/repair and maintenance) jobs arrived, the industry started using the available tables intensively - which still corresponded to the state of the art of the 1950s - and began treating divers for decompression sickness (DCS) as never before.

Because the industry was not sufficiently organized to collect the information and edit statistics, the British

Government in 1983 decided to handle the situation. They imposed a system of report collection and analysis: for each and every air dive on the UK sector, copies of the dive reports and accident reports would have to be sent to the National Hyperbaric Center in Aberdeen where they would be entered into a computer. This opened the era of the databases which would change the work and the mind of decompression modelers.

The first report on the UK database was presented in 1986 and was most disappointing (1). The information was there but the clusters of DCS would not fit any available models, and the data showed obvious trends but also puzzling singularities (Figure 1). The diagram confirmed the dependence of DCS occurrence on the severity of the dive exposures: the deeper the depth and/or the longer the bottom time, the higher the risk. This has been known for long and it could be argued that these limitations were just a matter of adjusting computation parameters. However these classic models also failed to explain the high variability observed in individual susceptibility, could not predict the type of symptoms encountered, and did not account for shallow type II DCS cases where little gas is loaded in the diver tissues.

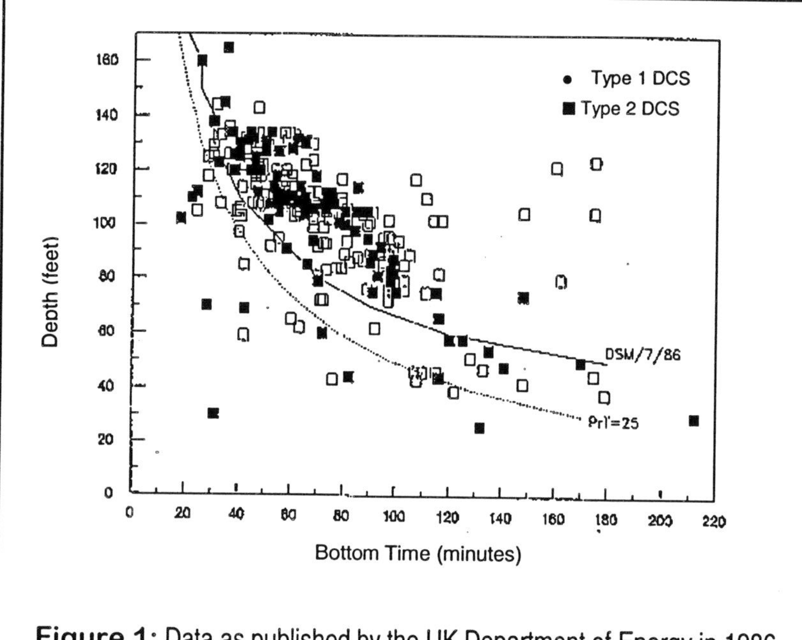

Figure 1: Data as published by the UK Department of Energy in 1986 after they organized the collection of commercial diving dive reports.

The diagram displays cases of decompression sickness over the depth and time exposures. Black squares represent type I DCS and white squares represent type II DCS. This pattern is typical in the sense that information from the recreational diving agencies has shown exactly the same partition of DCS cases over depth and time.

When faced with statistics showing an alarming incidence of DCS, the British government had to take a strong stand and issued a series of Safety Memoranda limiting air diving exposures in the UK sector. This approach, purely based on a depth/time limitation, has shown to be relatively efficient because the 1992 database report published an overall 0.10% DCS incidence, a great improvement over the 1986 results (2). However, it was still unsatisfactory because serious neurological accidents were reported in the authorized limits; this represented a threat for a population of around 800 commercial divers. This attitude is not specific to commercial diving since some recreational diving agencies have also limited diving to no-stop decompression in the hope to minimize their liability exposure. Sticking to this attitude, by successive adjustments of the borderline, one could conclude that the only safe diver is the diver that never gets wet. Something was obviously missing and it was time to introduce a good new idea.

Starting with Decompression Safety

Let me recall that the safety of decompression tables is defined in terms of the risk of DCS occurrence per dive exposure. DCS symptoms include a wide span of problems ranging from skin rash to articular pain and neurological symptoms which for operational reasons have for long been classified into two categories, type I and type II DCS.

Type I DCS includes simple symptoms like skin rash or articular pain. Because the symptoms are obvious, they are reported early and the treatment is initiated without hesitation. In most cases, administration of hyperbaric oxygen at 40 ft (12 m) will rapidly clear the symptoms. Safety wise, a type I DCS is a "good DCS" because the diagnosis is easy, the treatment is applied rapidly, and the symptoms are treated efficiently. Technical divers should not be afraid of type I symptoms. It hurts at the time but it has little consequence for your diving career once it has been treated. In fact type I is typically a problem in commercial diving (long bottom time, heavy work) where it builds up to 2/3rds of the reported diving accidents but is rare in recreational diving.

Type II DCS is always serious because it affects either the respiratory or the neurological systems. The symptoms which often only include fatigue, headache, or feeling unwell, are vague and the diagnosis may be difficult at an early stage. The treatment is complex and requires deep recompression, significant periods of hyperbaric oxygen breathing, fluid intake and sometimes steroid administration. Safety wise, a type II is a "bad decompression accident" because the diagnosis may not be easy, the treatment is often delayed, and its efficiency depends on the circumstances. Technical divers should consider type II DCS as their main risk because its consequences can be dramatic.

The point is that the classical models for decompression have adopted a general approach to DCS and cannot differentiate between symptoms (Figure 2). The problem is considered as a whole and type II symptoms are regarded as merely an aggravation of type I symptoms.

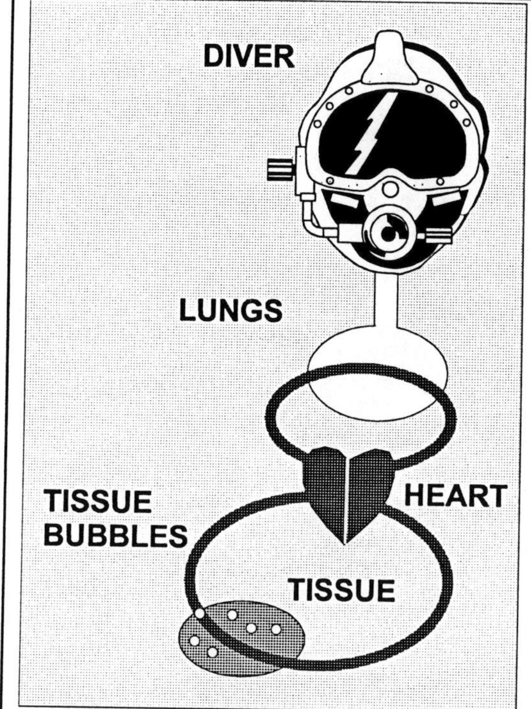

Figure 2: The classical approach. Being traditional about decompression involves the following assumptions:

- Diving requires compressed air breathing and causes nitrogen to dissolve in the diver's tissues. The critical issue is the amount of nitrogen stored in the tissues (dose) prior to the ascent.
- The primary insult is bubble formation during the ascent. DCS is considered as a whole. Limb bends and neurological symptoms are seen as different levels of severity of a general problem.
- The sites for bubble formation are the tissue or on the venous side of the blood circulation but none is specifically identified, and a series of "compartments" is considered. The decompression strategy consists in managing the amount of gas dissolved in the tissues to control bubbles formation and avoid DCS during the ascent.

Models like the Workman or the Bühlmann models are built on different assumptions but all consider DCS as unique continuous phenomena. These models cannot be denied certain efficiency since the present commercial diving tables have an overall safety record at around 0.5% DCS incidence (3). However, it is easy to show their limits by quoting numerous accounts of "undeserved accidents" where people did the right thing and got bent. We cannot accept these views with a light hearted attitude because it makes a lot of difference to us whether the risk is type I or type II when we dive, especially if we carefully follow the rules.

Models are just a simplified way of representing the reality and we are entitled to change them when the reality changes. My experience was that saturation divers tend to get pain in the articulation exclusively, air divers are very prone to neurological symptoms, and deep divers on short bounce decompression generally get nothing but a vestibular hit. If bends are so specific, then the alternative should be to study DCS through its different manifestations: one model for each problem, or a story for each bubble. A nice structuring idea that requires a different scenario for each of the symptoms. It is also a granny's rule to cut the piece into smaller chunks when it is difficult to swallow. This was idea no 1.

When Bubble Volume is Critical

Let start with the easy one: pain only DCS. In fact, Type I occurrences can be handled by the classic theories and in particular fits perfectly the predictions of Critical Volume Assumption or CV model. This hypothesis was published long ago by Haldane and refined later by Hennessy and Hempleman (4). They collected information on experiments where divers were saturated at a given depth and then decompressed until they bent, or nearly bent (I should say for ethical reasons). A linear relation was found between the initial saturation depth and the depth to which divers could safely ascend, and Hennessy worked out a simple equation to calculate the volume of gas phase generated in the tissue. They linked the symptoms to the critical volume of the gas phase. It is a sort of Haldane's critical ratio concept revisited for the benefit of type I symptoms only.

However, the important consequence is that only one tissue is critical (Figure 3). It corresponds to the tendons and the ligaments wrapping the articulations. Such tissues are very dense and strong. They are also very innervated (if you were to knock your elbow on a wall, you know it would hurt painfully). The explanation is that if there was a bubble forming in such a tissue, it will distort the fibers and the pressure will be transmitted to the nerve endings and cause pain.

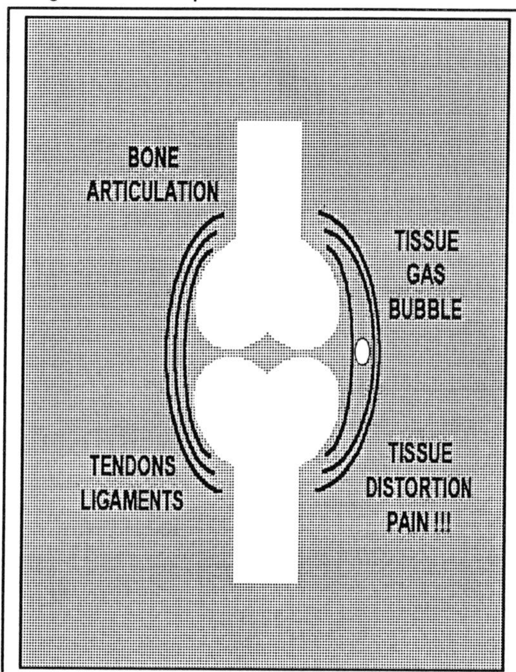

Figure 3: The Critical Volume model. The adaptation of the classic models to the specific case of type I DCS occurrence: Diving requires compressed air breathing and causes nitrogen to dissolve in the diver's tissues. Again, the critical issue is the amount of nitrogen stored in the tissues.

- The primary insult is still bubble formation during the ascent. However, the site for pain is now specified as the ligament capsule and/or tendons surrounding the articulations. These tissues are both very tight and highly enervated. The deformation induced in the tissue fibers is immediately transmitted to the nerve's endings and causes the pain.
- The pain is proportional to the deformation and thus to the size of the gas phase.
- The decompression strategy consists in managing and controlling the bubble size in one specific tissue to avoid type I DCS during the ascent.

Defining the connective tissues as the sites of type I DCS is not a novelty and all sorts of stories can be called in support of the CV model. For instance, during the decompression of Comex deep experimental dives, we knew that the divers often experienced pain in the knees in the last few meters of the decompression. On one experiment, Mazurel from the French Navy who was leading Doppler studies, prepared a cuff similar to the one used for taking blood pressure. As a diver reported pain at around 82 fsw (24msw), the cuff was locked inside the chamber and fitted around his knee. Raising the pressure of the cuff to about 200-300 mbar relieved his symptoms for a while, thus elegantly demonstrating the site and the role of a gas volume in the aetiology of limb bends.

One interesting prediction of the CV model is that it speculates that the gas phase is formed from the dissolved gas available in the surrounding tissue. This allows us to simply relate the risk of type I DCS to the dose of gas. All tissue models do just that by tracking gas in the various compartments and we know it works - more or less. Their imperfections have simply encouraged diving supervisors to introduce safety margins in the selection of decompression tables. It is well known in the commercial diving industry that the US Navy tables are the best tables in the world as long as you don't use them explicitly. Considering the present commercial diving safety records, this tends to demonstrate that an experienced diving supervisor can be worth a high-flying mathematician.

The CV model can also be handled mathematically without difficulties and used for computing decompression tables. I used it at Comex for designing new air diving procedures (5) that later became the French official air decompression tables in 1992 (6). However, because of the assumptions introduced, I must admit that these tables are limited to the prevention of type I DCS only. It might seem a little bit provocative, as they are still good tables, but let me explain this restriction. If you accept the idea that gas dissolved in tissues is only relevant when it comes to articular pain, then decompression tables which only track the amount of gas in the various compartments can only prevent type I DCS. I believe that they also prevent type II DCS but this is the by-product of built-in procedures - a slow rate of ascent to the first stop or restrictions on repetitive diving, etc.

If you are not ready to give away your confidence in decompression models based on multiple compartments, think in terms of tissue gas load and try to imagine what could be the worst tissue during a decompression. The answer is the fat on the belly. It grows with age and drinking, and is our largest reservoir of dissolved nitrogen. Well, have you ever heard of bend of the belly? No, not me either. Despite the fact that there is a large amount of gas available and that bubbles certainly grow during decompressions, this tissue is irrelevant because it is soft and poorly innervated and fat belly bubbles have no consequences.

Models are just models and there is no point in defining the hearsay but there are people who believe so hard in tissue compartments that they can give them a mind of their own. I once attended a conference in Aberdeen where Dr. Bühlmann came in and declared in front of the commercial diving community that his tables never produced bends. As the audience was recovering from this blunt statement, the chairman recalled that Bühlmann himself had published accounts of recompression treatments. Dr. Bühlmann then went on explaining that these cases were related to the 10 minute compartment but that he had changed its coefficients and that his tables were now fine. This dogmatic approach might relieve your anguish about DCS but I am not sure it will help you to go through it. The point is that present compartment models only cover part of the problem - pain only DCS. They are not bad; they are just limited. This was idea no 2.

When Bubble Diameter is Critical

That summer, Comex had a series of work sites in the southern part of the North Sea that is relatively shallow and intensively dived on air using surface decompression techniques. A diver got a hit, and then a second, and then a third and I did not know what to do. I had used up all my tricks; recalculating tables with more conservative coefficients, lengthening oxygen breathing periods; nothing worked and the client started to put pressure on us to resolve the problems.

Then came Dr. Philip James. Philip had recently joined the company as medical advisor and had been working intensively on micro embolism (7,8). Although it was known that the lungs not only exchange gases, but also filter the blood, the concept seemed to have been forgotten. He revived it in a strange way. Philip had to move his office and he found himself one morning in his new place, waiting for his crates to come. While standing in the empty room, Philip spotted a brain specimen that his pathologist predecessor had left on the top of a rusty cabinet. Doctors don't seem to have quite the same taste as us when it comes to decoration, but it seemed to Philip that the brain sample was from a case of DCS, but it turned out that the man had died in a car accident. The emboli that had affected his brain were not bubbles, but fat from the fractures and soft tissue injuries. The droplets of fat from the tissue destruction entered the circulation and were trapped in the lung, but were then carried in the arterial blood to the brain. So here was the parallel to bubbles in DCS.

Philip explained to me the arterial bubble model, which I call the AB model, which considers that the lungs act as a bubble filter. When people decompress, bubbles are formed and collected on the venous side and sent to the lungs (Figure 4). There, by size, there are trapped in the capillaries and evaporated in the lungs. If by chance a bubble passes the lung filter, it will be dumped at the wrong place, because the piping at the aortic cross level is designed to send blood preferably to critical centers, such as the nervous system or the heart. In case of a severe wound, this will save your life. In case of a gas bubble, this will raise a drama. This was idea no 3.

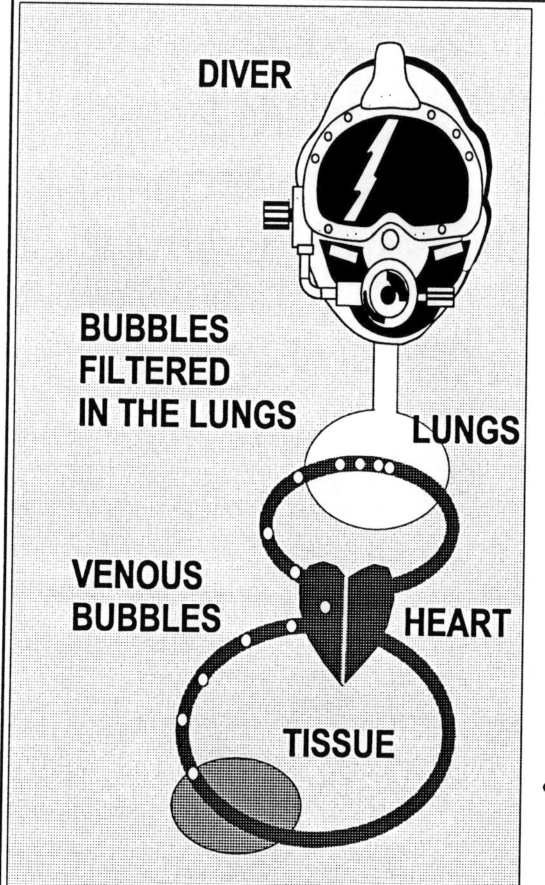

Figure 4: The Arterial Bubble model. A scenario for type II symptoms occurrences.

- Diving requires compressed air breathing and causes nitrogen to dissolve in the diver's tissues. Bubbles are normally produced during decompression in the vascular bed, transported by the venous system and filtered out in the lung. The critical issue is the filtering capacity of the lung system.
- In case a bubble crosses the lung and is injected in the arterial system, the distribution of blood at the level of aortic cross is such that a bubble is likely to reach a neurological tissue, there, the neurological tissue will act as a gas reservoir and the bubble will start growing, causing major alteration of the blood supply, and finally ischemia.
- The primary insult is now bubble growth and the specific site for such bubbles is defined as neurological tissues. However, the bubble is not generated on site, but simply amplified after it has crossed the lung system and has reached the tissue.
- The decompression strategy consists in preventing the occurrence of arterial bubbles to avoid type II DCS during the ascent. For this purpose, scenarios must be proposed for bubbles to pass through the lung.

The Beauty of the Arterial Bubble Model

The contribution of the AB model is to provide a separate explanation for the onset of type II DCS. It is nice to know that the very idea of arterial bubbles can be tracked to Haldane himself. Philip gave me a slide with the following text drawn from page 352 of Haldane's 1908 publication:

"If small bubbles are carried through the lung capillaries and pass, for instance, to a slowly desaturating part of the spinal cord, they will there increase in size and may produce serious blockage of the circulation or direct mechanical damage."

Thereafter, Haldane's idea became perverted and only the tissue and critical ratio concepts were remembered. But the basic idea was already there. During the 80s, the arterial bubbles were detected and their possible role discussed by the scientists running Doppler detection studies. Arterial bubbles were used to discuss the cerebral perfusion deficit in divers who had symptoms mainly referable to the spinal cord and the possible role of a patent foramen ovale in the divers susceptibility to type II DCS.

The first merit of the AB model is to introduce variability through the lung function. It is reasonable to accept that the filtering capacity of the lung may vary from person to person. Some filters are better than the other. Still, thinking in term of filter, we understand why some factors like age, physical fitness, smoking, fatigue or hang over may have an influence over DCS susceptibility.

The AB model also permits speculation on the possible role of CO_2 in the onset of neurological symptoms. You only have to figure out that CO_2 decreases the performance of the lung filter and may cause bubbles to pass through to the arterial side of the blood stream. In reality, the physiological response is not as simple, but think of all the situations that create CO_2 retention: stress, anxiety, hyperventilation, hard work, cold, low-flow regulator, etc.; and you will list all sorts of factors that have been known for a long time as inducing a higher risk of DCS.

Finally, and the most important contribution of the AB model is to explain how pressure variations during a dive may affect the decompression safety. Assume you were decompressing with some nice little bubbles stuck in your lung filter (so far so good) but suddenly re-immersed. The recompression will inevitably produce smaller diameter bubbles that might pass through the lung filter and become responsible for the occurrence of type II symptoms.

Normally, a diver is committed to keep a constant depth and follow a square profile that corresponds to the assumptions used to calculate and validate the decompression schedule. In practice, we know that the diver may perform repetitive ascents and descents between levels, or when in shallow waters, even repetitive ascent to the surface. These depth variations are termed "yo-yo diving". Yo-yo diving may kill you. Bubbles with a smaller diameter may pass through the lung capillaries and will be dumped into the arterial bed. Once arterial bubbles are formed, the rest of the scenario is known, but what is critical in yo-yo diving is that the process does not require much gas stored in the tissues. This explains why severe type II DCS cases have been reported in shallow diving operations, even in the no-stop decompression range.

The advice from the AB Model to technical divers is that they should plan their dives in order to **avoid repetitive pressure changes.** Divers should ban ascents to the surface in the middle of a dive or - even worse - during the course of a drift decompression to spot the dive boat or meet partners. They should also refrain from severe exposures in repetitive dives: The bubbles are still there from the previous dive when they start descent.

There is one tragic application of the AB model. Assume a diver has performed a stressful dive, or he/she is him/herself in poor physical condition, or let us say off-gassing seriously. As he/she climbs back on board, he/she realizes that the anchor is stuck and decides to make a quick jump to the bottom to free the anchor. When he/she recompresses, bubbles stuck in the lung capillaries might shrink enough to pass the lung filter. Fifteen minutes later, he/she would feel numbness, woollen legs, pins and needles, etc. The anchor does not need to be deep ... and this happened many times.

Open sea air divers should also avoid the 10 ft (3 m) stops and accumulate their stop times at 20 ft (6 m). The 10 ft (3 m) stop is difficult to perform and we should be aware that these slight pressure changes at a depth where Boyle's law is quite effective and the lung likely to be involved in the process of filtering bubbles. Moreover, the 10 ft (3 m) stop becomes quite uncomfortable when the sea is rough and divers may be tempted to perform a Valsalva.

Warning: A Valsalva in decompression is a nasty thing. It induces a significant lung over pressure and may produce arterial bubbles as "water is squeezed out of a sponge."

However, the best demonstration of the AB model came from commercial diving and surface decompression (Figure 5). Sur-D is a standard technique in the North Sea where divers directly ascend to the surface at the end of their bottom time and are immediately recompressed to 40 ft (12 m) in a deck chamber. The advantages are obvious in cold and difficult seas, because the diver is safer and much more comfortable in a chamber than in the water.

However, according to the AB model, the consequences are dramatic. The scenario is that the ascent to the surface generates bubbles and the recompression in the chamber facilitates their transfer through the lung.

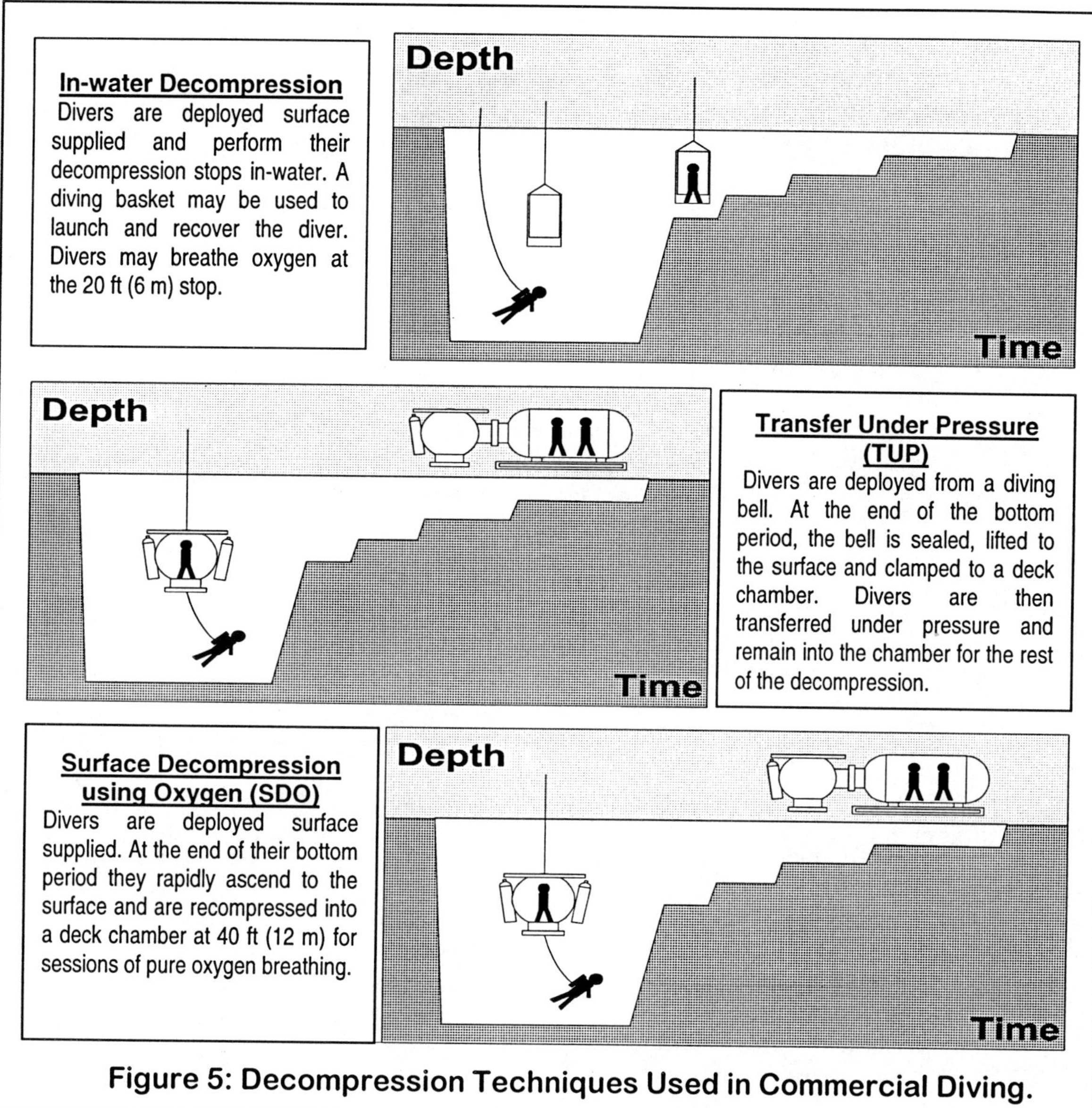

Figure 5: Decompression Techniques Used in Commercial Diving.

Working on the idea, I used the Comex database which I combined to the HSE database to gather 300,000 exposures and proved that Sur-D tends to produce 10 times more type II cases than in-water decompression (9). This is why Philip James continuously had to treat divers, before we understood that we had to switch to another method of intervention. Since then Philip has constantly crusaded against the use of Sur-D in the North Sea, and eventually lost his appointment with a main North Sea diving contractor in the process (not Comex!).

This is part of the disappointment. The concept of lungs as a filter is useful for qualitative analysis but not an operational tool. It is difficult to assess mathematically (who could put figures on the efficiency of your lungs?) and it will not help computing tables. The only way to go around it is to set up rules of thumb. Do's and don'ts, such as dive square profiles and "don't perform deep repetitive dives". It cannot yet be translated into quantitative terms such as stop times or rates of ascent, and no one will be able to tell you how many yo-yo dives you can afford before you get into trouble. It works on the procedure side, not on the table side.

Deeper Into Modeling

Whatever the merits of the CV and AB models, they are not applicable to the early stage of the decompression, a phase which is characterized by two factors, the depth of the first stop and the rate of ascent to this stop. It is too early for tissue bubbles to occur and bubbles are too small to be filtered out by the lungs. This is the era of the micro bubbles.

It must be recalled that the classic models cannot define a rate of ascent before a tissue is supersaturated.

There is a zone ranging from the bottom to the depth at which the compartments start directing the decompression where no guidance is available on how to conduct the ascent. For this reason the rate of ascent to the first stop has always been set to empirical values ranging from 60 to 50 ft (20 to 15 m) per min. Surprisingly, this rate has always been considered critical and diving manuals all recommend not to exceed the specified value. People must have learnt something the hard way there.

The same remark applies to Heliox tables. Comex used Heliox bell bounce diving intensively during the 1970s before it was replaced by saturation diving. The analysis of the table's performance showed that the long bottom time tended to induce type I DCS in the last few meters of the decompression (something which was predictable with the CV Model), but that the short bottom time, for some reason, preferably yielded vestibular symptoms. Note that a vestibular hit corresponds to a problem in the brain, the computer, not in the vestibular system, the sensor. These early tables were characterized by a high distance between the bottom and the first stop depth. Typically, a dive of 20 min at 216 ft (66 m) on Heliox 18 82 was associated to a first stop at 40 ft (12 m), that is a 170 ft (51 m) ascent performed in around 3 minutes. This is a real push, because at the time the strategy was to create a gradient to eliminate the inert gas.

Obviously, the rate of ascent for a 55 ft (18m) air dive has less relevance than for a 216 ft (66 m) Heliox dive, however the issue is serious as the risk seems to be neurological disorders. To explain why the first few minutes of the ascent have so much influence on the rest of the decompression which could last for several hours, a "ghost" element must be introduced; that is the microbubbles. These are bubbles that do not quite follow the physics of ordinary bubbles and are so small that they can freely pass through the lungs. If not controlled properly, they sow the seeds for true grown up bubbles later in the decompression. This was idea no 4.

The Tiny Bubbles Assumption

Microbubbles, or more precisely micro stabilized gas emboli, have been studied mathematically by Van Liew (10) who supposed they were pre-existing to the decompression. He showed that depending on the amplitude and the rate of ascent, these microbubbles could collapse or, on the contrary, increase in size until they reach the status of a bubble.

However, I believe that the merit of the Microbubble model, which I call the MB model belongs to Tom Hennessy, the designer of the BSAC '88 tables. Hennessy patiently collected evidences and finally published all the physical aspects of the arterial bubbles scenario in a remarkable paper (11). Unfortunately, his paper has remained confidential as it was presented at a meeting in Trondheim and nobody reads the proceedings of Norwegian conferences. He defined the origin of the microbubbles as being cavitation at the tips of the heart valves (see next page). The survival time of these microbubbles would depend on the amount of gas dissolved in the blood. At the surface, such microbubbles would survive only a few centimeters. At depth, the microbubbles would contain more gas and survive for a longer time (12). If microbubbles were allowed to last long enough, they could reach a tissue where they could receive more gas and grow. Hennessy imagined that these microbubbles could initially pass through the lung filter and cycle several times before they reach the size of a bubble in the arterial bed. Then, the rest of the story is the same as in the AB model and we know the scenario calls for type II symptoms.

Secondly, strategies for ascent are difficult to accurately define. Classic tables, such as the US Navy ones, use a rapid linear ascent to the first stop and slow stops close to the surface. No one, with some decent diving education would dare to do anything else. What is required are situations where special conditions made people use non-traditional decompression schedules. One famous case is certainly the procedures the Okinawan divers that were reported by Hills that built the foundation of his famous "thermodynamic" decompression model (14). Briefly, local people were very talented at manufacturing shirt buttons from oyster shells. These divers, who used to breath hold dive, suddenly got access to SCUBA equipment and compressors but not to tables. Bends after bends, they finally developed dive profiles where they would slowly ascend along the walls harvesting shells until they reached a depth near 33 ft (10 m) where they directly ascended to the surface.

Figure 6

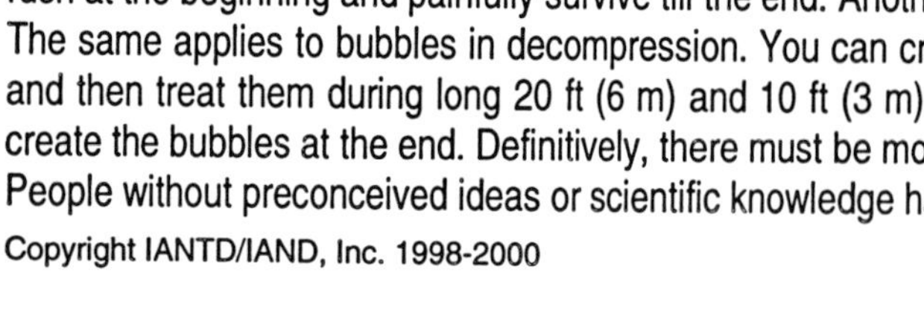

Traditional dive profile

Okinawan divers' dive profile

This way of doing decompression totally opposes our way of conducting dives but let us remain open-minded. There are two ways of running a marathon. One way is to rush at the beginning and painfully survive till the end. Another way is to make a slow start and may sprint at the end. The same applies to bubbles in decompression. You can create the bubbles by a rapid high amplitude initial ascent and then treat them during long 20 ft (6 m) and 10 ft (3 m) stops. Or you can slowly start to ascend and decide to create the bubbles at the end. Definitively, there must be more than one strategy to conduct a decompression profile. People without preconceived ideas or scientific knowledge have already tried all sorts of them.

The Microbubble Model Scenario (Figure 7)

(Proposed by Hennessy)

1. Microbubbles are produced by cavitation at the tip of the heart valve. At the surface, the survival distance of these microbubbles is only a few centimeters.

2. At depth, because of the increased amount of gas dissolved, their survival distance increases. The critical site is thus the blood. The critical issue is the survival time of the microbubbles.

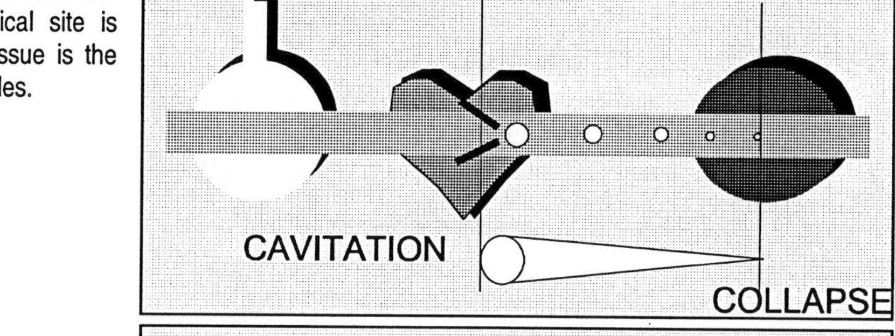

3. During decompression, microbubbles may reach a fast tissue off loading gas. The gas will diffuse inside the bubbles and increase their size.

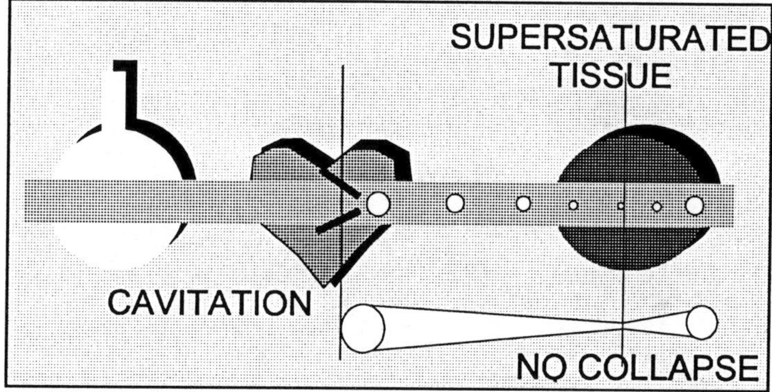

4. Microbubbles will pass through the lung filter because of their small size and cycle several times and be progressively amplified. In their last cycle, microbubbles will become full size bubbles. The rest of the story is then the same as for the Arterial Bubbles model. The primary insult is again an arterial bubble reaching a neurological tissue.

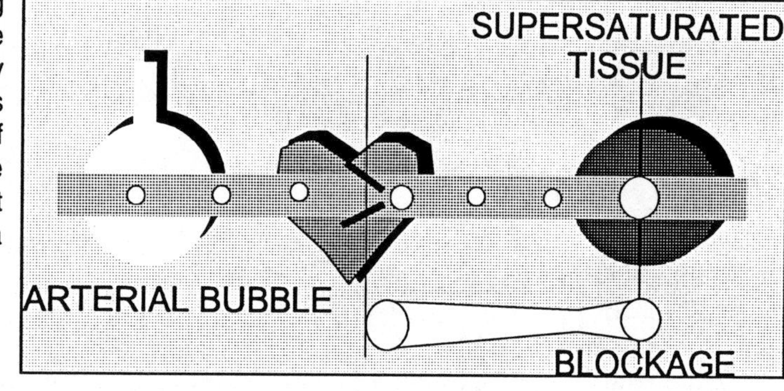

The Secret of Red Coral Divers

Red coral is fancied around the Mediterranean for jewelry and the tradition is to offer a coral pendant to male babies. The market of coral is organized from Napoli in Italy and there is a small community of coral divers in the south of France and Corsica. Diving for red coral is a tough job but it pays off. So, during the season coral divers usually dive twice a day, on air, to 260 ft (80 m), for 20 minutes. Coral divers do not have access to the modern diving expertise and use a variety of decompression procedures that they have developed themselves or adapted empirically. I have collected such decompression tables for a long time and they always look dramatically too short to me. When a coral diver bends, it is always serious but still they manage to get through a lot of decompressions. They do incredible things, like adding stops or lengthening the oxygen time depending on their feeling. They must be passing so many bubbles that they got a sensation of it. However, I have found that the reason why coral divers can go through such rapid decompressions is perhaps because they have adopted some specific operational procedures that change the profile of the decompression and obviously improve its outcome (Figure 6).

At the end of a 260 ft (80 m) 20 min bottom time dive, the divers ascend rapidly approximately 50 ft (15 m) above the bottom. The reason advocated is that they want to get rid of the narcosis. Then they slow down their ascent until they reach 130 ft (39 m) where they wait for the boat. When the boat is located, they send the basket with the precious harvest to the surface using a lift bag and only when the basket is secured do they proceed to the rest of their super fast decompression. This way, the dive profile is lengthened by some 10-15 minutes spent at mid-depth as presented below.

The mid-depth stop is an old trick that already appeared in the Royal Navy deep air tables. I also was told the story of two sponge divers who used to stop at mid-depth and sing a certain number of verses of a gospel before they proceeded to their decompression. However, it is interesting to note that this "fast/slow" ascent protocol is similar to the one proposed by Van Liew using his microbubble model. When such dives are analyzed in the light the MB model, it appears that the coral divers have developed a protocol which permits them:

To off-gas fast tissues such as the brain by the rapid initial ascent of small amplitude. This way, if a microbubble was transiting through them, it will not found supersaturated gas to feed its growth. Then control microbubbles to reduce their survival distance by following slower ascent to and a stage at 130 ft (40 m). This way, maybe, they avoid showers of microbubbles cycling through their body and prepare a clean decompression.

The Strange Properties of the "Log/P" Plot

The last account comes from decompression studies carried at the Comex Hyperbaric Center at Marseille in the mid-1970s. At the time, Comex planned optimistically to conduct deep diving operations on a large scale and wanted to select deep divers. Divers were offered to be pressurized in 15 minutes to 588 ft (180 m) and run a battery of tests on High Pressure Nervous Syndrome for two hours. The divers were a little bit shaken by the rapid pressurization and the tests were sensitive enough. However, the persons in charge of the decompression had difficulties defining a model to calculate profiles for such an advanced dive until they finally gave up the idea of any mathematical support and simply start drawing the ascent profile on paper. Decompression as a pure art. They discovered that plotting the deco profiles in a depth versus time diagram was always disappointing and could not really permit comparison of different decompression profiles. After some trials, they finally found that by plotting the rate of ascent in a logarithm scale versus depth the decompression ascents appear roughly as a line (Figure 8), a property they could use to design decompression.

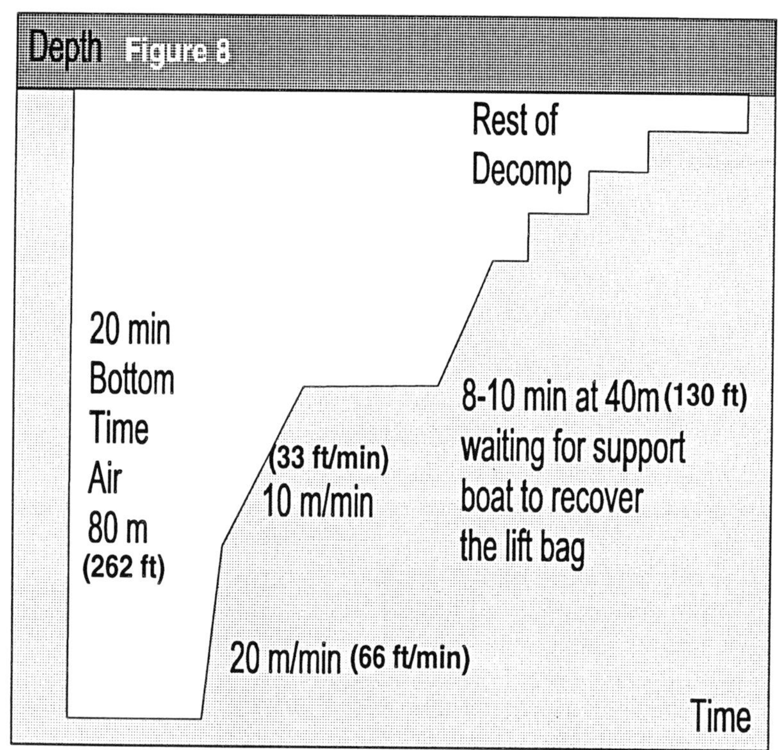

Although the method was deliberately empirical, it permitted defining a schedule with varying rates of ascent and very deep stops. After some adjustments, Comex produced a table for the 588 ft (180 m), 120 min dive that required 48 hours of deco and which was extremely successful. A total of 47 divers used it without any problem.

Years later, working with cave divers, and considering the difficulty of designing a increasingly deeper trimix decompression, I became interested in slower rate of ascent and deeper stops and the curious properties of the semi-log plot. This plot makes it possible by extrapolation to define ascent rates and even stops in the deepest part where traditional models fail to control the ascent. I have since built on it a method which I call the "Log/P" plot to adapt old Trimix tables to modern cave diving. All it requires is a sheet of semi-log paper. In that the "Log/P" plot, the x-axis is linear and represents the depth in meters. The y-axis is logarithmic and initially represented the rate of ascent in meters/min. In fact, I use a variation of it. Due to the property of the log function and because the stop increments are constant, I plot directly the stop times in a log scale versus the depth.

I found this way of plotting decompression profiles very instructive. It expands the initial part of the decompression and permits me to immediately evaluate the rate of ascent and initial stop depth. It also allows me to compare decompressions in the same diagram regardless of their duration, as for instance different depths for the same bottom time or various bottom times from the same depth. After some practice, we learn that:

- Decompression profiles appear roughly as lines in the "Log/P" plot.
- The slope of the line is related to the % of O_2. The higher the O_2 content in the mix, the faster the ascent.
- A change in deco mix accelerates ascent. Deco with several mix displays a sort of saw tooth shape.
- The longer the bottom time, the slower the ascent. Two dives at the same depth and same mixes but with different bottom times display parallel lines.
- If the bottom time increases, the deco's tend to adopt the same stop times close to the surface. This corresponds to the last tissue controlling the ascent, i.e. the saturation end of the decompression.

The secret of deep Trimix decompression is to start with a good classic table, plot them in the "Log/P" plot, and prolong the line in the deeper part to define additional stops and slower ascent rates for a safer decompression. I have computed such Trimix decompressions for my cave diver friends, and recently for Pascal Bernabé and Fred Badier who reached 560 ft (170 m) for 20 min in Fontaine de Vaucluse in France, and they all remained my friends, which means they came back safe and happy from the darkness!

Finally, my philosophy of decompression boils down to little: work an explanation for each manifestation. Then my techniques summarize to use tissue compartment models to avoid type I, use procedures to avoid type II, and use deep stops to avoid vestibular hits in deep fast decompression. I understand there is more to it. Other pieces of model can be thrown in the puzzle such as the blood/brain barrier and the long-term effects, also called the deco fatigue in saturation diving. However, the lesson learned is that no idea is so good or old that it should not be challenged. Don't listen to gurus, use your experience and follow your own good new idea. But what I like about deco modeling is that it is exciting. The fact that Comex was able to design a 588 ft (180 m), 120 min. deco that worked proves that there must be a meta-model hiding somewhere. There is something still to be understood that will allow us to design safe and efficient deco tables at least from surface to 588 ft (180 m). Up to now, the multi-model approach is the best I have found.

Works Cited

1. Shields TG, Lee WB. The incidence of decompression sickness arising from commercial offshore air-diving operations in the UK sector of the North Sea during 1982/83. Report to the UK Department of Energy, 1986.
2. Shields TG, Duff P, Wilcox SE. Decompression sickness from commercial offshore air-diving operations on the UK continental shelf during 1990. Report from the UK HSE. 1992
3. Imbert JP. Decompression safety. Proceedings of the Subtec '93 Conference. Volume 31, 239-249. Aberdeen, Scotland, Nov. 1993.
4. Hennessy TR, Hempleman HV. An examination of the critical release gas volume concept in decompression sickness. Proc. R. Soc. B179, 299-313, 1977.
5. Imbert JP, Bontoux M. A method for introducing new decompression procedures. Proceedings of the Undersea Medical Society Workshop on validation of deco schedules. Bethesda, Maryland, February 13-14 Th., 1987.
6. Travaux en Milieu Hyperbare. Mesures particuliaires de prévention. ISBN 2-11-073322-5-ISSN 0767-4538. Journal Officiel, 26 Rue Desaix, 75727 Paris cedex 15. France.
7. James PB. The size distribution of gas emboli arising during deco. A review of the concept of critical diameter of gas emboli. Proceedings of the XIIIth Annual Congress of the EUBS, Lubeck, Germany, October 5-8th, 1982.
8. James PB. Decompression sickness. In Clinical Neurology. Edited by Michael Swash and John Oxbury. Churchill Livingstone. Vol. 1;565, 1991.
9. Imbert JP. Multi-model approach to decompression safety. Proceeding of the Decompression Modeling Workshop. Ballater, Scotland, - November 1996.
10. Van Liew HD. Simulation of the dynamics of decompression sickness bubbles and the generation of new bubbles. Undersea Biomedical research, Vol. 18, No 4, 1991.
11. Hennessy TR. On the site of origin, evolution and effects of decompression microbubbles. Proceeding of the International Symposium on supersaturation and bubble formation in fluids and organisms. Trondheim, Norway, June 6-10th, 1989.
12. Van Liew HD, MP Hlastala. Influence of bubble size and blood perfusion on absorption of gas bubbles in tissues; Respiratory Physiology (1969) 7,11-12 &; North Holland Publishing Company, Amsterdam.
13. Mazurel G, Hee J, Giacomini L, Guillerm R. Ultrasonic detection of circulating bubbles in ewes exposed to simulated dives deeper than 800 m under isobaric conditions and with unchanged gas mixtures. Proceedings of the XIth Annual meeting of the EUBS. Goteborg, Sweden, August 1985.
14. Hills BA. Deco Sickness, Volume 1. John Wiley & Sons. Chischester. New York. 1977. ISBN 0 471 99457 X.

CHAPTER 13
Psychological and Physical Fitness for Technical Diving

Tom Mount

Introduction

Each time man ventures forth to explore new environments, he encounters new physical and mental challenges and faces new hazards. In order to cope with and overcome these challenges, he must learn new adaptations and behaviors. This chapter will discuss some of the adaptations, behavioral modifications and conditionings that relate to the specific challenges and demands of technical diving.

Andrew Driver, Nick Jewison and Dough Howard preparing for a Cis-Lunar MK5p dive. Photo: Don Townsend

Advances in scuba technology and dive planning have allowed divers to reach depths and underwater durations unthinkable even a decade ago. But there is a price that must be paid for such advances. As divers go deeper and travel greater distances than ever before, they must be prepared to face the hazards and challenges that accompany these extended limits.

Today's exploratory dives push and often exceed the comfort level of even the most experienced and hardened diver. Adapting to and overcoming the physical and mental challenges of such dives is a matter of behavior modification - a process that requires the diver to develop a unity of the mind, body, and spirit.

There are many factors that will influence the way in which a diver reacts to the demands and hazards of his environment. These factors include his attitude, awareness, physical fitness, self-discipline and his ability to separate perceptions from reality. To understand this phenomenon, we must examine the various mental and physical stimuli that influence a diver's attitude and performance.

Stress in Technical Diving

Stress plays a major role in our actions and reactions in all facets of our lives. Underwater, one's reaction to stress can easily determine the difference between an enjoyable dive and an accident. Stress is a phenomenon that may, if unchecked, lead to panic and result in an accident. Technical divers are exposed to most known stresses measured by psychologists. In this chapter we will identify and provide examples of the major stresses to which divers may be exposed.

Wrecks and caves present us with an overhead environment. This means we cannot escape directly to the surface as we do in no-decompression stop open water diving. Caves and wrecks are dark. They usually present us with "tough" choices. Deciding which passage or companionway to take in a seemingly endless maze can create its own sources of stress. As we review each stress source, it will become apparent how these environmental hazards add to stress.

Time-pressure stress is present in a wide number of scenarios. In its most simple form, time-pressure stress involves matching the gas supply to the duration of the dive. This expands into a major problem when a dive plan has been exceeded and the gas supply is running low. In this instance, uninformed or unskilled divers may actually compound the problem by increasing their breathing rates. Time-pressure stress can also build when a diver looks at his/her decompression "clock".

Distance presents a major time-pressure stress. The greater the distance to open water, the more time stress has to build. The greatest danger in distance-related stress is the perceived time-pressure threat. In this case, the perception is usually greater than the actual threat. There have been numerous instances when divers have become so distressed they forgot basic, but important, rules for safe diving.

Preparing for a dive can also cause time-pressure stress. For example, if one diver is already suited and enters the water and his (or her) buddy has an equipment problem and removes his/her gear to make repairs. Time stresses both divers - the one who has to wait and the one who is causing the delay because he/she has to play catch up.

If stress is not controlled, it may lead to panic. Panic is a life-threatening event!

Confinement is an obvious source of stress. This is usually lurking in the recesses of the mind and comes into play when other stresses are introduced. Confinement couples time-pressure stress with the distance factor. The "knee jerk" reaction to bolt toward the surface must be overcome by overhead training that discourages thinking about the "traditional escape route". In this way, confinement stress is managed.

Task loading stress occurs when divers must perform more tasks than they feel they can handle. Task loading can happen when a diver is trying to do three simple things at once - manage a reel, manage two stage cylinders and swim in a normal, correct, relaxed manner. Add to this a Diver Propulsion Vehicle (DPV) or other specialized items, and the diver's ability to function may be impaired. With experience, divers will learn to handle multiple tasks with greater ease, but each time an additional action or responsibility is added to the diver's task load, stress will increase.

Incorrect breathing patterns are tied to stress in a two-way cause/effect cycle. Incorrect breathing patterns will create stress, but stress will also cause incorrect breathing, which will in turn compound the diver's original stressed condition. Once a pattern of incorrect breathing has begun, a vicious cycle develops. The pattern is often so subtle a diver may not even recognize it. Examples of stressful breathing include hyperventilation, rapid breathing (usually shallow), resulting in a feeling of air starvation. This is frequently sensed as regulator failure. A diver who fails to exhale and keeps inhaling in small "gulps" until his lungs are full often thinks that his regulator is faulty.

To break this cycle, a diver must become aware of and regain control of his/her breathing. Divers should practice diaphragm breathing exercises and, when diving, should concentrate on breathing slowly and deeply until it becomes a reflex reaction.

Hypoventilation usually results from a concerted effort to skip breathe. This often produces excess CO_2 that may lead to unconsciousness.

When a diver first becomes aware of stress or a feeling of discomfort, it's important for the diver to stop all activity, exhale slowly and fully, and then inhale slowly and fully. This breathing pattern should be repeated at least 3 times before resuming the dive. The diver should then continue breathing slowly and fully using the diaphragm muscles. Discomfort can almost always be alleviated by this method.

A good way to avoid breathing stress is to develop a swim pace that allows acceptable forward momentum while maintaining a correct, comfortable respiratory pattern. Accelerating one's swimming stroke will frequently lead to uncontrolled breathing, and can even produce a sensation of uneasiness.

Divers who maintain good physical conditioning will discover that the human body is much like a boat's hull. Once a boat reaches hull speed, doubling the power produces little or no increase in forward momentum. Divers' bodies behave similarly. Human bodies, like boat hulls, come in different shapes. Some shapes pass through the water easier and faster than others. Exceeding our "hull speed" takes more work and produces a minimal increase in performance. Unwanted respiratory induced stress will result.

Unlike boats, divers can change the shape of their "hulls". A lean profile generally produces less drag and is more efficient in the water. Divers should be encouraged to maintain a lean personal profile through exercise and proper diet, but a lean profile also involves the diver's swim posture and equipment configuration.

Poor swim posture may lead to stress, and will typically require more energy to maintain. This increased energy demand, in turn, makes increased demands on our respiratory system.

Exertion and thermal imbalance produce stress, as the diver is either too hot or too cold. An aware diver should be able to control these stressors simply by monitoring his comfort level and using adequate and appropriate thermal protection.

Ego threats, or peer pressure, are indirect sources of stress, particularly if they cause a diver to attempt feats beyond his/her personal ability or comfort level.

Disorientation is always a problem when exploring overhead environments or deep water. Most overhead environments feature multiple passages. Deep water allows little time for correction of navigational errors. Both environments create the very real possibility of becoming lost.

The proper use of navigation aids such as visual referencing, compasses, and in overhead environments, line arrows and guidelines can offset the stress of disorientation and the risk of becoming lost. One of the leading causes of deaths in overhead environment dives is the failure to follow a continuous guideline.

Darkness or loss of visibility produces stress due to sensory loss. This can be a result of a light malfunction, low visibility, turbid water, or silt outs. While this should not be a major concern in and of itself, when combined with other stresses and performance inhibitors, loss of visibility can lead to threatening situations.

The most serious form of stress is "compound stress". It occurs when more than one stress source is involved. Compound stress is more difficult to manage than individual sources of stress. However, in reality, it is very common to have more than one source or form of stress on a dive.

Other stresses include buoyancy problems, excessive dependency on another diver, and real or perceived physical threats. Early recognition of the telltale signs and symptoms of stress can help reduce or prevent the escalation of the stress reaction. Personal indicators of stress often include an uneasy feeling, unusual anxiety, apprehension or irritability. Our intuitive hunches will attempt to tell us if there is a reason for stress. Becoming tuned in to our inner self is an important step towards stress-free diving. Developing such a degree of awareness requires training and the use of mind control techniques.

VISUAL INDICATORS OF STRESS INCLUDE, BUT ARE NOT LIMITED TO...		
BIG-EYED LOOK	FIXATION ON GAUGES	FREEZING UP
INCREASED RESPIRATION	CHANGES IN SWIM PACE	CLUMSINESS
FAILURE TO COMMUNICATE	INABILITY TO DO SKILLS	TENSING UP

Stress control can be accomplished through increased self-awareness. Frequently, the stressed diver is unaware of an increase in respiration. A buddy, who notices his dive partner breathing quickly or unusually, should immediately alert him to momentarily remain at rest until the breathing problem is solved. To control stress, we must first be aware of it and then execute a corrective action. When dealing with stress, we must remember that while its cause may be either real or perceived, the results are equally dangerous. Also keep in mind that stress frequently manifests itself by a change in respiration.

As divers, we must learn to recognize some common behavioral modifications that can result in "mental narrowing", or more aptly stated, becoming unfocused as it relates to problem solving. By becoming overtly focused, the diver may lose the ability to correctly analyze situations and to perform both newly learned and well-known skills. Mental narrowing can compound the problem because of falsely perceived task loading. This type of behavioral change, if not corrected, may lead to panic.

The body's physical reactions to the psychological trauma of stress may include increased respiration, increased heart rate, abnormal adrenaline release, and the instinctive urge to flee.

For survival, it is imperative that we compensate for behavioral and physiological changes. The tools that will enable us to control stress in all its manifestations include awareness, adequate training and the application of newly acquired skills. In addition, we must develop a new discipline (or attitude). We must be able to instantly recognize a real threat as opposed to a perceived one, and we must instinctively make the appropriate corrective actions in order to avoid disaster.

Awareness is developed through a process of both self and group analysis. Awareness must become automatic. One of the best ways to accomplish this is by employing the process of mental visualization prior to the actual dive. Running the dive through your mind prior to diving can result in a safer dive. Awareness also opens the mind's ability to detect changes in dive performance that otherwise would go unnoticed in either yourself or your dive companions. During the dive, periodically ask yourself, "Am I comfortable? Is everything really OK?" Observe buddies and their comfort levels and listen for changes in respiratory rates.

The need for intensive, repetitive training of all pertinent skills becomes apparent when a situation takes a critical turn. Poorly learned skills will be forgotten in times of duress, and only those skills that were practiced to the point of becoming virtually instinctive will remain with the diver.

The first step in any stress control and behavior modification program should be a personal training program. Personal training needs to be ongoing. It is key to maintaining a record of safe diving. To do this, we must continue to regularly practice relevant skills. As part of this exercise, we must practice efficient breathing. We must continually evaluate and configure equipment so it's easy to use and every element is accessible and works dependably. Routinely review your skills, and as your interests expand, seek additional training for specialty areas in diving. Select dive buddies who share your interests and training objectives.

Risk Management

Risk management is key to becoming a good technical diver. By employing the concept of risk management, divers learn to establish realistic objectives. They can then decide what kind of diver they really want to be - a recreational diver, a technical diver or an explorer.

As we continue to emphasize, there are many risks in diving. There are various solutions to most of the risks. Once you decide to accept a given level of overall risk, you must also consider what compromises you will need to make. You must, for example, weigh efficiency with safety. You must recognize the hazards as well as the benefits and deal with the positives as well as the negatives.

Various factors will enter into these compromises, including the size of the dive team, equipment configuration, compromises involving capabilities, the degree of decompression risk and the level of acceptable discomfort. As technical divers, we must review all of these factors and determine the limits of your personal control zones. Many paths lead to the same destination in exploration or enjoyment. The quickest path often yields the greatest risk, but may produce a more immediate return. The more deliberate path may take longer to arrive at the same destination, but will provide greater safety. It all comes down to individual risk management and how much risk you're prepared to take.

Equipment configuration can provide a good illustration of the risk evaluation and risk management process, as it allows a diver to weigh the advantages and disadvantages of a given piece of equipment with regards to the overall safety of the dive.

For example: the more streamlined our equipment, the greater our in-water efficiency. Our gas consumption is lower, we swim easier and more efficiently, and our stamina improves. So, why not always opt for the maximum efficiency? Risk may cause some divers to configure equipment with some added drag to compensate for equipment failure. For instance, one diver may decide to dive with a single BC bladder, although failure of the single bladder may prevent him from being able to surface. Another diver, making this same dive, may elect a backup BC as insurance for a safe ascent, even though the redundant bladder creates added drag and a very slight increase in gas consumption.

Given a choice, most divers would prefer a configuration that reduces drag. But, if there's a chance your single bladder could fail and this failure could be life threatening, it makes good sense to sacrifice being streamlined by increasing redundancy. If doing so, however, the divers should take into account the additional gas consumption that will result from the increase in drag, and plan for this increased usage accordingly.

You need to ask yourself: "How often has your BC malfunctioned and is this a significant risk to be considered?" In the past 5 years, I have had two malfunctions that made my BC absolutely useless for ascent, and I have witnessed other incidents of BC bladder/inflator malfunction. These incidents convinced me that redundancy was a small price to pay for safety. If you decide to use a backup BC, you should select one that offers as little drag as possible while providing adequate lift to achieve neutral buoyancy.

Additional considerations regarding equipment configuration should be evaluated in a similar fashion. Some divers use two submersible pressure gauges (SPGs) on their primary gas supplies. Others feel this is just added drag. They feel that if their primary gas supply components fail, the dive should be terminated. Given this choice, one submersible gauge is enough. In fact, many feel the extra SPG is just something else that could break. Those who feel redundant SPGs are necessary say that safety is the overriding issue for them. It all comes down to a matter of personal choice and comfort.

When configuring equipment, consideration must be given for each piece of redundant equipment. The idea of "bringing it along" must be coupled with the corresponding increased drag. Thus, we must choose carefully. We must realistically decide what produces personal safety and what is simply redundancy for redundancy's sake.

There are any number of additional topics to which risk assessment and risk management should be applied, and these topics could fill an entire text by themselves. Hopefully, listing a few examples will prove sufficient to stimulate you into thinking about, recognizing, and evaluating just what risks might really be encountered during a given dive.

You must opt for a level of risk you can live with. The best determination is, perhaps, one which you feel allows you control over your own destiny - worded another way, a profile that acknowledges, "Only you can breathe for you, swim for you or think for you." A dive plan determined by you as survivable is a matter of personal choice.

If this is your 1st or 1,000th dive, you should approach risk management the same way for every dive. The first step is to list all of the anticipated risks associated with the dive. Once this list is completed, define how each risk can effect safety. Second, prepare a plan of action to cope with known stresses on the dive. Third, determine which risks are acceptable to you. Fourth, outline your equipment needs (for dive accomplishment and for your feelings of personal safety). Last, develop an operational plan providing a set of limits which makes you comfortable.

Regardless of what you decide, expect others to probably challenge your decisions. The debate of risk management vs. efficiency is an eternal one. There are minimums all should agree on, but the specifics are totally individual.

The overall application of risk recognition and management was stated aptly by psychiatrist Gil Milner MD: ***"If known, you have the responsibility to fully explain the risk of any activity to all who choose to pursue this endeavor. As an individual, you must be responsible for discovering all the apparent risks in activities you want to pursue. Once all risks are fully understood, you have the right to subject yourself to whatever degree of risk you chose even if it is life threatening."***

Mind Control

Behavioral Failure: In this presentation we will discuss diver capability failure points and also some suggested variations and approaches based on whether one is cave or open water diving certified. Safe diving depends on many variables that can be classified as failure points. What exactly is a failure point? Is this a breakdown in the diving system, diver behavior and/or education that may lead to an accident?

Diver Capability

Herein lies the critical point in being a safer diver. There are many issues that contribute to this and offer increased performance. Life support systems, equipment configuration, equipment reducing failure points, all can enhance performance but it is the raw capability of the diver that will determine the safety foundation.

To discuss diver capability, some definitions must be established. Capability is defined as having ability or competence. It includes qualities that may be used or developed, thus one's potential can be determined. So, to have or to develop capability then is a combination of becoming aware of the environment, becoming skillful in specific diving technique for efficient swimming, developing detailed techniques for specific environments, evolving to a good body attitude and, of course, practicing. Experience is a valuable contributor to diver capability. Experience may also be a positive contributor by continued use of correct skills and techniques. However, experience may also be a negative influence if the diver's early experience did not lay a firm foundation in basics skills, technique, body attitude and risk awareness. If one routinely practices a bad technique, then this bad technique is "perfected" and becomes a stumbling block for growth as a diver.

Diver capability begins in the first open water class and evolves through continuing education and practical application of diving skills, and knowledge. It is therefore important that the initial training be strict in the basics. Today, unfortunately, many dive instructors, even instructor trainers and course directors do not have a good foundation in dive technique. It is quite common in advanced and technical training to have to (re)teach highly "experienced" instructors the correct way to kick or achieve proper body attitude in the water. In many cases these persons have "perfected" a bad technique, sometimes accompanied by the attitude of "because I'm an instructor, therefore I can do no wrong". In these cases not only does technique have to be developed and old habits broken, but the attitude must be altered. In most sports, optimum performance is gained by mastering technique first, then concentrating on "going for it". Technique is everything. I (also) teach martial arts and one of the most difficult things to tell people is to relax, breathe out as they strike or prepare to get hit, and develop proper technique.

The same is true in diving: relaxed and correct breathing combined with relaxed (untensed) muscles when executing correct form and even calculated movements is how performance is improved. For instance, on a kick, just ensuring the toes are pointed in a relaxed manner makes a world of difference in power on a flutter kick. With a frog kick, technique is the difference between being almost useless or having a strong and efficient tool. During this kick, being relaxed as the legs spread out and then cupping the toes followed by an inward thrust that brings the toes together is very important. If one is flexible enough, this thrusting before the heels touch provides the majority of forward momentum. When a diver does not bring the fins together, they are quite inefficient in realizing the full potential of this technique. Learning ascent techniques, especially in dry suits, also adds to diver capability.

Thus, in diver education the primary goal at all levels is to increase diver capability in the environments she/he is trained in. The secondary goals will include equipment selection and configuration that will enhance performance. But remember these will be wasted if a capable diver is not using them.

I recently overheard two technical instructors discussing the most important aspects of a technical course. The least experienced was trying to explain how the most important thing was equipment configuration. The 20-year veteran instructor just smiled and then started listing the entire component that a technical diver had to master, such as stress management, body posture and advanced skills. The list continued for about five minutes. At the end, the new instructor conceded that capability was the number one objective followed then by ways to increase performance, and agreed that configuration, although quite important, is included in the increased performance category rather than the primary goal of a training program.

A capable diver, once efficient in technique, must also become capable of managing stress. Diving is an activity that removes us from our natural habitat; therefore, one must anticipate that a stressful event will occur at some point someday on some dive. A diver trained in stress management will not yield to a perception of stress but will in fact automatically respond with a corrective measure. To insure this type of response, the diver must be exposed to simulated reality-based situations during training. The most serious are gas failure problems. Other areas include equipment failure and most importantly, behavior failure. IANTD programs emphasize these areas as IANTD feels diver capability is the single most important aspect of diver safety.

A capable diver is one who has a foundation in good diving technique and skills. They continue training either in formal programs or by self-improvement. The capable diver employs a good attitude and has self-confidence. This individual defines a personal safety envelope of limits and establishes goals and direction as a diver. Once capable, this person reaches out to find avenues to increase performance, thus extending accomplishments while still maintaining a safety envelope.

Several years back, former Vice President Dan Quayle was asked to speak at the Alliance of Black Colleges and Universities. Being one who often got things mixed up, he said with all honesty and sincerity, "It's a terrible thing to lose one's mind." What he should have said was, "A mind is a terrible thing to waste."

Seriously, our minds are the most powerful tool we possess. Scientists believe the power of the mind may be infinite. They say most of us use less than 5% of our brain's potential. Imagine for a moment what you might accomplish if you could suddenly tap into your brain's total potential.

Thoughts direct our conscious mind. In fact, we are what we think. Each and every one of us is a product of our thoughts. Our happiness, our success, and our health are all influenced by what we think. These thought patterns have been embedded in our minds from the moment we began to think. They were shaped by our upbringing, past experiences, and education. If we want to improve ourselves, the first step is to improve our outlook and, perhaps, our beliefs and thoughts.

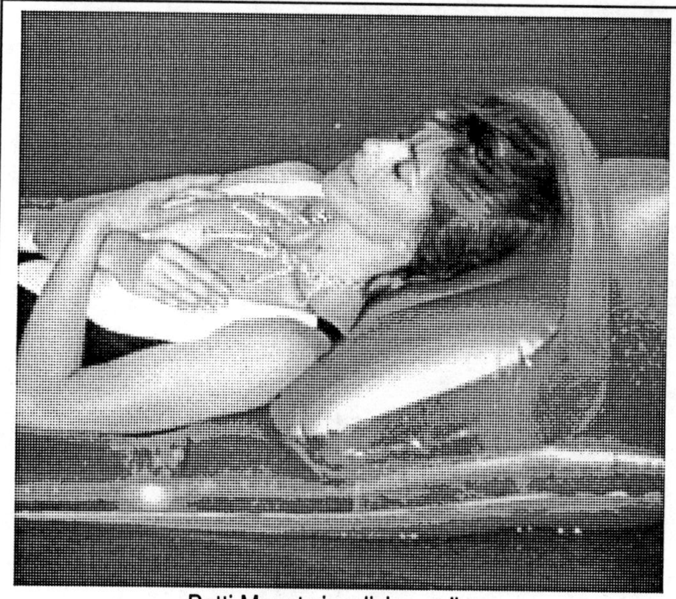

Patti Mount visualizing a dive.

Photo: Tom Mount

By controlling our minds, we have the potential to improve our lives. Sound simple? It is. However, few of us have developed the discipline to think strategically. It appears most people seem to merely respond to their environment. Being ahead of the game, people with foresight and judgment plan and shape their world. Yet, developing mental discipline and the ability to think strategically takes time. It requires you to exercise your mind. The mental exercise techniques I use include meditation, affirmations, goal setting, breathing exercises and concentration.

I am convinced that a physically conditioned body is necessary for creating a healthy mind. For the body to experience outstanding health, the mind must remain healthy. The mind, body and spirit all work in unison. We are, indeed, what we think. In time, we can probably make our life what we want it to be by using mind control. Some people have called it the "right stuff". Perhaps it is. Having the right stuff means having increased self-confidence. It means being able to accomplish important goals. Moreover, it means being able to survive when mentally and physically challenged.

Even before you begin technical diving, you must prepare your mind. You must tell yourself, "I'm going in. I'm going to do everything right. And, I'm coming back. There's nothing in there I can't handle. I've done my homework thoroughly." Being able to say this is important, because your mind must be conditioned to adjust to environmental changes once you enter a dive.

In mind training, there are numerous facets to be considered. It is often necessary to overcome ingrained negative beliefs. Self-confidence is a major component in making the right decision, especially when faced with unforeseen adverse situations. A positive self-image and self-confidence go hand-in-hand.

Often in our society, people are "brainwashed" more by what they can't accomplish rather than by what they *can* achieve. Many people live their lives in fear. They fear the unknown. They're afraid to walk out of their homes at night. All of these are negative thoughts. When you were younger, how often did someone say you couldn't do such and such, or that you were a bad person?

These statements, directed at us during our formative years, became embedded in our minds. Over time, this conditioning evolved into a belief system. To produce a positive belief system, it is often necessary to recondition our inner beliefs.

In my own experience when investigating accidents, I have found that when accidents occur, one or more team members had bad feelings or premonitions about the dive.

As we've said, when it comes to becoming a good technical diver, we must develop an "I can" belief system. We must program our minds. We can accomplish this with the techniques of visualization and affirmation. These powerful mechanisms change and improve belief systems. They also provide the most clear cut approach for helping us to accomplish all our desired diving goals. As stated by Tom Ford, "Believe you can, believe you can't, either way you are right." As stated in the bible, "What so ever a man thinketh, so he is." Our total being is a reflection of what we think we are. Our thoughts are our reality.

Visualization is an excellent tool for developing mental control and changing belief systems. The process is quite simple. Here's how it works: Close your eyes and concentrate on breathing slowly and deeply. You are going to slowly relax every muscle in your body. You will begin with your feet. Once these muscles feel relaxed, you'll move to the calves of your legs. Then, continuing this relaxation technique, you'll move slowly upward relaxing each and every muscle group from your big toe to the top of your head. As soon as you feel totally relaxed, form an image in your mind. This image may involve the performance of a given skill or the completion of a goal. These are the first steps to becoming your own master.

Most champion athletes and many successful business people use visualization to manage their lives. It is merely a part of their total training program. If you want to achieve greater success, we strongly recommend you begin a program of mental conditioning, if you aren't already doing so.

To visualize an upcoming dive, use this relaxation and visualization technique. Picture in your mind the entire dive from beginning to end. Include all dive team members. Visualize what you might see as well as what challenges you may face. Be thorough. Do the dive step by step in your mind. Once this dive has been mentally rehearsed, it's easy for your body to duplicate this performance.

When you are in a relaxed state, it's easy to communicate with your subconscious mind. If your mind "tells you" something can go wrong during your upcoming dive, sort it out. Talk to your buddies. Tell them about your concerns. Go back and run the dive through your mind again. If you still get "bad vibes", bail out. If you're the team leader, cancel the dive.

There are numerous self-help tapes available to guide you to learn the technique of visualization. They include, for example, self-image improvement, correct breathing, goal setting, and increased concentration. While tapes are excellent materials to help you get started, eventually you'll need to customize your training to include your specific needs. No tapes are available to help you visualize an upcoming dive. The tapes will show you how to do the visualization, but after that, you're on your own.

Your pre-dive visualization can be as brief as three minutes or up to a half-hour. The more serious the dive profile, the greater the detail you should devote to the visualization. I visualize all my dives. When possible, I try to do one meditation session daily. I usually average about three sessions weekly, plus pre-dive visualizations.

Once you incorporate a meditation program into your lifestyle, you'll find yourself becoming more relaxed and able to handle stress more quickly and easily. You should also see immediate improvements in your dive performance. When diving, you should feel more relaxed and have a greater sense of confidence. Gradually, you'll discover not only your lifestyle has changed, but your entire belief system has changed as well.

When you begin the process of visualization, be patient. Negative feelings, or a sense of inadequacy, which have been a part of your life for years, cannot be changed overnight. Improvements will come gradually. Before you laugh or dismiss this idea, *remember* the process does work. I use it, as do most of my friends and dive buddies.

Visualization enables you to increase your self-confidence. It permits you to see yourself as you really are. Being honest with yourself is very important, not only with your abilities as a diver, but in your life as well. It is excellent for expanding awareness and for becoming more intuitive. It enables us to get to know our own selves. For the serious diver, visualization is an essential part of the dive planning process. This is the means by which you can go within yourself and make a major life commitment. Importantly, it is in these moments when we discover our real feelings about life's meaning. When this energy is channeled toward dive planning, we are able to reach new levels of excellence and control.

Affirmation is the concept of stating something as if it has already happened. It is another means of communication with the subconscious mind. Affirmations can be spoken, written, or repeated during the process of visualization. A great deal of research on the effective use of affirmations has been performed in recent years. Psychiatrists, psychologists and social workers, as well as self-help tapes are now using the results of this research. All of these are using the findings of this research to successfully help patients establish realistic goals and belief systems.

Verbal affirmations are quick, beneficial, and efficient. They play a key role in helping you re-program your mind. Written affirmations are more effective than verbal ones. Writing down what you want to accomplish is the best way to reach your brain's subconscious realm. Any time is good to do affirmations, but many researchers conclude that the best time is about 30 minutes prior to falling asleep.

> Personal attitudes are a controllable part of our philosophies. They determine our outlook toward life and how we believe the world looks at us.
>
> Through our attitudes we shape the quality of our lives. Cause and effect relationships in our lives also mirror our attitudes. Simply speaking, we get back what we put out. Our environments are reflections of ourselves.
>
> A positive attitude produces great results. A poor attitude produces nothing except, perhaps, thoughts of inadequacy and self-doubt.

It's a good idea to keep a ledger to log your affirmations. The best way to do this is to divide your log into three sections. First, set personal goals. Second, each night write down the steps you have made to accomplish each goal. Third, log the affirmations reflecting accomplishment of an individual goal. Stating an affirmation while visualizing it is probably the best way to create an accurate personal goal or objective.

The right attitudes cause us to be responsible and expectant. We expect our actions to produce pleasant experiences. Our attitudes cause us to receive what we expect. Attitudes reflect our "inner person". Success in diving, or in business, is simply a reflection of our attitudes. Luck happens when preparedness meets opportunity. A positive attitude causes good luck. A person with a winning attitude expects and achieves success. Winning attitudes don't just happen. We create them through practice. Remind yourself daily to continue to develop and sustain a good, positive attitude.

As our attitudes develop, we begin to learn more about ourselves. We become honest with ourselves and, more importantly, we begin to believe in ourselves. As this belief strengthens, it is easy to exhibit self-discipline. Thus, as our attitudes develop, our ability to know ourselves becomes a natural outcropping, and the ability to be true to ourselves becomes a reflex. A winning attitude helps us deal favorably with stress. Most importantly, it helps us conquer the impossible!

A winning attitude causes life's energy to flow positively. As divers, we can accomplish more. As individuals, we become happier and more content. Five statements summed up by Earl Nightingale, the renowned motivator, best explains the role of attitude:

> 1 - "It is our attitude at the beginning of a difficult task that will bring about its successful outcome."
>
> 2 - "Our attitudes toward others determine their attitudes towards us. Our success depends largely on how we relate to others."
>
> 3 - "We must think, act, talk and conduct ourselves in all affairs as if we were the person we wish to become. We must keep a mental image of that person in front of us throughout the day."
>
> 4 - "Note, the more successful a person, the better the attitude, and that attitude is not the result of success rather success is the result of attitude
>
> 5 - "Recognition and self esteem represent the major need of our lives. To provide this, develop a habit of making all thoughts constructive and positive. Do not waste time discussing negative values."

"When it comes down to it, all life is just a matter of thoughts and beliefs. We are simply acting out our thoughts. The mind is capable of achieving everything it can conceive and believe. Realistic beliefs originate from thought and are improved by exercise. In the process, some minor goals evolve providing a path to achievement of major goals. Overall, long term goals are ultimately accomplished."

All the world's major philosophies and doctrines share fundamental beliefs. The Christian Bible says, "Whatsoever you ask for, ask for believing and you will receive it." If you ask with disbelief or doubt, it is unlikely your prayers will be fulfilled. Confucius ironically stated, "Do not unto others what you would not want done to you."

Taoism teaches universal duality, the Ying - Yang. Over two thousand years ago, the Chinese philosopher Lao Tzu noted, "For every positive action there is a positive reaction." He also taught, "If a tree does not bend with the wind, it will break." For us, this means we need to open our minds, be receptive to new ideas, and be willing to change for the better! Thomas Ford, the inventor of the automobile, sums up the idea of "belief" most aptly,

"Believe you can. Believe you can't. Either way you are right."

We do, in fact, achieve what we believe in. This includes survival in a life threatening situation or success in any of life's ventures. Our only limit is the depth of our belief system. Our outlook is the greatest influence on that belief. If we do not believe it can be achieved, we will not achieve it unless we can change our attitude.

The material discussed in this chapter will help you develop a positive belief system. By developing positive attitudes, we can change our thought patterns. When we change our thought patterns, we change our belief systems. When we change our belief systems, we change our lives. When we believe we can, we accomplish all we set out to do. Success, survival, happiness, honesty in self and with others, self-discipline, and good relationships all depend on positive attitudes.

Another key ingredient necessary for success in technical diving, or in life in general, is goal setting. This is the process of defining an objective we desire to accomplish. Success is simply the achievement of our goals. To effectively utilize the technique of setting and realizing goals, we must follow a three step process. First, we must define exactly what we want. Second, steps must be defined to consummate the goal. Third, we must develop a belief in the attainment of the goal.

Goals are achieved one step at a time. When we accomplish one step, we move on to the next. A belief system also develops in the steps we pursue. Once the mind believes in a realistic goal, it can be fulfilled. Steps taken in orderly progression allow the mind to fully believe in success.

It's a smart idea to write down your goals. In business, it's common to set long term goals. The long-term goal is then broken down into short-term goals, usually annual goals. Accomplishing each intermediate goal brings long-term success much closer.

The same process works in diving. This is true whether your goal is to simply be a good diver or a record-setting explorer. Once written, the subconscious mind begins to program itself. The use of affirmations and the act of visualizing the goal will speed up its occurrence. Once a given goal is attained, new goals should be envisioned.

The ability to focus, a talent which is mainly developed through meditation, can be enhanced by a few simple exercises. One of the best exercises is simply observing a clock's second hand sweep and concentrating on its movement. The key to this exercise is to dismiss all other thoughts that may present themselves during the exercise. This type of control is essential when facing threatening situations. The key is learning to focus and direct the mind in a selective fashion.

Survival depends on being capable of rejecting negative thoughts. A diver who masters the ability to focus can overcome nearly all threatening situations. Under duress, negative emotions and thoughts will flow in an unconditioned mind. If these negative thoughts are allowed a mental audience, they lead to worry which amplifies stress and can lead to reactions that culminate in death.

We all must think!
We must analyze!
We must be focused!

Several years ago, I read an article in some dive publication praising some diver who died. The name of the publication or that of the diver doesn't matter. The article described how the dead diver was found, dive slate in hand. It went on to say that the diver wrote a letter in wonderfully long and articulate prose to his loved ones. A touching story was presented, one of love and concern for those dear to him. While it's admirable that this person could devote the last moments of his life to those he loved, it also brought up another thought. In his perceived moment of tragedy, it appears the diver stopped fighting. I think, perhaps, the diver died because he simply gave up instead of trying to solve his problems. In this case, I think it is quite possible that had the diver spent the time swimming and **THINKING**, he would most likely be alive today!

As I was completing this book, I came across a true story I thought you'd like to read. It gives a good example of the desire of a very disciplined individual to survive. A cave diver in his late 40's was diving in a popular North Florida site. He was in extremely good physical condition and worked out every day. On the day of the incident, he was diving with two buddies. The three divers became separated. During the ensuing events, our diver found himself separated and disoriented.

When he finally figured out where he was, 2,000 feet (610 meters) back in the cave, he only had 400 psig (27 bar) in his primaries and he was 200 feet (61 meters) away from his stage bottle. When he was 100 feet (30 meters) from his stage bottle, his air ran out. Through sheer willpower and a desire to survive, our diver swam the last 100 feet (30 meters) with only the air in his lungs.

There are two points to this story. First, by all accounts, the dive team followed all the rules. What happened to them could happen to anyone. Second, our out-of-air diver survived because he kept his head together by fighting stress and panic. He never stopped thinking! He analyzed the situation and he remained focused throughout the ordeal. And, most importantly of all, he didn't stop to write us a letter. He did not quit. He kept on kicking and kicking, and as a result, he's still alive and able to tell the story!

If all the steps and procedures referenced in this chapter are incorporated in your habits, you will achieve any goal you set providing that you develop a positive, realistic belief in these processes. Saying, "I wanna do it" does not accomplish anything. It is kind of like the Janis Joplin song, " Oh Lord, won't you buy me a Mercedes Benz." Want and belief are not the same thing.

Wanting something does not produce it. Belief accomplishes all. You must program your mind to believe. You must THINK and mentally picture the goal continuously. You must train and make whatever sacrifices are needed to realize your goals!

Survival Training

To merely say that survival training is extremely important would be an understatement. In fact, it's necessary if you want to keep on living! Survival training's benefits are summed up in the book *Safe Cave Diving*, which I, along with several contributing authors, wrote in 1973. Bob Smith, a contributing author, stated in the stress chapter,

"When faced with dying or achieving the impossible, some people choose to live."

Survival training enables divers to exemplify Bob's very apt statement. In fact, it teaches you how to focus your mind on the job of staying alive while, at the same time, making wonderful discoveries. And, importantly, it teaches you how to be physically tough and mentally disciplined through a winning attitude.

This training program addresses the risk of technical diving for both recreational and exploratory divers. We have learned it is essential to be able to make informed decisions. A problem 2,000 feet (610 meters) into an overhead environment is far more difficult to manage than a problem in open water. By reviewing the accidents in diving, it is apparent that technical diving does have risk. We must be aware of the risks and how to evaluate them.

Several years prior to his death, Sheck Exley introduced the merits of breaking down accidents into steps and analyzing the mechanisms that produced the incident. The majority of accidents are the result of divers' mistakes. In other words, your life may depend on your ability to think fast and to get it right the first time. If you're tired, or hurt, a buddy may be able to help you swim for a little while, and, if necessary, share gas; however, you're the only one that can really control your breathing rate. And, when your "you know what" is in a sling, ultimately only you can save it!

To react favorably in the face of a physical threat, your mind must be preconditioned to as many uncomfortable yet life-dependent variables as possible. A good example would be your ability to survive in the event of a real gas-sharing emergency. In a real emergency, your buddy is going to be more than an arm's length away. Your buddy is probably swimming and not looking directly at you.

In your mind, visualize this scenario: You're 60 feet (18 meters) down. Everything beyond your beam of light is pitch black. What's worse, you're just a "mere" 1,000 feet (305 meters) from the upline. You've had a total gas supply failure. Perhaps your regulator has broken. Picture yourself not panicking. All you have to do is just swim nonchalantly over to your buddy and tap on their shoulder to get their attention. They signal, "What's wrong?" You casually indicate, "I'm out of air. Notice how blue my face is?" They acknowledge that you've looked better. You go on to inquire ever so meekly, "Would you please let me share your air?" They say, "Sure. No problem!"

Gas sharing rarely goes as smoothly as the above scenario. In fact, gas sharing requires precision teamwork to work smoothly. All team members involved must know their roles and be able to execute them without making mistakes. Not only is the life of the out-of-air diver at stake, but probably those of the team members as well. After all, it's their air that's being shared.

The best way to insure that buddy breathing never becomes a nightmare is through the regular practice of out-of-air drills that simulate the stress of a "real" situation. Prior to implementing gas sharing and breath holding survival skills, begin by swimming a set distance underwater without breathing. If this is hard, remind yourself of the importance of being able to cope with the feeling of needing to breathe.

Keep in mind that in a real situation, your buddy will be swimming. You will have to get their attention and/or overtake them in order to find an air source. In these drills, the actual breath holding duration rarely exceeds 35 to 45 seconds. There is no real danger of blackout and no true physiological demand for air. There is a psychological scream as the mind and body exceed the time at which it is conditioned to breathe. This skill is paramount for divers who may be exposed to real out-of-air situations. It is not, and is not approached as, a fitness test or "toughness skill".

The gas sharing exercise involves swimming without air 60 to 75 feet (18 to 23 meters) to a buddy, gaining their attention and initiating gas sharing. Both divers will then remain at rest for at least three breaths to allow the out-of-air diver to regain respiratory control. Both divers then perform a timed swim. The timed swim is not for speed. The divers must maintain a normal swim pace. If the divers swim too fast, additional stress is developed and gas consumption is increased. This, of course, may inhibit them from making it to the surface. On the other hand, if the pace is too slow, they may not have enough gas to reach the surface. The key is that the timed swim be based on a normal swim pace.

Now, let's analyze why this skill helps divers develop survival instincts. If faced with a "real" out of air situation, the subconscious mind "knows" it can deal with it. The mind has been preconditioned to handle the emergency. It means that the diver knows how it feels to need and really want air without being forced to "turn blue". It means being disciplined and in control when faced with adverse conditions.

Additional training skills include the performance of other life support and equipment familiarity skills. A few essentials include: gas shutdowns, use of safety lines, lost diver procedures, and navigating a line in blacked out conditions (simulated by closing the eyes). Training and certification, if done properly, prepare divers for the stress that coincides with in-water emergencies.

The Importance of Fitness

The ideal technical diver is a finely tuned individual, both mentally and physically. Good physical fitness allows the diver to handle his equipment without staggering under its weight. It permits him/her to swim long distances without tiring. Even the diver who uses a DPV must be physically fit. Indeed, this diver is at special risk if unfit should the DPV malfunction during the course of a dive.

Out-of-shape divers are prone to cramps, unable to control respiration, and incapable of providing physical assistance in an emergency. Their work and resting RMV is dramatically different. Fit divers tend to develop coordination as part of their training. This enables them to become more skillful diving technicians. Mental fitness is a must for maintaining self-discipline. Much of the training in a technical program is aimed at developing mental control.

Patti getting in a CV workout.
Photo: Tom Mount

It is appropriate to say that physically unfit divers should avoid technical diving. The non-thinking diver is not qualified for technical diving. Serious deficiencies in either mental or physical fitness place a diver at much greater risk in the diving environment.

A diver needs to be physically fit to prevent injury. Cardiovascular fitness provides the stamina to be comfortable while swimming extended distances in SCUBA gear. It has been documented that unfit divers may retain up to 50% more CO_2 than physically fit divers. This is important. CO_2 is additive to early fatigue, decompression illness, inert gas narcosis and oxygen toxicity. In other words, excess CO_2 may hurt you. Increased CO_2 may also lead to uncontrolled respiration. It is a major factor in loss of consciousness with resultant drowning.

The first step on the road to survival training involves getting a complete physical at your doctor's office. The second step is to begin a physical conditioning program. The initial training should incorporate some exercises for muscular toning and a graduated level of cardiovascular conditioning. In selecting the muscular toning exercises, resistance with weights or machinery is effective. This part of the regime should simulate actions using muscles that you will need for your style of diving. (For example, high pull-ups will simulate the act of lifting tanks.)

Resistance training needs to be balanced. Extending and contracting muscles prevents an imbalance by working both groups of muscles. Unbalanced musculature may lead to injury when an overdeveloped area creates excess tension on its opposing muscle. Special attention should be placed on stomach and lower back muscles. These muscle groupings are subjected to strain in technical diving environments. This is especially true when managing equipment in and out of the water.

Believe it or not, this two-step approach to fitness is also the first level of survival training. The survival benefit is developing the discipline to enter and maintain a fitness program. Even the most devout athletes require discipline.

There are days when excuses abound to avoid a training session. There will be days when you literally drag yourself into a workout. Getting the job done means you are developing a good survival instinct. It is on these days you are going beyond your comfort zone. The days you give in and do not workout can be viewed as diminished survival days.

Points to remember for safe diving...

"Only YOU can think for you.
Only YOU can swim for you.
Only YOU can breathe for you."
In short, no one but YOU can guarantee your survival.
YOU must be a responsible diver.

Once the first two basic steps have been initiated and a reasonable degree of fitness has evolved, it's time to begin the third step. Hard-core survival training takes all you can muster mentally and physically. This is an ongoing, increasingly tough and demanding pace. The benefits will greatly enhance your ability to overcome adversity and to survive. In this training, we select a given exercise and assign three goals. The first goal is a time factor. The second is a distance or performance measurement. The third separates us from the pack. We will accomplish these goals at all cost! Keep in mind, this is a gradual process. Training becomes addictive once current goals become less challenging. Mentally these must be viewed as life or death achievements.

Survival abilities can be developed, enhanced and maintained on land even more conveniently and effectively than underwater. The programs to develop survival conditioning, however, go beyond the level of cardiovascular training. Many physical trainers and physiologists define cardiovascular-level training as the point where an elevated pulse is maintained for at least 20 minutes. During this period, the individual should be able to carry on a conversation without interrupting the exercise pace.

However, when performing survival training, exercises should be well beyond the "conversation level". When you've reached this plateau, the only voice you'll be able to muster is the one in your mind that says, "Don't quit. Keep on going!" This is unquestionably a maximum level performance. The entire program is aimed at functioning beyond your comfort level and maintaining that level. The parameters involve maintaining maximum, sustained effort while maintaining a constant respiratory rate. To function in this manner requires discipline to allow increased volume without a corresponding increase in respiratory rate. Obviously, it takes more than a few training sessions to master.

Controlling the respiratory rate under stress means overcoming interfering messages generated by the autonomic nervous system (ANS). Efficient respiration is vital for developing good discipline when using SCUBA gear. As divers, we deal with an assortment of variables requiring us to maintain a slow inhalation and exhalation rate. A few of these variables include a regulator's breathing resistance, drag while swimming, and the density produced by the depth and/or gas mixture. By controlling our respiratory rates, we have taken the first step in mental control. In this instance, limited control of the ANS has been gained.

A stair climber, or step machine, is an excellent tool for survival training. This is an exercise I personally use and recommend. I begin by establishing the maximum comfortable level I can maintain. Next, I gradually boost the level exercising a minimum of 40 minutes.

As your fitness improves, you can incorporate interval training. After the first 2 minutes on the climber, boost the level by one. Remain at this level for 2 minutes. Then, resume the previous level and repeat every 2 minutes. Throughout the exercise, maintain a constant slow respiratory rate. A good initial respiratory rate is achieved by inhaling approximately 6 seconds. Pause no more than 3 seconds. Finally, exhale 6 seconds with an exhalation pause of 3 seconds or less.

Once you've mastered the initial step in interval training, increase your work level to the absolute maximum that can be maintained for 20 minutes. Next, reduce the level by one and complete 5 additional minutes at this level. Start increasing the intensity of interval training. After 3 minutes, boost the level one step and maintain it for 3 more minutes. Drop to the previous level and remain there for 3 minutes. Return to the next higher level for 3 minutes. Finally, repeat this procedure for 30 minutes and set the "bump up" intervals to 5 minutes in length.

This concept of maximum exercise should be maintained throughout the entire exercise session. Gradually increase the total time from 20 minutes to 40 minutes. When you've reached the upper level and can maintain it, it's time to begin survival training.

Survival training exceeds the limits of normal interval training. It means your workout session is a maximum effort from beginning to end. I do the following. On my stair climber I set the upper level at 12. This translates to 20.3 flights of stairs-per-minute. I do the entire 40 minutes at this level. My performance goal is 40 minutes and 820 floors, or an average of 20.5 floors-per-minute. The acceptable range is from 770 floors to 820 floors.

On those days when I maintain this level, my survival ability is rated as certain. On days when I climb less than 770 floors, I score myself as having reduced survival abilities. In my scoring system, as long as I complete the time and remain between 725 and 750 floors, a good survival probability exists. If less than 725, but more than 675 floors are completed, the survival probability is average. When the total floors climbed is between 650 and 675, the probability of survivability is low. With less than 650 floors, the rating is poor. When I'm unable to complete the exercises, I rate my odds for survival at zero. In my training philosophy, I "die" on those days.

In diving, quitting is the unforgivable sin!
Quitting in a life threatening circumstance leaves one alternative - death!
Continuing, regardless of the odds, provides the option of survival!

When accomplishing these drills, attempt to complete all goals. Even on those days when you cannot maintain the accelerated rates, at least complete the time objective. Occasionally, it will be necessary for you to actually stop (just as in a stressful diving situation), regain respiratory and/or mental control, then resume exercising. Going the full time limit is paramount. The survival probability is lower when only two or more objectives are completed. However, going the distance greatly increases discipline and improves your possibility of survival. Quitting too soon means you probably won't survive. Everyone of us has read about divers who quit trying. When they quit trying, they died!

The level of intensity in survival training varies from person to person. Everyone should be able to discover a personal system and rating code. The tougher the training, the greater the survivability factor. Jim Lockwood, for example, has survived near impossible situations. His workouts on the stair climber last over 1½ hours. He goes "flat out". He also finds time for a 70 to 100 mile (112 to 161 kilometer) bicycle ride 2 - 3 times a week. In season, he combines swimming and kayaking with the same intensity of training.

Experiment with a level of exercise that will force you to become more mentally and physically disciplined. This combination of mental and physical self-control is paramount to your survival. While training, your body and mind will often cry out for relief. When this happens, visualize yourself in a critical situation. Your only hope of survival is to keep going. When you want to stop and rest, dig deep within yourself and produce that extra burst of mental power to drive your physical body to success. On those really tough days, give yourself a reward for completing a survival session. Getting the job done when it's the hardest improves your survivability factor. On the easy days, and they are few, you simply maintain and reconfirm your abilities.

Cross training is an excellent tool to help you increase fitness and prevent boredom. Swimming, especially with fins, is an excellent way to improve stamina and endurance. When cross training, set up your program for maximum effort. This may sound extreme. It is. However, it also conditions both your body and mind for a better survival level. I know this to be true from dozens of personal experiences, including a plane crash.

Both Patti Mount and I survived a plane crash with multiple injuries. We were in the water fighting for our lives for over 3½ hours. Patti was semi-conscious and unconsciousness for much of this time. The entire 3½ hours was spent swimming, as our raft sank faster than our plane. The only flotation device I could think of involved using my blue jeans, which I made into a float for Patti. Thanks to our survival training, we are both alive today.

The importance of physical fitness should be evident by this time, but as it relates to both mental and physical discipline, we will take a more in-depth look at the benefits of fitness for technical divers.

By incorporating the survival training I have described, a positive belief system evolves. Inner awareness is created. We become in tune with our "intuitive selves" as well as with our physical and mental abilities. We accomplish what our belief system dictates. People achieve their beliefs, not undirected daydreams. However, through some of the above practices, it is possible to turn daydreams into belief systems.

If we truly believe, we do accomplish the inconceivable, and we survive the impossible. ***Think! Meditate and Visualize!***

Focus! Affirm! Train! Accomplish all things! Beginning this moment, experience a magnificent rebirth in philosophy. "Think about it, act on it and enjoy safer diving."

CHAPTER 14

Operational Safety

Kevin Gurr

Safety, while it should be of primary concern to all divers, becomes increasingly important as one ventures into technical or extended range diving. In these more advanced forms of diving, the increased duration and scope of the dive plan will cause a corresponding increase in risk exposure. A simple analogy might be; "If I stand in the street long enough I am more likely to get run over."

The longer a diver remains underwater the more the effects of equipment reliability, diver error and environmental changes become an issue. Complex dives often involve extended decompressions, depth outside of the accepted sport limits, large amounts of gas and support equipment as well as sophisticated dive platforms such as boats and underwater habitats. The following is offered as a general guide of questions to be addressed when planning such dives.

To define a safe operating procedure we must first look at several specific issues:

- The type of dive and it's associated hazards
- Risk
- Safety planning
- Dive platforms
- Standby divers
- Rescue management and equipment.

Types of Dive

The range of dives available to recreational divers is almost limitless. In recent years, the concept and scope of recreational diving has expanded into the realm known as Technical Diving. Now, there is Recreational diving and there is Technical diving, but what is the difference? Divers are often diving for fun past the recreational norms of 130 fsw (40 msw) or 165 fsw (50 msw), so depth is not necessarily the issue. It is now fairly common in certain parts of the globe to see divers hiring boats to take them out into 240 fsw (70 msw) of water and do a "recreational" Trimix dive. So where does recreational diving really stop? Should the analogy be that as long as the diver is doing it for fun it is still recreational diving irrespective of depth and time submerged? What makes diving "technical"?

Perhaps the difference is based on the functions of time and exploration. Exploration is going somewhere no one else has been before, which generates its own risks. Likewise, extending bottom times past the accepted recreational norms - at any depth - exposes us to increased risk. For example, we might consider an open water dive to fall outside the realm of recreational diving if the divers went to depths beyond the sport diving limits - 130 fsw (40 msw) - and/or spent sufficient time at any depth to generate a decompression obligation.

For our purposes, a description of technical diving might be:

"Technical diving involves a range of knowledge, skills and suitable equipment which, when combined correctly, allow the recreational diver to increase their safety while underwater. This information may be employed in either shallow or deep water, is often used to safely extend the divers submerged duration well into the realms of extended decompressions," and may be used as a tool for exploration. The types of diving discussed in this section can be broken down into three general categories. They are:

1. Shore Diving
2. Boat Diving
3. Cave Diving

Diving Hazards

Items 1 and 2 can be subdivided into reef or wreck. All dives can obviously be fresh or salt water and may be at altitude or at night. There are a variety of different cave dives. Looking at each one in turn (and in order to identify the risk involved) let's list some of the hazards.

Type of Dive	Scenario	Hazard
Shore - Reef	Entry / exit point	Physical injury
	Current	Swept away from safe egress
	Marine life	Physical injury
	Boat traffic	Physical injury
	Sea state	Physical injury, inability to safely egress
	Weather	Changing sea state, reduced surface visibility
	Gas failure	Drowning
	Underwater visibility	Loss of dive partner
Shore - Wreck	All of the above	
	Entrapment	Drowning or other physical injury
Boat - Reef	All of the above	
	Underwater visibility	Loss of line to surface
Cave	Line loss	Inability to find exit
	Silt out	Inability to find line or partner

The above is a table of some but not all of the general hazards (both physical and environmental) which might occur. This should be completed for the specific dive being planned and where necessary, corrective actions defined for any high risk scenarios.

Risk

Looking at all of the above the overall risk for each item can be defined as a combination of the probability of any event occurring and how life threatening it is. As all dives involve risk, all dives should have varying levels of safety planning. In some cases such as gas supply failure where the probability of failure is potentially low (due to reliable regulators) but the life threatening potential is extreme; the combined risk is high and hence detailed safety plans should be made. In another case the probability of losing a safe egress from a shore dive in bad weather is fairly high but the potential for rescue and hence the life-threatening factor might be low, making the overall risk minimal.

In general low risk dives normally have their safety requirements covered by standard diving equipment and practices such as those often employed on a normal recreational dive, where as high risk dives need specific emergency plans for any of the highlighted hazards. So how do we assess risk and define which scenarios need more planning than others?

Life threatening factor should be graded as:

0. No risk
1. Low
2. Medium
3. High

Probability of a hazard occurring should be graded as:

1. Not likely
2. Possible
3. Probable

Generate a table to assess risk.

For example, look at the table below under hazard 1. A diver uses a single high quality regulator that has a low failure probability of 1. However if it does fail, as there is only one, the potential for loss of life is high due to drowning, etc. Hence the overall risk is high. In this instance the most practical safety plan for this scenario would be to carry a backup or redundant regulator (see chapter on equipment configurations). The same type of assessment can be made for the other examples and a safety plan generated.

Scenario / Hazard	Probability	Life Threatening Factor	Overall Risk
Loss of gas	1	3	4
Loss of boat	1	1	2
Loss of partner	1	0	1

As all dives do involve risk the need to execute them must be balanced against that risk and the potential reward (see chapter on psychological aspects). In some cases the reward is worth the ultimate risk. The point of this chapter is to make you think about the hazards and define which require detailed safety planning to reduce the overall risk.

Safety Planning

Having defined the hazards which require detailed safety planning (scoring 3+), it is important to review the environments effect on those hazards after which a safety plan may be generated. The worlds diving environments are not only varied across the globe, but may vary from day to day and even hour to hour at any one site.

Each type of dive has it's own specific environment due to it's location. Especially in open water; dives that require extended decompressions or long submerged durations may be affected by a range of changing environments. It is important to plan for these changes and include them as part of our risk assessment. As both the dive environment and any physical hazards affect our overall safety, let's now include both of these in our safety plan (for those that score a 3+ on the risk scale) and define possible corrective action in the event of them occurring to reduce any risk. This will be done for a range of dives.

Proper planning, training and equipment reduce risk.

Shore Diving

Scenario / Hazard	Risk Score	Safety Procedure
Difficult access / egress to site	3	Carry kit in stages / employ "Sherpas" Use ropes and slings.
Ocean swells	3	Submerge ASAP to identify underwater hazards. Deploy exit line and floats. Use shore cover personnel.
Ice	6	Always use line to surface and shore personnel. With thick ice, ensure surface cover has safety cutting equipment.
Bad surface visibility	3	Carry surface signaling equipment. Sonic alerts or EPIRB'S work in most instances.
Bad underwater visibility	3	Use buddy lines and compasses.
Boat traffic	4	Use surface marker buoy.
Nets and lines	5	Carry cutting equipment.
Current	4	When planning long dives in a tidal area, planning to predict an egress point is vital. At a minimum, shore and probably boat cover are needed. Drifting divers should always use a surface marker.

Shore diving generally requires that a diver has good navigational skills especially when ocean diving along cliffs, where specific access / egress points are limited. Where drift dives are to be performed with an extensive floating decompression ensure boat cover is adequately equipped. For specifics on safety equipment to be carried by the diver see equipment configuration chapter and the IANTD equipment configuration video. With all diving, but especially where land is to be crossed, remember: Always respect the environment and landowners wishes.

Boat Diving

Scenario / Hazard	Risk Score	Safety Procedure
Rough seas	3	Deploy diver pick-up and kit. Drop lines with buoys tethered to the boat. Do not attempt to egress in full kit.
Current	3	In the event of being swept away carry signaling equipment, flares, EPIRB'S, sonic alerts, etc. Plan for a lost diver drill and search pattern at a predetermined time point after the divers should have
Other boats	4	Never surface without a marker or being on your boats shot line.
Entrapment	4	Avoid penetration. Check structures for safety before entering. Dive with a partner who may be able to assist.
Nets and lines	3	Carry cutting equipment.
Poor underwater visibility	5	Use strobes or reels on the down line to ensure a safe return.

Cave Diving

Scenario / Hazard	Risk Score	Safety Procedure
Current	4	In extreme cases work against the flow going in. Test for changes in current and tidal affects before entering. Lay strong lines.
Low in water visibility	3	Always use continuous exit lines. Remain in-touch-contact where possible in emergencies.
Collapse / Entrapment	3	Dive as part of a team. Do not enter unsafe structures.
Line loss	4	Conduct established / practiced search patterns.

Summary

So now we have looked at a range of dives and their possible hazards, we have defined the probability of that hazard occurring and the life threatening potential if it does. This gives us our overall risk. For those hazards that produce a score of 3 or more we have then formulated detailed safety plans.

Dive Support Platforms

Dive platforms can be subdivided into those that remain on the surface and those that stay submerged during the dive. In the simplest form these range from the shore safety personnel to the boat through to decompression stations and habitats. Shore personnel have been basically discussed, suffice to say they must be aware of the team plan, carry safety equipment such as oxygen and ropes and slings and have good communications (phone/radio).

Boats

Let us first define the functions of a boat in a Technical diving operation. Put briefly these can be listed as follows:

- Safe transport to and from the dive site
- Protection from the elements
- Accommodation
- A dive support platform
- A rescue platform

Taking each in turn. The first three categories of the above list are almost always defined by the physical size of the boat. Boats as operational platforms tend to fall in four size-related categories. These categories will also define the range of the vessel and possibly it's suitability to a specific operation.

Type	Construction	Size	Suitability
Dory/dingy	GRP or aluminum	Up to 10 ft (3 m)	In-shore open boat work. Can be used for small team technical operations
Inflatable	Rigid or soft hull inflatable	Up to 30 ft (9 m) as a sport boat	In shore and off shore work. All levels of technical operation.
Day boat	GRP, wood or steel	Up to 50 ft (15 m) approximately	As above
Liveaboard	As above	Generally over 50 ft (15 m)	As above plus expeditions

While each of the above may be suitable for technical operations, each has it's own problems. While weather will often decide the range and type of diving undertaken on the smaller vessels, larger boats also generate problems in strong weather particularly with diver egress. Even though larger vessels may get divers more comfortably to the dive site in strong weather, diver safety may still be compromised during the entry and exit phase. In short, anything much above a force 5 on the Beaufort scale will preclude safe diving. Extended decompressions in strong seas also become uncomfortable unless precautions are taken (see section on Decompression Stations and Habitats).

Accommodation will only normally be found on the larger live on board/expedition sized vessels. Suffice it to say, find out as much about the boat as possible prior to chartering. Three things that can make a trip miserable above all others are poor or inadequate food, inability to rest comfortably and poor sanitation. All of these also affect team safety.

Boats as Dive Support Platforms

As defined in all diving the boat is used to deliver the divers to and retrieve them from the water, allow an area for suiting up and suiting down, provide protection while they are submerged and transport equipment specific to the operation. The following is a list of practical suggestions to overcome some of the associated problems.

Entry and Exit

Smaller vessels basically allow the diver to roll backwards to enter the water and once in, clip on additional equipment and cylinders (if boat space is limited). Exit, at worst, will involve removing the equipment prior to returning into the boat. This is especially true of the inherently stable inflatable technology. Larger vessels may have a similar entry method although stern entry doors are becoming more popular and do provide more safety and less potential for physical injury with multiple cylinder set-ups. With larger vessels re-entry to the boat will often be via some form of ladder. While side ladders are extensively used in some countries, on non-cathedral hull boats (where the pitching of the vessel can be extreme), this type of entry can be hazardous. In general, stern platforms provide for a much more stable base for entering the boat. In any event one of the safest ways to re-enter any vessel is to remove excess equipment prior to doing so. Two proposed methods for achieving this are:

Method 1: Use a small support boat (inflatable) to retrieve heavy equipment (side mounts, etc.).

Method 2: Deploy a kit retrieval line. This is basically a long line [16.4-32.7 ft (5-10 m)] with loops positioned along it and a large float at one end. The other end is tied to the stern of the boat, preferably at a high point away from the propeller. If surface conditions are slight, simply return to the line and, remove one side mount clip at a time and clip it to the line (this stops accidental dropping and loss of the cylinder).

If conditions are severe, undo the rear side mount clip while still submerged (at the last stop), rather than in the surface swell. Again attaching one clip at a time to the line to prevent loss. Then pull yourself back to the boat using the line allowing the skipper/support crew to retrieve the cylinders. If twin sets are to be removed, provide a firm anchor point on the set by which it can be lifted (not the manifold).

Kiting and De-kiting

While kiting areas on smaller boats may be limited, on larger vessels there can often be too much space leading to a confusion on the boat. Boat loading plays a crucial role especially should an emergency occur.

In summary:

- Ensure personnel team equipment is accessible in the order in which it is to be used. In other words the first pair in should have their kit nearest the kiting area or exit point.
- Ensure that all safety equipment is easily accessible and space can be made to treat a casualty
- Where possible make a separate kiting up to travel area for the equipment. In rough seas equipment tends to move around and should be firmly locked in a stowage area to prevent equipment damage. It is often far safer to fully rig equipment on land prior to loading and then firmly secure it in the boat rather than trying to assemble and test it in a pitching sea. This also reduces the number of kit bags required (hence space needed). Simple benches or a central table make good kiting areas once on site, empty bags being stowed underneath.
- Where support divers can be used (see section on Standby Divers), employ them to kit team members. If these are not available, educate your boat skipper!
- Upon re-entry to the boat, de-kit as quickly as possible and stow equipment (see section on rescue procedures and equipment).

Protection while Submerged

While the dive is being conducted, it is the boats function to protect the dive team. The vessel itself can offer physical protection from other sea users by employing such things as radar and communications equipment. It's ability to do this for the whole team relies on the divers acting as a unit. In tidal areas it is just not acceptable that extended decompressions be carried out on an individual basis where there is a possibility that the group will become fragmented.

Separation of the team is hazardous for the following reasons:

- The boat cannot offer protection from other vessels for all team members.
- As weather and sea states change divers may become lost.
- If a pair or individual has a problem (see section on Decompression stations and habitats system 2), the boat may not be in the right place at the right time.
- If separated pairs or individuals have problems, the boat cannot be in two places at once.

The only real answer to this problem is the use of decompression stations or habitats (see below).

Whichever boat platform is used there are several golden rules which should not be broken:

- Never leave the boat unattended.
- Carry a 100% oxygen supply system (see section on Oxygen Delivery Equipment).
- Carry a medical kit (see section on Minimal First Aid Equipment).
- Carry communications equipment (radio, phone, flares, etc.).
- As a minimum carry a compass and/or other suitable electronic navigational aids.

Decompression Stations and Habitats

The function of a decompression station or habitat is to provide a stable platform on or within which the team can complete the decompression phase. Advantages and disadvantages of such systems can be listed as:

Advantages:

- A place to stage emergency equipment.
- Allows the team to stay together in a tidal environment.
- Provides a visual reference to assist with buoyancy control (stations).
- Allows the team to exit the water (habitats).
- Provides extra safety in the event of an oxygen incident. Employ Habitats when the casualty is dry. Employ Stations when the other divers can assist casualties or are recovered by the Standby divers.

Differing environmental conditions require different adaptations to the decompression station concept. Four basic layouts of decompression stations will be discussed as well as simple and complex habitats although there are others.

Decompression Station Layout
System 1

Use Area:

Low tidal flow, good in water conditions and generally good surface visibility. Small or large dive teams. Possibly heavy shipping traffic.

Method:

This system normally involves the support boat being tethered into the wreck/reef on a fixed single point bow mooring. The boat then deploys a line under the stern of the boat that joins a horizontal line or bar at 20 ft (6 m) connected to the main mooring line. In good visibility, where a return to the up-line is simple, decompression cylinders may be staged on this 20 ft (6 m) line or at a point on the mooring line where they will be first needed. The boat may also provide surface supplied oxygen or indeed any decompression gas. In light current divers may use Jon Lines to clip off to the main line.

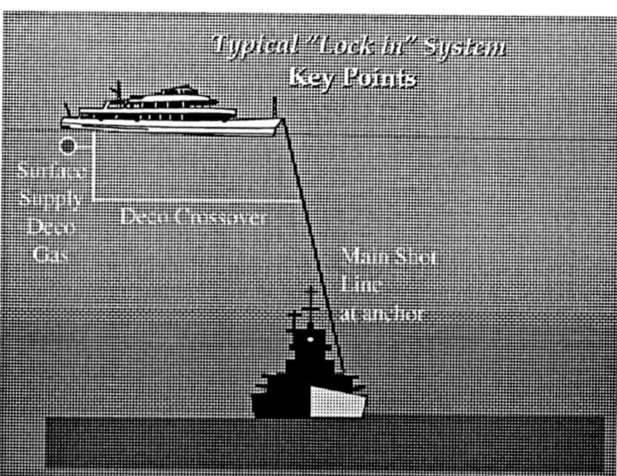

Safety Systems:

Each diver carries an inflatable surface marker should they lose any of the lines. Unless a return to the mooring line is guaranteed, divers will always carry all their own gases. Divers should carry some form of surface signaling device (flares/EPIRB).

Decompression Station Layout
System 2

Use Area:

High tidal flow. Low in-water visibility. Possibility of poor surface conditions. Small or large dive teams. Possibly heavy shipping traffic.

Method:

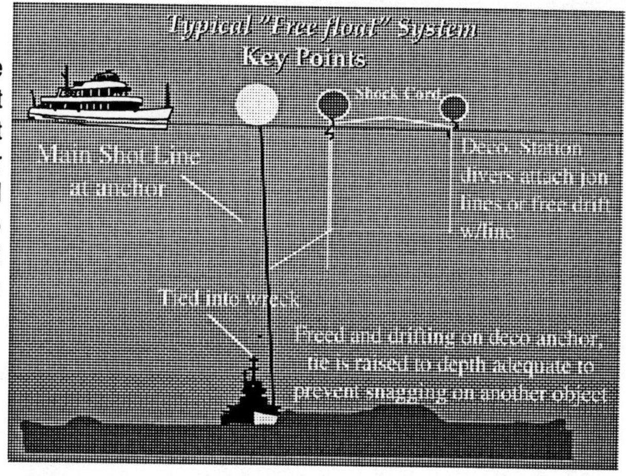

Main buoy line sunk (shot or grapnel) to the site with a large surface buoy. The boat is not fixed to this line and works as a safety boat at all times. At the end of the dive the anchor or shot is retrieved and tied up the line several meters and hooked in place allowing the line to free float with all divers using it as a visual reference. Trimix diving safety decompression gas may be staged at the first gas switch point.

Safety Systems:

Divers will always carry all their own gases.
Boat must be equipped with radar and radios.
Divers carry some form of surface signaling device (flares/EPIRB).
Each diver carries an inflatable surface marker should they lose any of the lines.
The surface vessel will carry emergency gas to be deployed on measured and buoyed depth lines, (dependant on the dive plan) in the event of a yellow emergency buoy being deployed. An orange buoy indicates "diver solo but all is well" whereas a yellow buoy signals an emergency. Slates with pencils affixed can be attached to buoys for additional information.

Decompression Station Layout
System 3

Use Area:

High tidal flow. Low in-water visibility. Possibility of poor surface conditions. Small or large dive teams. Possibly heavy shipping traffic.

Method:

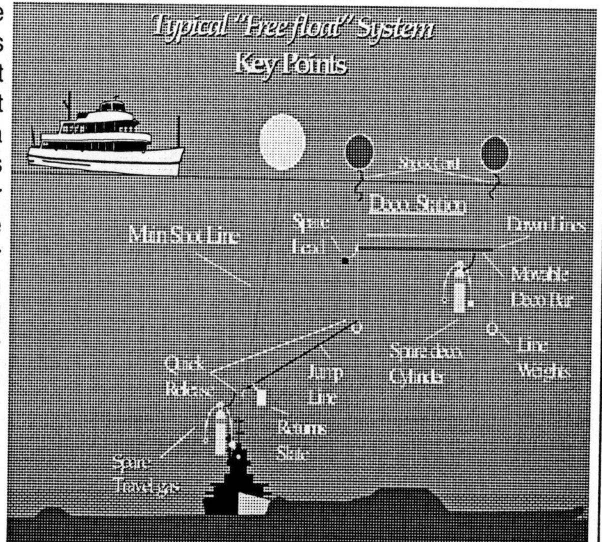

Main buoy line sunk (shot or grapnel) to the site with large surface buoy. Two 30 ft (9 m) lines with a buoy at the top and a weight (2-4 kg) at each base. Each line will have loops every 10 ft (3 m). The lines are joined as in a trapeze with a movable bar 6 - 10 ft (2 - 3m) long. This station is attached to the main buoy line by a jump or travel line. Dependant on the amount of tide expected this line will be 20 ft (6 m) or longer than the point to the deepest decompression stop, allowing for the angle on the line the tidal affect will have. With Trimix diving safety decompression gas will be staged at this first gas switch point. Adaptations to this system for larger groups may include several down lines and a triangular bar system.

Safety Systems:

Divers will always carry all their own gases.
Boat must be equipped with radar and radios.
Divers will carry some form of surface signaling device (flares/EPIRB).
Each diver carries an inflatable surface marker should they loose any of the lines.
The surface vessel will carry emergency gas to be deployed on measured and buoyed depth lines, dependant on the dive plan, in the event of a yellow emergency buoy being deployed An orange buoy indicates "diver solo but all is well" whereas a yellow buoy signals an emergency" (as above).

Decompression Station Layout
System 3

Use Area:

Good underwater and surface visibility. Low surface traffic. Small teams.

Method:

Each diver or pair is allowed to deploy their own surface marker as the decompression starts.

Safety Systems:

Each diver carries at least one inflatable surface marker should they lose any of the lines.
The surface vessel will carry emergency gas to be deployed on measured and buoyed depth lines, dependant on the dive plan, in the event of a yellow emergency buoy being deployed. An orange buoy indicates "diver solo but all is well" whereas a yellow buoy signals an emergency" (as above).
Divers will normally carry some form of surface signaling device (flares/EPIRB).

Team Management

With System 2 above and in extreme tidal areas, team management is vital. If team members are late arriving back at the station the current may be so strong as to drag down the surface buoys and hence sink the station. Should this situation occur the only option is to deploy the individual surface markers (orange) and start solo decompressions. To ensure team members return to the station within a safe tidal window it is vital that tidal conditions are assessed and a team plan devised. The key point being to define what is often known as a "cut-off time" or the time point in a runtime schedule when the jump line will be disconnected from the main line, thus allowing the station to free float. This can either be a fixed time of day in the team plan or a time point in the runtime schedule of the last pair to enter the water (i.e. entry plus 30 minutes). Each team member signs in on a slate positioned where the jump line joins the main line. Should the majority of divers return within the time and other team members not yet be back, the "on station" team has the option to disconnect the jump line at the station end (rather than descending again).

Divers on the decompression stage system used at Bikini Atoll.

Photo: Kevin Denlay

Members not managing to return by the cut off time will realize this and simply deploy their markers and not waste energy or gas trying to return to the station. There may be several adaptations to this system. Which ever is employed, teams are advised to practice all eventualities before fixing on a system. The above systems are primarily focused on open water use. Cave or quarry dives have their own specific problems but generally involve the staging of gases and emergency equipment at fixed points. The use of any system that requires a return to a fixed point should employ visual markers such as strobes, reels or lights to ensure a safe return.

Habitats

Dependant on the climatic conditions, extended decompressions where there is either a cold environment or a risk of oxygen toxicity should involve decompression habitats where the divers may exit the water to complete the decompression phase. Habitats can be simple affairs that allow a portion of the diver to exit the water (almost like an up-turned bucket) or more complex arrangements that allow a complete team of divers to totally exit the water. Habitats both reduce the possibility of hypothermia as well as help control the risk of drowning should an oxygen convulsion occur.

Habitat construction can be a detailed science especially when one is designed for open water use. If a unit is to be constructed that is capable of allowing a team of divers to fully exit the water this will take considerable engineering skill and resources. A list of problems that face the would be habitat designer might encompass:

- **Total internal space required.** This defines the buoyancy the construction will experience (Archimedes principle). This may vary from a few kilos of uplift to several tons. To give the reader some idea, a habitat capable of taking 6 people may experience an upthrust of some six tons and hence (ignoring construction and personnel weight) need six tons to hold it down. If it cannot be tethered then suitable ballast will need to be sunk.
- **Ruggedness and strength of construction.** The materials used must be suitable for the force exerted per square meter when the construction is filled with air. Also if the habitat is to be deployed for a period of time it must stand up to the rigors of the environment.
- **Deployment.** The larger and more complex the arrangement the greater the risk of damage or even loss during deployment and retrieval.
- **Equipment staging and gas supply.** The system may need detailed mounting systems to handle primary and emergency gas supplies as well as other equipment.
- **Venting.** To reduce the risk of fire and other gas related problems, the habitat needs to be continually flushed with fresh air. Positioning and running of compressors capable of this may prove difficult especially in the open ocean.

Standby Divers

In any technical operation the welfare of the dive team is of prime importance. This welfare must begin prior to the dive taking place and end after all divers have exited the water. A large portion of this responsibility lies with the Standby divers. So when should Standby divers be used and what are their responsibilities? At what level of operation should Standby divers be used? There are several things that can affect this decision.

- Site conditions
- Level of risk on the dive, primarily during the decompression phase
- Level of complexity and additional equipment to be employed

As a general rule if any of the above phenomena result in the dive team not being able to concentrate on the prime task (i.e. the dive itself) and find themselves undertaking excessive additional work other than conducting the dive plan, then Standby divers should be used. Put basically the Standby divers role is to "help out". The specific areas of assistance might be defined as follows:

- **During the planning phase**

  Dealing with some of the logistics. This could range from ensuring fluid is available for a simple dive defining and assembling sufficient gas quantities and it's management for an extended operational period.
- **During preparation**

  Ensuring all equipment is in place and that the support platform is correctly loaded. Assembling any emergency equipment and verifying it's functionality.
- **Prior to diving**

  Assisting the divers to kit up. Deployment of the decompression station and any in-water emergency equipment. Ensuring divers safely enter the water and all shallow water checks are conducted successfully.
- **During the dive**

  At least one Standby diver should descend to the first gas switch point and ensure emergency gas is staged and functioning. If possible waiting until all divers have returned safely past that point. The Standby diver should then make sure all divers are safely on the

decompression station prior to setting the station loose (if applicable).
If two divers can be used then one should remain top side. In the event that a rescue has to be performed this "shallow water" Standby is best suited to this role. Also if one of the team becomes separated this Standby diver would be deployed to define the extent of the problem and assist where possible.

- **Post dive**

  Pump gas. Cook. Keep records. Assist the team with exiting from the water and de-kiting. Provide fluids and any surface gas for the team. Stow equipment. Help with an overall assessment of the operation and provide useful input for next time.

In short Standby divers are essential parts of any dive team and ideally team members should rotate through the Standby diver role. There have been instances where Standby divers have saved the life of a convulsing team member. Make no mistakes, although for some the use of Standby's may seem a luxury, they are a skilled member of the team and may in fact need additional skills over and above other team members. Additional skills which may be required could encompass:

- First Aid training
- Hyperbaric training
- Gas blending
- Equipment servicing

Obviously it is important that as many of the dive team as possible have a range of skills, depending on the complexity of the operation more skills and more skilled team members may be required.

Rescue Procedures and Equipment

In all diving emergencies it is prudent to assume that Decompression Illness (DCI) will be a factor in that emergency. This assumption should be made until information is gathered to affirm the precise nature of the trauma. As such DCI rescue and avoidance play a major part in any safety planning. This chapter will deal with a range of diving emergencies including DCI and the relevant First aid procedures.

DCI Avoidance

The following is a collection of scientific (if the analysis of DCI can be defined as such), commercially attained knowledge and personal observations from a range of experienced divers. In many cases an incident and especially DCI is a serious and frightening experience and these resultant paragraphs are offered as a method of practical avoidance drawn from the above spheres of knowledge.

As most divers are aware, the majority of recreationally available decompression tables are based on the Haldane theory of decompression which expresses the body as a group of parallel tissue compartments. Each theoretical compartment may on- and off-load gas at different rates and compartments have different tolerances to over pressurization or, put simply, the amount of expansion they can tolerate after a period of saturation (submersion at elevated pressures) while experiencing a reduction in external pressure (as during an ascent). Put basically, the amount of saturation and the tolerated over pressurization broadly define the decompression profile from a given dive.

Currently there are a variety of differing adaptations to decompression models that attempt to take in to account phenomena such as micro bubbles forming in the blood and a host of other DCI problems. As most divers, particularly those operating outside of the air range, tend to use a derivative of the Haldane model, more often than not that developed by Professor A. A Bühlmann of Zurich, Switzerland; execution of schedules using the Bühlmann tables will be discussed.

Nitrox

Nitrox is a combination of two gases, Nitrogen and Oxygen. The formation of bubbles of nitrogen during or after a dive in the body is a well-known phenomenon but it is not common knowledge that oxygen bubbles may also temporarily form. This has been noted by the navies of the world in long duration swims on high PO_2's. This activity being out of the sport diving range will allow us to discount the phenomenon.

General Guidelines Covering All Dives

- **Analyze** all gases prior to diving.
- Ensure all gases are properly and **visibly labeled** prior to diving.
- Use **1.4 PO_2** on technical level exposures as a bottom and **1.6** as a maximum decompression mix PO_2.
- After a period of **activity at the surface** (kiting up), allow for a short rest period in order to get breathing and heart rates back under control prior to entering the water. Experienced divers may use visualization techniques or bradycardial breathing to achieve this. In short, stop whatever you are doing and breathe deeply for a period of time.
- During the **descent**, stop at 20 ft (6 msw). Perform a leak and general equipment check. This wait time of an additional minute or so further allows the body to **acclimate** to the new environment. Temperature and light level acclimatization may take several minutes (up to 25 minutes for a major light level change), however this brief stop will allow the cardio-vascular system to return to near normal rates.
- Make a **slow descent** without excess exercise. Either free fall or use hand over hand techniques with shot lines in tidal areas. Finning down the line will use a lot of energy and produce CO_2 that in turn predisposes us to narcosis and a range of other problems.
- Having reached the bottom take another brief period to adjust equipment and attain the **correct buoyancy**. All of these extra stabilizing minutes are simply an attempt to return the body to a near surface functioning state such that it operates to maximum efficiency.
- During the dive, whenever possible use "pull and glide" techniques rather than **heavy finning** (with suitable respect for the environment). Use of the arms reduces breathing stress.
- If at any point during the dive a **stressful situation** arises, Stop, Take 3 deep breaths (focus on breathing out), Think and Act in that order. Try and prioritize the problems. The bottom line being if I have gas I can breathe. There is no urgency to start an ascent if at the end of the planned time something happens which slows egress providing bailout schedules are (and should be) carried.
- If the depth of the dive is known, carry a **schedule** for the dive time and the dive time plus 5 minutes. If the depth is uncertain carry a schedule for the depth and the time and the depth plus at least 10 ft (3 m) and the same time. Carry an additional schedule for the longest time and deepest depth assuming a decompression on bottom mix (see suggestions for Trimix schedules).
- Always plan for the **deepest** part of the dive even if this portion is only a bounce, i.e. if the wreck bottoms at 229 fsw (70 msw), but most of the dive is at 223 fsw (68 msw), plan for 229 fsw (70 msw). Maintain **ascent rates** of 33 ft/minute (10 m/minute) or less, even from deep water.
- As with a no-stop dive where it is wise not to return directly to the surface (as this is a calculated pressure ceiling), it is also wise not to return directly to the **first decompression stop**. One or two minutes spent waiting 10 fsw (3 msw) below the first stop are beneficial when considering tissue over pressurization and will have no noticeable affect on the remaining decompression.
- Avoid unnecessary **delays in deep water** on bottom mix, such as starting up a wall after the planned bottom time and then taking time to stop and look.
- Do not **reduce stop times** arbitrarily. Do not make assumptions on stop time reduction if using a non planned gas without first computing for the effects. In a team plan this would mean carry a schedule for the worst gas scenario of the team (most deco).
- When reaching the first stop and if using a time device which works in **whole minutes**. Wait until the minute has incremented and then start the timing at that stop.
- If the stop involves a **gas switch**, start the stop timing after at least 3-4 breaths using the gas.
- Maintain **stop accuracy** to +/- 1 fsw (0.5 msw).
- After completing the **final stop**, ascend half way to the surface and stop for a further 2-5 minutes.
- While waiting for the **boat** to pick you up, stay on the highest available FO_2.
- Upon entry into the boat after a period of decompression, spend at least 5 minutes breathing your highest available **FO_2 on the surface**.
- **Hydrate** with non-acidic drinks at least 12 hours before a planned extended decompression dive. Hydrate again prior to the dive and immediately afterwards.
- Avoid **alcoholic beverages**, caffeine and decongestants prior to diving.
- Do not **smoke**, especially immediately before and after a dive.

Trimix Dives

Trimix is a combination of oxygen, helium and nitrogen. Trimix dives require specialist training in the use of decompression tables or software and often employ multiple decompression gases.

- Apply **general rules** as above.
- Where the FO_2 of the bottom mix is less than **16%** avoid using it at or near the surface.
- On dives requiring a **travel gas** (ideally where the bottom mix FO_2 is LESS than 16%), use the travel gas down to a PO_2 of 1.4ata. This travel section may be programmed in as a part of the decompression profile or the assumption may be made that the downward travel is on bottom mix (from a tables standpoint) although travel mix (Nitrox) is used. This provides an extra level of decompression safety.
- On the **ascent, switch** away from Helium as soon as possible. If possible slightly before the planned first stop.
- If the planned first stop (in order to maintain decompression gas efficiency) occurs at a gas switch point (1.6 as a PO_2) then conduct a 1 minute stop half way between the bottom and the first stop on bottom mix. Research has indicated that these deep-water stops help limit **microbubbles**.
- Apply **air breaks** once the CNS clock exceeds 80%.
- Take submersible dive plans for depth and time scenarios as above with an additional schedule assuming a loss of the **deep-water decompression** (travel) gas. This will normally mean completing the deep stops on bottom mix.
- Wherever possible dive as a **team** such that spare gas is always available. Wherever possible stage spare deep-water decompression gas at the first stop depth, especially in low visibility situations.
- If an **ascent from deep water** has delayed the time to the first stop by more than 10% of the planned bottom time, use the next most conservative schedule to complete the decompression (greater depth or time). Wherever possible, leave the bottom early to avoid this problem.
- Employ **team ethics** wherever possible, this means employing decompression stations where conditions allow and staging emergency decompression gas, especially for the deep stops and in shallow water if possible.

DCI First Aid & Equipment

Arterial Gas Embolism (AGE) and Decompression Sickness (DCS) are the two most common diving related accidents. Symptoms may occur on surfacing or within 36 hours. Other common conditions are listed later. Additional information can be found in various reference works.

The following will detail suggested emergency equipment and procedures for DCI and a range of diving related injuries.

DO:

Always carry...

- Oxygen and 100% delivery system
- Resuscitation equipment
- Marine radio & Cellular Phone (if possible)
- Emergency contact numbers
- Fluids (powdered form)
- Water
- Basic First Aid kit
- Pen and paper
- Diver recovery system (ropes/sling, etc.).

Consider carrying...

- Specialized in-water recompression equipment for remote locations. This should include:
  - Full face mask
  - Harness system with attachment line to boat or decompression station
  - "Air break" system (air cylinder and separate regulator).

In any incident, assume DCI until informed otherwise. First Aid for DCI is:

- Administer O_2 Immediately (First 15 minutes are critical.)
- Keep warm and dry
- Lay casualty flat
- Stay calm
- Administer a small amount of fluids
- Check urination, continue fluids if successful
- Note any changes
- Contact emergency services

DO NOT:

- Do not administer pain killers
- Do not give fluids if casualty is unable to urinate regularly (25 minute intervals)
- Do not delay in giving oxygen
- Do not stop O_2 administration if pain worsens (allow for transient worsening)
- Do not leave casualty unattended
- Do not elevate to a higher altitude

Neurological Test

The purpose of this test is to ascertain the extent of any DCI. Recording of this information will give chamber technicians a good idea of the casualty's previous condition and any improvements, on arrival.

Ask questions: Where does it hurt?
When did symptoms occur?
When was it the worst?

Orientation: Does the diver know name and age, day and date?
Does the diver know their current location?
Does the diver appear alert?

Eyes: Check eyes separately, hold up fingers and ask them to count different numbers.
Get the diver to follow one finger for 0.5m (18 inches).
First up and down and then side to side.
Is the movement smooth and are the pupils the same size?

Face: Ask them to smile.
Is muscle contraction the same for both sides?

Tongue: Stick out tongue. It should come straight out with no sideways deviation.

Muscle strength: Push down on shoulders while they shrug. Is the pressure equal and strong?
Lay them flat and ask them to raise each leg and push against your outstretched hands.
Are both sides equal and strong?
The same can apply to the arms.

Sensory: Close divers eyes and lightly touch points down each side of the body.
Where do they *not* feel it?

Co-ordination: Have them stand with feet together and arms stretched out front and eyes closed.
Be prepared to catch them.
Do they wobble or fall? Note if one arm drops.
Ask them to touch their nose and your finger [18 inches (0.5m) away] rapidly, a few times.

Feet: (*Babinski Reflex*). Take off socks and gently run a pointed instrument up the sole.
If the toes curl down, this is normal. If nothing happens no conclusion can be drawn.
If they curl up, this is a reliable sign of spinal involvement.

With any DCI assessment it is important to look for and record any changes without causing the patient unnecessary emotional stress. When asking a question such as: "Do you have pain?" Ask for the answer on a scale of one to ten. Ask the same question again after a short period (say 15 minutes) and note any changes. Record all results and send these results with the casualty. Make sure these records get to the physician.

Type I (minor neurological) and Type II (major neurological) DCI have not been sub-divided as one may lead to the other. In general Type I starts as joint pains or skin rashes.

If in doubt assume DCI and, at the very least, administer 100% oxygen. With all incidents contact the emergency services as soon as possible. Monitor the buddy as well as the injured diver and ensure they stay together throughout the rescue.

Speed of administration of 100% oxygen is vital. After 10 to 15 minutes of onset of symptoms, permanent damage may have taken place. Denying the onset of DCI is very dangerous. If you have any symptoms from mild pain, headache, nausea through to muscle weakness, do not hesitate - **ADMINISTER OXYGEN.**

Oxygen Delivery Equipment

The important thing is that virtually 100% oxygen reaches the diver. In most cases, the diver will be breathing and hence free flow masks are not recommended. The suggested ideal system is two demand regulators (oxygen serviced diving type are acceptable) and at least an 8 liter (60 cu ft) oxygen bottle. Gas wastage and diluted oxygen % delivery make free flow impractical.

Where breathing is labored an Ambubag type resuscitator is recommended with an oxygen attachment.

Other Diving Incidents - Diving Accident Management

Information in this section is offered as Emergency First Aid for any casualty and is not a complete treatment. Any diving related incidents should be reported to trained medical/hyperbaric staff as soon as possible.

In any diving incident:

Rule 1. Remove casualty from danger.

Rule 2. As a rescuer, do not put yourself in unnecessary danger.

Rule 1 normally means removing the casualty from the water which may be a complex operation involving ropes and slings in an extreme situation. In any event, all accident scenarios should be practiced and planned for.

Primary First Aid For the Following Incidents:

Shock:

Symptoms

- Loss of blood, pale and clammy skin.
- Pulse rapid and weak or shallow breathing, nausea.

Treatment:	Always	Never
	Keep patient lying down and QUIET. Ensure good breathing and circulation. Control bleeding. Give oxygen and prevent heat loss. Reassure (talk to) victim.	Give anything by mouth. Make them stand up.

Bleeding:

Symptoms

- External will be apparent.
- Internal may be seen at the mouth. This could also be a burst lung.

Treatment:	Always	Never
Internal	Place in recovery position. Treat for shock.	
External	Apply local pressure, preferably with sterile dressing.	

Carbon Dioxide Poisoning:

Symptoms

- Rapid breathing.
- Headaches, dizziness and weakness.

Treatment:	Always	Never
	Give oxygen and CPR as required.	

Carbon Monoxide Poisoning:

Symptoms

- Breathless on exertion.
- Nausea.
- Vertigo.
- Confusion.

Treatment:	Always	Never
	Give oxygen and CPR as required. If a chamber is nearby recompress to 30 ft (9 m) on 100% oxygen.	

Drowning:

Symptoms

- Cyanosis.
- No vital signs.
- Unconscious.

Treatment:	Always	Never
	Give ECM (CPR)/EAR (Rescue Breathing). Give Oxygen. Continuously monitor. Secondary drowning can occur.	Leave alone.

Hypothermia:

Symptoms

- Shivering
- Complains of cold, pale skin
- Slurred speech
- Possible cardio-respiratory arrest

Treatment:	Always	Never
	Prevent further heat loss, use blankets, cloths (avoid foil space blankets), other bodies, etc. Cover head, neck and torso. Replace wet clothes with dry ones. Monitor pulse and breathing. Warm drinks are allowed.	Rapidly re-heat. Give hot drinks. Give alcohol.

CNS Oxygen Toxicity:

Symptoms

- Convulsions
- Unconsciousness
- Confusion

Treatment:	Always	Never
	Allow convulsions to cease. Remove from danger, preferably onto the boat. If patient recovers in-water and stops could be completed, continue on as low a PPO_2 as possible, extending the stop time. This type of rescue is really only possible with full face masks.	Restrict a convulsion.

Cardio-Pulmonary Resuscitation

The key points in any rescue are Airway, Breathing and Circulation. Detailed as follows:

- Airway.
  Look for and clear any obstructions.
- Breathing.
  Look for signs of breathing. Listen for air sounds and watch for chest movement. If there is none, administer EAR (Rescue Breathing)
- Circulation.
  Check carotid pulse and control bleeding. If there is no pulse, administer ECM (CPR).

EAR (Rescue Breathing) and ECM (CPR) Sequence

1. Ascertain whether conscious, ask what is wrong? Reassure casualty. If conscious put in recovery position, check symptoms and administer first aid as required.
2. If unconscious (use pain test - ear lobe pinch), check A, B, C's (above).
3. If EAR (Rescue Breathing) is required, extend airway, pinch nostrils and give two breaths. Check pulse and breathing.
4. If ECM (CPR) is needed, locate base of sternum, move up two fingers.
   Place a flat palm on this point (heel of the palm central) with the second hand on top of the first.
   Lock elbows. Depress using short steady 2 inch (5 cm) movements.
   Administer 15 compression's followed by two inflation's. If working with two people 5 to 1 is advised.
   Do this in a sequence of four then monitor pulse. Repeat until victim recovers.
5. When pulse and breathing return, place in recovery position and administer oxygen.

Never give up until someone more medically qualified takes over.

Minimal First Aid Equipment

- 100% breathing grade oxygen and dual supply system.
- Marine radio.
- A by size selection of standard wound dressings.
- A selection of crape bandages.
- Assorted sterile adhesive plasters.
- 1 pair tweezers.
- 1 eye bath and ointment.
- 1 bottle Aspirin.
- 1 bottle Antiseptic fluid.
- Resuscitation mask.
- 1 pencil and notebook.
- Fresh water.
- 1 bottle vinegar (jelly fish stings, etc.).

Helicopter Rescues

Important points to remember are:

- Remove all obstructions (aerials, etc.) from pickup point.
- Always follow the pilot's instructions.
- Never touch the winch man, lines or stretcher until a ground wire has touched the boat or sea. There is a risk of electric shock.
- Do not attach any lines from the helicopter to the vessel.
- Do not haul on the winch line.
- Attach detailed written information about the incident to the casualty.
- Position the boat into the wind at an angle of 30 degrees off the port bow. You may be asked to slowly motor (5 knots).

In the event of a lost diver scenario, the dive boat should mark the last known position prior to leaving the site.

Insurance

Internationally, medical insurance is available to cover diving incidents and taking out Divers Alert Network (DAN) insurance (see resources section) can cover any subsequent treatment. DAN can also advise on chamber locations and rescue facilities.

Conclusions

The safety planning of any single dive or series of dives may range from the simple to the extremely complex. Remember, define the hazards, assess the risks, plan for the specific scenarios and stay in practice.

"One of the best weapons in your arsenal is *you*, providing you are a prepared and practiced logical thinking diver."

Glossary of Abbreviations and Selected Terms

Glenn Forest

Air Cell: Another term for a buoyancy compensator (**BC**). See **BC**.
AB Model: The Arterial Bubble Model for Type II **DCS** symptoms.
ABS: A type of high impact plastic. **Abs,** slang for abdominal muscles or it also refers to 'absolute.'
ACE: Angiotension Converting Enzyme.
Adenosine Triphosphate: The energy currency of life. **ATP** is the biomolecule in which cells store energy. **ATP** is composed of an Adenosine molecule with three high-energy phosphate molecules attached, one after the other. Adenosine Diphosphate (**ADP**) has only two phosphate molecules attached. Adenosine monophosphate (**AMP**) has only one phosphate molecule attached. The more phosphate molecules the more stored energy.
ADP: Adenosine Diphosphate, see **Adenosine Triphosphate** above.
AMP: Adenosine Monophosphate, see **Adenosine Triphosphate** above.
AMTE/PL: Admiralty Marine Technology Establishment, Physiological Laboratory.
ANS: Autonomic Nervous System.
ASAP: As Soon As Possible.
ATP: Adenosine Triphosphate. See **Adenosine Triphosphate** above.
Antioxidants: Essential chemicals (vitamins) that inhibit **free radical** formation or repair **free radical** damage.
Arteriosclerosis: A disease of blood vessels caused by plaque (fatty deposits usually) accumulating on the walls of blood vessels or at the junction of blood vessels.
ATA: Atmospheres Absolute. May be used interchangeably with the term 'Bar' when referring to Partial Pressures.
ATM: Atmospheres, Imperial-US measurement of pressure equal to 14.7 **psi.**
Alveoli: Miniature sacks of tissue in the lungs on the surface of which gas exchange takes place.

Bar: Metric measurement of pressure approximately equal to 1 atmosphere (**atm**) or 14.7 **psi**. May be used interchangeably with the term 'ATA' when referring to Partial Pressures.
BC or BCD: Buoyancy Compensating Device. A device used to either adjust a divers buoyancy or provide surface floatation. **BC**'s are not considered Personal Floatation Devices (PFD's) which are required equipment by certain state and federal agencies under certain circumstances.
BT: Bottom Time.

C: Centigrade, see **Centigrade/Celsius.**
Capillaries: The smallest of all blood vessels.
Carbon Dioxide: See **CO_2.**
Carbon Monoxide: See **CO.**
Cardiac: Having to do with the heart.
cc: Cubic Centimeters.
Centigrade/Celsius: Metric measurement of temperature. To convert **Centigrade/Celsius** to **Fahrenheit,** multiply by 9/5 (1.80) and add 32.
CFM: Cubic Feet per **Minute,** Imperial-US measurement of volume flow.
Cis: A stereochemical term meaning the subject chemical groups are on the same side of a carbon to carbon double bond. Used in this text to describe certain configurations of fat molecules. 'Cis-fats' are the good fats. See also **Trans.**
cm: Centimeter, metric length measure. 1 inch equals 2.54 centimeters.

CNS: Central Nervous System.

CNS% or %CNS: The percent of central nervous system oxygen exposure.

CO: Carbon monoxide, a highly toxic, colorless, odorless, and tasteless gas produced by the combustion of hydrocarbons (petroleum fuels used in engines, and smoking tobacco or cannabis).

CO_2: Carbon dioxide. A normal by-product of **respiration**, Carbon dioxide can be harmful if allowed to accumulate. See **Hypercapnia.**

CO_2 Retention: The build up of carbon dioxide in body tissue. Individuals that tend to accumulate carbon dioxide more than average are termed **CO_2 retainers.**

CON-VENTID: Mnemonic for the symptoms of oxygen poisoning.

CPR: Cardiopulmonary Resuscitation.

Cubic Feet: Imperial-US measurement of volume. Another way of expressing this volume is **feet cubed** or **Ft^3**.

Cu. Ft.: Cubic Feet, see **cubic feet.**

CV Model: The Critical Volume Model for type 1 **DCS** symptoms.

DAN: Divers Alert Network.

D-ring: A 'd' shaped ring used for attaching equipment.

DCI: Decompression illness/injury, the direct result of not allowing for the safe elimination of excess or accumulated gas in body tissue. Also referred to as **DCS**, decompression sickness. Although there are subtle differences in medical terminology for decompression illness, decompression injury, and decompression sickness, the end result is the same - treatment in a very expensive recompression chamber.

DCS: Decompression Sickness. See **DCI.**

Deco: Slang for the word 'decompression', i.e., deco bottle or deco stop.

DIN: Deutsches Institut für Normung, a European regulatory association.

DM: Diabetes mellitus.

Doppler Effect or **Doppler Studies**: An acoustic measuring device or method used by scientists to measure the passage of bubbles in the arteries or veins of divers. A Doppler device for divers would be, in essence, a bubble counter.

Doubles: Two **SCUBA** cylinders joined together by a manifold to create a <u>single</u> gas supply. (In effect, 'doubling' the available gas supply.) Although some use the terms **twins** and **doubles** almost interchangeably, there is a very critical, life or death, difference between the two concepts. See also **twins** which is a different and very dangerous concept. See also **side mount.**

DPV: Diver Propulsion Vehicle, alias scooter, sled, torpedo, etc.; Any motorized device used for transporting submerged divers.

EAD: Equivalent Air Depth.

EAR: European term for Rescue Breathing.

EAN: Enriched Air **Nitrox.**

EANx: Abbreviation used to describe a generic **Nitrox** blend. A 36% oxygen **Nitrox** blend is EAN 36.

ECM: European term for **CPR.**

EDU: United States Navy Experimental Diving Unit.

EEG: Electroencephalograph, an instrument that measures brain wave activity.

END: Equivalent Nitrogen Depth.

Enzyme: A highly specialized, biologically active protein. **Enzymes** are the tools with which the body controls **metabolism.**

EPIRB: Emergency Positioning Indicator Radio Beacon that is compact and self contained.

EST: Electroshock Therapy.

Fahrenheit: Imperial-US measurement of temperature. To convert **Fahrenheit** to **Centigrade/Celsius**, subtract 32 and multiply by 5/9 (.556).

Feet: Imperial-US measurement of length or depth. 1 **foot** equals .305 **meters.**

Feet cubed: Imperial-US measurement of volume. 1 **cubic foot** equals 28.32 **free liters.**

FFW: Feet fresh water. Imperial-US measurement of depth in feet of fresh water. Very rarely used.

Fg: Fraction (percentage) of a gas in a mix.

FLPM: Free Liters Per Minute.

FN_2: Fraction of Nitrogen.

FO_2: Fraction of **Oxygen** in a mix.

Free liter: See **liter.**

Free Radical: A highly destructive, 'hot' molecule of usually some oxygen compound. **Free radicals** are short lived because they are so energetically active (looking for something to bind to or combine with). They can and will bind to just about any other molecule either destroying that molecule or disrupting its function.

FSW: Feet Salt Water. Imperial-US measurement of depth in feet of salt water.

Ft: Feet, see **feet.**

Ft^3: Cubic Feet, see **feet cubed.**

GABA: Gamma-aminobutyric Acid. **GABA** is a neuro-transmitter responsible for brain functioning.

GI: Gastrointestinal tract.

g/l: Grams per **liter.**

HBO: Hyperbaric Oxygen or Hyperbaric Oxygenation.

HDL: High-density Phospholipids (High-density Fat). See Also **LDL.**

He: See **helium.**

Heliair: Any mixture of air and helium.

Heliox: Any mixture of oxygen and helium.

Helium: An inert biologically unreactive gas.

Hemoglobin: A complex protein and iron molecule found in **RBC**s that transports **oxygen** and **carbon dioxide. Hemoglobin** literally means iron-bearing glob. It is the iron atom embedded in the protein that actually binds the **oxygen** or **carbon dioxide** molecules. If **carbon monoxide** binds to the iron molecule first, the hemoglobin molecule can carry no **oxygen** or **carbon dioxide.** This is why **carbon monoxide** is so dangerous to divers because it reduces **oxygen** flow to tissue and reduces **carbon dioxide** removal from tissue.

Hgb: Abbreviation for **Hemoglobin.**

HIV: Human Immuno-Virus. The causative agent for Acquired Immune Deficiency Syndrome (AIDS).

Hogarth or **Hogarthian Style**: A particular gear configuration, some say gear configuration philosophy, named in honor of William Hogarth Main.

HPG: High Pressure Gauge.

HPNS: High Pressure Nervous Syndrome.

HSE: Health and Safety Executive, United Kingdom.

Hydrox: Any mixture of hydrogen and oxygen or hydrogen, helium and oxygen.

Hypercarbia: Elevated **carbon dioxide** in the blood.

Hypercapnia: A potentially fatal condition for divers caused by an excessive build up of **carbon dioxide** in either body tissue or inspired air.

Hyperoxemia: Insufficient oxygenation of the blood.

IANTD: The International Association of Nitrox and Technical Divers.

No J's

K: Chemical symbol for Potassium.
Kit: European term referring to the dive gear or equipment needed for a dive. Somewhat analogous to the American terms 'rig' or 'gear'.
Kiting or kiting up: European terms referring to the act of outfitting or dressing for a dive. Analogous to the American term 'suiting up' or 'gearing up'.
kPa: KiloPascals. Metric measurement of pressure. See also **mmHg**.

L: Liter, see **liter.**
LDL: Low-density Phospholipids (Low-density fat). See also **HDL**.
LED: Light Emitting Diode.
Liter: Metric measurement for volume. 1 **liter** equals 0.035 **cubic feet**. One of the finer points of the metric system is that a **liter** of gas is referred to differently from a **liter** of a liquid. **Liters** of gas are formally referred to as **free liters**. Off the record, unless one is a chemist, a **liter** of gas is basically the same as a **free liter** of gas. Many of our international colleagues, especially British colleagues, request that IANTD use the 'proper' terminology to refer to a **liter** of gas as being a **free liter** of gas.

m: Meter, see **meter.**
MB Model: The Microbubble Model. See Chapter 12.
mbar: Millibar.
Meds: Medications.
Metabolic: see **metabolism.**
Metabolism: The biochemical cycle of life. A complex system of chemical reactions that produce the biochemical molecules necessary to sustain and maintain living organisms. Loosely translated, **metabolic** means "with the ball," or "with the cycle" because **metabolism** is a cyclic process.
Meter: Metric measurement of length or depth. 1 **meter** equals 3.28 **feet**.
Mitochondria: A crucially important cell structure. The **mitochondria** (a tiny bean shaped structure found in all living cells) is the factory in which a cell makes its energy (fuel) **ATP**. Inhibiting Mitochondrial function has widespread detrimental effects on a diver that includes loss of mental acuity, loss of motor control, loss of muscle strength, loss of consciousness, convulsions and death.
MFW: Meter Fresh Water. Metric measurement of depth in meters of fresh water.
ml: Milliliter. Metric measurement of volume.
mm: Millimeter. Metric measurement of length.
mmHg: Millimeters of mercury. Imperial-US measurement for pressure.
MOD: Maximum Operational Depth.
"Mr. Murphy": American slang name for a fictional character. See **Murphy's Law**.
MSW: Meters Salt Water. Metric measurement of depth in meters of salt water.
Murphy's Law: Anything that can go wrong will go wrong.

Na: Chemical symbol for Sodium.

NOAA: The National Oceanic and Atmospheric Administration (United States).

Narcosis: A detrimental physiological and mental state produced by high levels of absorbed nitrogen (**nitrogen narcosis**) or inert gases (**inert gas narcosis**) such as Hydrogen or Neon

Ne: Neon, an inert biologically unreactive gas.

Nitrogen: An 'inert' diatomic (2 atom) gas. Air consists of approximately 78% diatomic nitrogen. Actually, diatomic nitrogen is chemically unreactive (not inert) in higher life forms because the two molecules are so tightly bound together. Lower life forms, such as nitrogen-fixing bacterial, can use (metabolize) diatomic nitrogen.

Nitrogen narcosis: See **narcosis.**

Nitrox: Any gas mixture of oxygen and nitrogen other than air (Air being approximately 21% oxygen).

NREM: Non-Rapid Eye Movement. See **REM.**

NSAIDS: Non-steroidal anti-inflammatory drugs.

O_2: The chemical representation for diatomic **oxygen.** See **oxygen.**

OMS: Ocean Management Systems. A manufacturer of technical diving equipment. Other manufacturers that specifically cater to technical diving include DiveRite, Zeagle, etc.

OTC: Over The Counter.

OTU: Oxygen Toxicity Unit.

Oxygen: Required to sustain life (ie., run **metabolism**), **oxygen** is nature's most common oxidant and is a necessary ingredient required for combustion/**respiration**.

P: Usually refers to 'pressure.'

$PaCO_2$: Pressure of carbon dioxide.

Pg: Partial pressure of a gas.

pH: A measurement of the hydrogen ion concentration in solution (such as blood).

Pi: Used in this text to indicate a single phosphate molecule. Actually, scientifically it would be written P_i. See **Adenosine Triphosphate**.

PO_2: Partial pressure of **oxygen.**

PPO_2: Same as **PO_2.**

PSI: Pounds per Square Inch. Imperial-US measurement for pressure.

PSIG: Pounds per Square Inch Gauge. Imperial-US measurement for gauge pressure (for absolute pressure, add 14.7 pound per square inch to PSIG)

Pulmonary: Having to do with the lungs.

No Q's.

RBC: Red Blood Cell.

REM: Rapid Eye Movement. A behavior usually associated with dreaming.

Renal: Having to do with the kidneys.

Respiration: A metabolic process that involves the exchange of gases. In air breathing mammals (most divers would qualify), Inhaled **oxygen** (an oxidizer), is exchanged with exhaled **Carbon Dioxide** (a waste by-product of metabolism).

RMV: Respiratory Minute Volume.

RNT: Residual Nitrogen Time.

RNPL: Royal Naval Physiologic Laboratory.

Rule of Thirds: A simple gas management technique specifying that divers use only one third of their available gas supply for 'penetration' (or descent into a dive). Upon expending the first third of air, the diver exits (ascends) using the second third of air. Upon reaching the exit point, the diver should have the full measure of the last third of their gas supply remaining.

S-Drill: 'Safety' drill performed before all technical dives.

SAC: Surface Air Consumption.

SCUBA: Self Contained Underwater Breathing Apparatus.

SDO: Surface Decompression using Oxygen.

Side Mount: Term used to describe a rig that enables a diver to wear two **SCUBA** cylinders, one cylinder on each side of the diver. Unlike **twins** that are also independent, **side mount**ed cylinders allow the diver to directly inspect and manage the two independent systems. Note: Some sources occasionally refer to stages as **side mount**.

SIT: Surface Interval Time.

SPG: Submersible Pressure Gauge.

SRF: Surface Ratio Factor.

Sur-D: Surface Decompression.

TOD: Target Operating Depth.

Trans: A stereochemical term meaning the subject chemical groups are on the opposite side of a carbon to carbon double bond. Used in this text to describe certain configurations of fat molecules. 'Trans-fats" are the bad fats. See also **Cis**.

Trimix: Any breathable mixture of **Nitrogen, Oxygen,** and **Helium.**

TUP: Transfer Under Pressure.

Twins: Term used in the United States to describe a rig where two independent **SCUBA** cylinders are worn on the back creating 'twin' independent air supplies. [British sources - such as author Kevin Gurr - often refer to **doubles** (see **doubles**) as 'twins'.] Back-mounted dual independent gas supplies (what divers refer to in the United States as **twins**) have been shown to be a major cause of diving fatalities.

UHMS: The Undersea and Hyperbaric Medicine Society.

V_E: Is actually pronounced "V dot E" and refers to expired total ventilation.

VO_2: A measure of a divers ability to utilize oxygen.

VPA: Sodium Valproate, enhances **GABA**, see chapter 11.

WBC: White Blood Cells.

No X, Y or Z's.

TABLES & CHARTS

Imperial-US and Metric

INTERNATIONAL ASSOCIATION OF NITROX AND TECHNICAL DIVERS/IAND, INC.

"The Leader in Diver Education"

Photo above by Tom Mount of Patti Mount on the wreck of the Doc de Milly in South Miami, Florida.

CHARTS & TABLES
TABLE OF CONTENTS

IANTD Dive Planning Tables and Charts – Imperial-US

IANTD Gas Management Tables – Imperial-US

IANTD Dive Planning Tables and Charts – Metric

IANTD Gas Management Tables – Metric

⚠ Warning: DO NOT attempt to use these tables unless you are fully trained & certified in the use of gas mixtures other than air, or are under the supervision of a gas mixtures other than air instructor. Proper use of these tables will reduce the risk of decompression sickness & oxygen toxicity, but no table or computer can eliminate those risks.

TABLE OF CONTENTS - CONTINUED

IANTD Gas Management Tables – Metric - continued

Imperial-US and Metric Combined

IANTD Diving and Decompression Tables

INTERNATIONAL ASSOCIATION OF NITROX AND TECHNICAL DIVERS/IANTD, INC.

"The Leader in Technical Diver Education"

⚠ Warning: DO NOT attempt to use these tables unless you are fully trained & certified in the use of gas mixtures other than air, or are under the supervision of a gas mixtures other than air instructor. Proper use of these tables will reduce the risk of decompression sickness & oxygen toxicity, but no table or computer can eliminate those risks.

IANTD/IAND, Inc. PO_2 TABLE

Table1

	Oxygen Content																															
FSW	0.21	0.22	0.23	0.24	0.25	0.26	0.27	0.28	0.29	0.30	0.31	0.32	0.33	0.34	0.35	0.36	0.37	0.38	0.39	0.40	0.45	0.50	0.55	0.60	0.65	0.70	0.75	0.80	0.85	0.90	0.95	1.00
10	0.27	0.29	0.30	0.31	0.33	0.34	0.35	0.36	0.38	0.39	0.40	0.42	0.43	0.44	0.46	0.47	0.48	0.50	0.51	0.52	0.59	0.65	0.72	0.78	0.85	0.91	0.98	1.04	1.11	1.17	1.24	1.30
15	0.31	0.32	0.33	0.35	0.36	0.38	0.39	0.41	0.42	0.44	0.45	0.47	0.48	0.49	0.51	0.52	0.54	0.55	0.57	0.58	0.65	0.73	0.80	0.87	0.95	1.02	1.09	1.16	1.24	1.31	1.38	1.45
20	0.34	0.35	0.37	0.39	0.40	0.42	0.43	0.45	0.47	0.48	0.50	0.51	0.53	0.55	0.56	0.58	0.59	0.61	0.63	0.64	0.72	0.80	0.88	0.96	1.04	1.12	1.20	1.28	1.37	1.45	1.53	1.61
30	0.40	0.42	0.44	0.46	0.48	0.50	0.52	0.53	0.55	0.57	0.59	0.61	0.63	0.65	0.67	0.69	0.71	0.73	0.74	0.76	0.86	0.95	1.05	1.15	1.24	1.34	1.43	1.53	1.62			
40	0.46	0.49	0.51	0.53	0.55	0.58	0.60	0.62	0.64	0.66	0.69	0.71	0.73	0.75	0.77	0.80	0.82	0.84	0.86	0.88	1.00	1.11	1.22	1.33	1.44	1.55	1.66					
50	0.53	0.55	0.58	0.60	0.63	0.65	0.68	0.70	0.73	0.75	0.78	0.80	0.83	0.86	0.88	0.91	0.93	0.96	0.98	1.01	1.13	1.26	1.38	1.51	1.63							
60	0.59	0.62	0.65	0.68	0.70	0.73	0.76	0.79	0.82	0.85	0.87	0.90	0.93	0.96	0.99	1.01	1.04	1.07	1.10	1.13	1.27	1.41	1.55	1.69								
70	0.66	0.69	0.72	0.75	0.78	0.81	0.84	0.87	0.91	0.94	0.97	1.00	1.03	1.06	1.09	1.12	1.15	1.19	1.22	1.25	1.40	1.56										
80	0.72	0.75	0.79	0.82	0.86	0.89	0.92	0.96	0.99	1.03	1.06	1.10	1.13	1.16	1.20	1.23	1.27	1.30	1.34	1.37	1.54											
90	0.78	0.82	0.86	0.89	0.93	0.97	1.01	1.04	1.08	1.12	1.16	1.19	1.23	1.27	1.30	1.34	1.38	1.42	1.45	1.49	1.68											
100	0.85	0.89	0.93	0.97	1.01	1.05	1.09	1.13	1.17	1.21	1.25	1.29	1.33	1.37	1.41	1.45	1.49	1.53	1.57	1.61												
110	0.91	0.95	1.00	1.04	1.08	1.13	1.17	1.21	1.26	1.30	1.34	1.39	1.43	1.47	1.52	1.56	1.60	1.65	1.69													
120	0.97	1.02	1.07	1.11	1.16	1.21	1.25	1.30	1.34	1.39	1.44	1.48	1.53	1.58	1.62	1.67																
130	1.04	1.09	1.14	1.19	1.23	1.28	1.33	1.38	1.43	1.48	1.53	1.58	1.63	1.68																		
140	1.10	1.15	1.21	1.26	1.31	1.36	1.42	1.47	1.52	1.57	1.63	1.68																				
150	1.16	1.22	1.28	1.33	1.39	1.44	1.50	1.55	1.61	1.66																						
160	1.23	1.29	1.35	1.40	1.46	1.52	1.58	1.64																								
170	1.29	1.35	1.41	1.48	1.54	1.60	1.66																									
180	1.36	1.42	1.48	1.55	1.61	1.68																										
190	1.42	1.49	1.55	1.62																												
200	1.48	1.55	1.62																													
210	1.55	1.62																														

Produced by: Tom Mount / Mark Owens / Don Townsend

1. Find the depth on the left side of Table.
2. Go across horizontally until you are in the column of the mix you are using.
3. Read the PO_2 indicated.

Example: 110 FSW using EAN 28 = 1.21 PO_2

Note: This table may be used for determining both the TOD and MOD values for a given dive.
To use the IANTD/IAND, Inc. OTU / CNS O_2 Tracking Table with this Table, simply round the PO_2 obtained to the nearest 0.5.
YOU MUST ALWAYS ROUND TO THE NEXT HIGHEST PO_2

⚠ Warning: DO NOT attempt to use these tables unless you are fully trained & certified in the use of gas mixtures other than air, or are under the supervision of a gas mixtures other than air instructor. Proper use of these tables will reduce the risk of decompression sickness & oxygen toxicity, but no table or computer can eliminate those risks.

Table 2

IANTD HYPOXIC PO_2 TABLE

	Oxygen Percent												
FSW	0.20	0.19	0.18	0.17	0.16	0.15	0.14	0.13	0.12	0.11	0.10	0.09	0.08
10	0.26	0.25	0.23	0.22	0.21	0.20	0.18	0.17	0.16	0.14	0.13	0.12	0.10
15.0	0.29	0.28	0.26	0.25	0.23	0.22	0.20	0.19	0.17	0.16	0.15	0.13	0.12
20	0.32	0.31	0.29	0.27	0.26	0.24	0.22	0.21	0.19	0.18	0.16	0.14	0.13
30	0.38	0.36	0.34	0.32	0.31	0.29	0.27	0.25	0.23	0.21	0.19	0.17	0.15
40	0.44	0.42	0.40	0.38	0.35	0.33	0.31	0.29	0.27	0.24	0.22	0.20	0.18
50	0.50	0.48	0.45	0.43	0.40	0.38	0.35	0.33	0.30	0.28	0.25	0.23	0.20
60	0.56	0.54	0.51	0.48	0.45	0.42	0.39	0.37	0.34	0.31	0.28	0.25	0.23
70	0.62	0.59	0.56	0.53	0.50	0.47	0.44	0.41	0.37	0.34	0.31	0.28	0.25
80	0.68	0.65	0.62	0.58	0.55	0.51	0.48	0.45	0.41	0.38	0.34	0.31	0.27
90	0.75	0.71	0.67	0.63	0.60	0.56	0.52	0.48	0.45	0.41	0.37	0.34	0.30
100	0.81	0.77	0.73	0.69	0.64	0.60	0.56	0.52	0.48	0.44	0.40	0.36	0.32
110	0.87	0.82	0.78	0.74	0.69	0.65	0.61	0.56	0.52	0.48	0.43	0.39	0.35
120	0.93	0.88	0.83	0.79	0.74	0.70	0.65	0.60	0.56	0.51	0.46	0.42	0.37
130	0.99	0.94	0.89	0.84	0.79	0.74	0.69	0.64	0.59	0.54	0.49	0.44	0.40
140	1.05	1.00	0.94	0.89	0.84	0.79	0.73	0.68	0.63	0.58	0.52	0.47	0.42
150	1.11	1.05	1.00	0.94	0.89	0.83	0.78	0.72	0.67	0.61	0.55	0.50	0.44
160	1.17	1.11	1.05	0.99	0.94	0.88	0.82	0.76	0.70	0.64	0.58	0.53	0.47
170	1.23	1.17	1.11	1.05	0.98	0.92	0.86	0.80	0.74	0.68	0.62	0.55	0.49
180	1.29	1.23	1.16	1.10	1.03	0.97	0.90	0.84	0.77	0.71	0.65	0.58	0.52
190	1.35	1.28	1.22	1.15	1.08	1.01	0.95	0.88	0.81	0.74	0.68	0.61	0.54
200	1.41	1.34	1.27	1.20	1.13	1.06	0.99	0.92	0.85	0.78	0.71	0.64	0.56
210	1.47	1.40	1.33	1.25	1.18	1.10	1.03	0.96	0.88	0.81	0.74	0.66	0.59
220	1.53	1.46	1.38	1.30	1.23	1.15	1.07	1.00	0.92	0.84	0.77	0.69	0.61
230	1.59	1.51	1.43	1.35	1.28	1.20	1.12	1.04	0.96	0.88	0.80	0.72	0.64
240	1.65	1.57	1.49	1.41	1.32	1.24	1.16	1.08	0.99	0.91	0.83	0.74	0.66
250		1.63	1.54	1.46	1.37	1.29	1.20	1.11	1.03	0.94	0.86	0.77	0.69
260			1.60	1.51	1.42	1.33	1.24	1.15	1.07	0.98	0.89	0.80	0.71
270			1.65	1.56	1.47	1.38	1.29	1.19	1.10	1.01	0.92	0.83	0.73
280				1.61	1.52	1.42	1.33	1.23	1.14	1.04	0.95	0.85	0.76
290					1.57	1.47	1.37	1.27	1.17	1.08	0.98	0.88	0.78
300					1.61	1.51	1.41	1.31	1.21	1.11	1.01	0.91	0.81
310						1.56	1.46	1.35	1.25	1.14	1.04	0.94	0.83
320						1.60	1.50	1.39	1.28	1.18	1.07	0.96	0.86
330							1.54	1.43	1.32	1.21	1.10	0.99	0.88
340							1.58	1.47	1.36	1.24	1.13	1.02	0.90
350							1.62	1.51	1.39	1.28	1.16	1.04	0.93
360								1.55	1.43	1.31	1.19	1.07	0.95
370								1.59	1.47	1.34	1.22	1.10	0.98
380								1.63	1.50	1.38	1.25	1.13	1.00
390									1.54	1.41	1.28	1.15	1.03
400									1.57	1.44	1.31	1.18	1.05
410									1.61	1.48	1.34	1.21	1.07
420										1.51	1.37	1.24	1.10
430										1.54	1.40	1.26	1.12
440										1.58	1.43	1.29	1.15
450										1.61	1.46	1.32	1.17
460											1.49	1.34	1.20
470											1.52	1.37	1.22
480											1.55	1.40	1.24
490											1.58	1.43	1.27
500											1.62	1.45	1.29

Produced by: Tom Mount / Mark Owens / Don Townsend

⚠ **Warning: DO NOT attempt to use these tables unless you are fully trained & certified in the use of gas mixtures other than air, or are under the supervision of a gas mixtures other than air instructor. Proper use of these tables will reduce the risk of decompression sickness & oxygen toxicity, but no table or computer can eliminate those risks.**

IANTD CNS% PER MINUTE BY PO_2 CHART

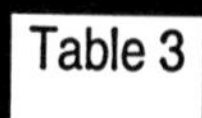
Table 3

PO_2	CNS% MIN.	PO_2	CNS% MIN.	PO_2	CNS% MIN.
0.60	0.14	1.02	0.35	1.42	0.68
0.62	0.14	1.04	0.36	1.44	0.71
0.64	0.15	1.06	0.38	1.46	0.74
0.66	0.16	1.08	0.40	1.48	0.78
0.68	0.17	1.10	0.42	1.50	0.83
0.70	0.18	1.12	0.43	1.52	0.93
0.72	0.18	1.14	0.43	1.54	1.04
0.74	0.19	1.16	0.44	1.56	1.19
0.76	0.20	1.18	0.46	1.58	1.47
0.78	0.21	1.20	0.47	1.60	2.22
0.80	0.22	1.22	0.48	1.62	5.00
0.82	0.23	1.24	0.51	1.65	6.25
0.84	0.24	1.26	0.52	1.67	7.69
0.86	0.25	1.28	0.54	1.70	10.00
0.88	0.26	1.30	0.56	1.72	12.50
0.90	0.28	1.32	0.57	1.74	20.00
0.92	0.29	1.34	0.60	1.77	25.00
0.94	0.30	1.36	0.62	1.78	31.25
0.96	0.31	1.38	0.63	1.80	50.00
0.98	0.32	1.40	0.65	1.82	100.00
1.00	0.33				

The above Table 3 is valuable on longer dives where exact CNS% values must be computed to insure a safe exposure. In the following text, you will be presented with a table that is expressed in 0.05 ata increments and is easier on which to calculate dives. For the majority of technical dives, and for all examples in the remainder of this text, Table 5 will be used. The additional advantage of Table 5 is that it combines information from both Table 3 and Table 4.

Table 4

SINGLE DIVE	
PO_2 (ATA)	OTU per MINUTE
0.50	00
0.55	0.15
0.60	0.27
0.65	0.37
0.70	0.47
0.75	0.56
0.80	0.65
0.85	0.74
0.90	0.83
0.95	0.92
1.00	1.00
1.05	1.08
1.10	1.16
1.15	1.24
1.20	1.32
1.25	1.40
1.30	1.48
1.35	1.55
1.40	1.63
1.45	1.70
1.50	1.78
1.55	1.85
1.60	1.92
1.65	2.00
1.70	2.07
1.75	2.14
1.80	2.21
1.85	2.28
1.90	2.35
1.95	2.42
2.00	2.49

MULTIPLE DAY ALLOTMENT OF OTUs		
EXPOSURE DAYS	AVERAGE DOSE	TOTAL DOSE
1	850	850
2	700	1400
3	620	1860
4	420	2100
5	380	2300
6	350	2520
7	330	2660
8	310	2800
9	300	2970
10	300	3100
11	300	3300
12	300	3600
13	300	3900
14	300	4200
15-30	300	AS REQUIRED

Note! An important point of the Repex Table is it tracks multi-day whole body oxygen exposure limits.

For additional safety, IANTD has designed tables to track the oxygen risk exposure. The values used in the tables have been converted into a linear representation making them slightly more conservative than if the raw values reflected in Table 3 are used. Refer to Table 5 for calculating CNS % and OTU accumulation on a given dive.
Example of OTU and CNS% tracking and planning using IANTD Table 5. OTUs are tracked in units. CNS O_2 is tracked in percent of the clock.

If PO_2 is not exact, use the next higher PO_2 on the chart. Slight differences may occur in rounding depending on column used in chart.

EXAMPLE: Total dive time is 80 minutes at 1.3 PO_2

60 minutes column used	33.33% CNS O_2	88.63 OTUs
20 minutes column used	11.11% CNS O_2	29.54 OTUs
Total for dive:	*44.44% CNS O_2*	*118.17 OTUs* *or if the*
1 minute column is used:	**44.80% CNS O_2**	**118.40 OTUs**

⚠ **Warning: DO NOT attempt to use these tables unless you are fully trained & certified in the use of gas mixtures other than air, or are under the supervision of a gas mixtures other than air instructor. Proper use of these tables will reduce the risk of decompression sickness & oxygen toxicity, but no table or computer can eliminate those risks.**

IANTD/IAND, INC. OTU / CNS TRACKING TABLE

Table 5

PO_2	1 In OTU - CNS O_2	5 Min OTU - CNS O_2	10 Min OTU - CNS O_2	20 Min OTU - CNS O_2	30 Min OTU - CNS O_2	40 Min OTU - CNS O_2	50 Min OTU - CNS O_2	60 Min OTU - CNS O_2
0.60	0.26 - 0.14	1.31 - 0.69	2.63 - 1.39	5.26 - 2.78	7.89 - 4.17	10.52 - 5.56	13.15 - 6.94	15.78 - 8.33
0.65	0.37 - 0.16	1.84 - 0.78	3.68 - 1.55	7.36 - 3.10	11.04 - 4.65	14.73 - 6.20	18.41 - 7.75	22.09 - 9.30
0.70	0.47 - 0.18	2.34 - 0.88	4.67 - 1.75	9.35 - 3.51	14.02 - 5.26	18.70 - 7.02	23.37 - 8.77	28.05 -10.53
0.75	0.56 - 0.20	2.81 - 0.98	5.63 - 1.96	11.25 - 3.92	16.88 - 5.88	22.50 - 7.84	28.13 - 9.80	33.75 -11.76
0.80	0.65 - 0.22	3.27 - 1.11	6.54 - 2.22	13.09 - 4.44	19.63 - 6.67	26.18 - 8.89	32.72 -11.11	39.27 -13.33
0.85	0.74 - 0.25	3.72 - 1.23	7.44 - 2.47	14.88 - 4.94	22.31 - 7.41	29.75 - 9.87	37.19 -12.34	44.63 -14.81
0.90	0.83 - 0.28	4.15 - 1.39	8.31 - 2.78	16.62 - 5.56	24.93 - 8.33	33.24 -11.11	41.55 -13.89	49.86 -16.67
0.95	0.92 - 0.31	4.58 - 1.57	9.16 - 3.14	18.33 - 6.27	27.49 - 9.41	36.65 -12.54	45.81 -15.68	54.98 -18.81
1.00	1.00 - 0.33	5.00 - 1.67	10.00 - 3.33	20.00 - 6.67	30.00 -10.00	40.00 -13.33	50.00 -16.67	60.00 -20.00
1.05	1.08 - 0.37	5.41 - 1.85	10.82 - 3.70	21.65 - 7.41	32.47 -11.11	43.29 -14.81	54.12 -18.52	64.94 -22.22
1.10	1.16 - 0.42	5.82 - 2.08	11.63 - 4.17	23.27 - 8.33	34.90 -12.50	46.54 -16.67	58.17 -20.83	69.80 -25.00
1.15	1.24 - 0.44	6.22 - 2.19	12.43 - 4.39	24.87 - 8.77	37.30 -13.16	49.73 -17.55	62.16 -21.93	74.60 -26.32
1.20	1.32 - 0.48	6.61 - 2.38	13.22 - 4.76	26.44 - 9.52	39.67 -14.29	52.89 -19.05	66.11 -23.81	79.33 -28.57
1.25	1.40 - 0.51	7.00 - 2.56	14.00 - 5.13	28.00 -10.26	42.00 -15.39	56.00 -20.51	70.00 -25.64	84.01 -30.77
1.30	1.48 - 0.56	7.39 - 2.78	14.77 - 5.56	29.54 -11.11	44.31 -16.67	59.09 -22.22	73.86 -27.78	88.63 -33.33
1.35	1.55 - 0.61	7.77 - 3.03	15.53 - 6.06	31.07 -12.12	46.60 -18.18	62.13 -24.24	77.67 -30.30	93.20 -36.36
1.40	1.63 - 0.65	8.14 - 3.33	16.29 - 6.67	32.58 -13.33	48.86 -20.00	65.15 -26.67	81.44 -33.33	97.73 -40.00
1.45	1.70 - 0.72	8.52 - 3.62	17.04 - 7.25	34.07 -14.49	51.11 -21.74	68.14 -28.99	85.18 -36.23	102.2 -43.48
1.50	1.78 - 0.83	8.89 - 4.17	17.78 - 8.33	35.55 -16.67	53.33 -25.00	71.11 -33.33	88.88 -41.67	106.7 -50.00
1.55	1.85 - 1.11	9.26 - 5.56	18.51 -11.11	37.02 -22.22	55.53 -33.34	74.05 -44.45	92.56 -55.56	111.1 -66.67
1.60	1.92 - 2.22	9.62 - 11.11	19.24 -22.22	38.48 -44.44	57.72 -66.67	76.96 -88.89	96.20 -111.1	115.4 -133.3

Produced by: Tom Mount / Mark Owens ♠Copyright 1993-2000: IANTD/IAND, Inc./Repetitive Diver, Inc.

⚠ **Warning: DO NOT attempt to use these tables unless you are fully trained & certified in the use of gas mixtures other than air, or are under the supervision of a gas mixtures other than air instructor. Proper use of these tables will reduce the risk of decompression sickness & oxygen toxicity, but no table or computer can eliminate those risks.**

Table 6 may be used as a quick reference for END values on a known mix. If a trimix 14 /45 is used at 270 feet, by finding the mix and going down the page to 270 feet the END will be 120 feet.

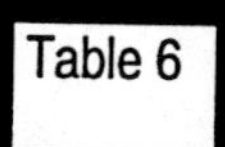

Equivalent Nitrogen Depths For Trimixtures

% Oxygen →	16%	14%	12%	15%	13%	12%
% Helium →	24%	33%	40%	45%	50%	63%
FSW	FSW	FSW	FSW	FSW	FSW	FSW
180	129	110	96	75	67	34
190	136	117	102	80	71	38
200	144	123	109	85	76	41
210	152	130	115	90	81	44
220	159	137	121	95	85	47
230	167	143	127	100	90	50
240	174	150	133	105	95	53
250	184	157	139	110	100	57
260	190	164	145	115	104	60
270	197	170	151	120	109	63
280	205	177	157	125	114	66
290	212	184	163	131	118	69
300	220	190	169	136	123	72
310	228	197	175	141	128	76
320	235	204	181	146	132	79
330	243	211	188	151	137	82
340	250	217	194	156	142	85
350	258	224	200	161	146	88
360	265	231	206	166	151	91
370	273	237	212	171	156	95
380	281	244	218	176	160	98
390	288	251	224	181	165	101
400	296	257	230	186	170	104

Produced by: Mount / Owens / Townsend

Note: Please be advised that the PO_2 of some of the mixes at certain depths will exceed 1.6 ATA. This chart is intended to show Equivalent Narcosis Depths only.

Table 7

Planning Information for Simplified Mixes

(PO_2 = 1.4 ATA)

MAXIMUM OPERATING DEPTH (MOD) FOR TRIMIXTURES IN FEET

	21%		26%		30%		32%		34%		36%	
END (FSW) →	187		133		103		91		81		71	
	Mix		Mix		Mix		Mix		Mix		Mix	
He %	O_2 %	MOD	O_2 %	MOD	O_2 %	MOD	O_2 %	MOD	O_2 %	MOD	O_2 %	MOD
2	21	191	25	148	29	124	31	114	33	106	35	98
4	20	196	25	152	29	127	31	117	33	109	35	101
6	20	201	24	156	28	131	30	121	32	112	34	104
8	19	206	24	160	28	134	29	124	31	115	33	106
10	19	211	23	164	27	138	29	127	31	118	32	110
12	18	217	23	169	26	142	28	131	30	121	32	113
14	18	223	22	174	26	146	28	135	29	125	31	116
16	18	229	22	179	25	150	27	139	29	129	30	120
18	17	235	21	184	25	155	26	143	28	133	30	124
20	17	242	21	189	24	160	26	147	27	137	29	127
22	16	249	20	195	23	164	25	152	27	141	28	132
24	16	256	20	201	23	170	24	157	26	146	27	136
26	16	264	19	207	22	175	24	162	25	151	27	140
28	15	273	19	214	22	181	23	168	24	156	26	145
30	15	281	18	221	21	187	22	173	24	161	25	150
32	14	291	18	228	20	193	22	179	23	167	24	156
34	14	300	17	236	20	200	21	186	22	173	24	161
36	13	311	17	245	19	208	20	193	22	179	23	168
38	13	322	16	254	19	215	20	200	21	186	22	174
40	13	334	16	263	18	224	19	208	20	193	22	181
42	12	346	15	273	17	233	19	216	20	201	21	188
44	12	360	15	284	17	242	18	225	19	210	20	196
46	11	374	14	296	16	252	17	234	18	219	19	205
48	11	390	14	309	16	263	17	245	18	228	19	214
50	11	407	13	322	15	275	16	256	17	239	18	224
52	10	425	12	337	14	288	15	268	16	250	17	234
54	10	445	12	353	14	302	15	281	16	262	17	246
56	9	467	11	371	13	317	14	295	15	276	16	259
58	9	491	11	390	13	334	13	311	14	291	15	273
60	8	517	10	411	12	352	13	328	14	307	14	288

Produced by: Mount / Owens / Blunt

⚠ **Warning: DO NOT attempt to use these tables unless you are fully trained & certified in the use of gas mixtures other than air, or are under the supervision of a gas mixtures other than air instructor. Proper use of these tables will reduce the risk of decompression sickness & oxygen toxicity, but no table or computer can eliminate those risks.**

Table 8

IANTD EAD/MOD TABLES

30 % O2

	ACTUAL DEPTH FSW										
	40	50	60	70	80	90	100	110	120	130	140
EAD	32	41	49	58	67	76	85	94	103	111	120
PO2	0.66	0.75	0.85	0.94	1.03	1.12	1.21	1.30	1.39	1.48	1.57
OTU MIN	0.40	0.57	0.74	0.89	1.05	1.19	1.34	1.48	1.62	1.75	1.88
% CNS O2	0.16	0.20	0.24	0.29	0.35	0.42	0.48	0.56	0.65	0.79	1.30

PO2	MOD/FSW
1.30	110
1.35	116
1.40	121
1.45	127
1.50	132
1.55	138
1.60	143

32 % O2

	ACTUAL DEPTH FSW									
	40	50	60	70	80	90	100	110	120	130
EAD	30	38	47	56	64	73	81	90	99	107
PO2	0.71	0.80	0.90	1.00	1.10	1.19	1.29	1.39	1.48	1.58
OTU MIN	0.48	0.66	0.83	1.00	1.16	1.31	1.46	1.61	1.75	1.90
% CNS O2	0.18	0.22	0.28	0.33	0.41	0.47	0.54	0.64	0.79	1.47

PO2	MOD/FSW
1.30	101
1.35	106
1.40	111
1.45	117
1.50	122
1.55	127
1.60	132

28 % O2

	ACTUAL DEPTH FSW											
	40	50	60	70	80	90	100	110	120	130	140	150
EAD	34	43	52	61	70	79	88	97	106	116	125	134
PO2	0.62	0.70	0.79	0.87	0.96	1.04	1.13	1.21	1.30	1.38	1.47	1.55
OTU MIN	0.30	0.48	0.63	0.79	0.93	1.07	1.21	1.34	1.47	1.60	1.73	1.86
% CNS O2	0.14	0.18	0.21	0.26	0.30	0.36	0.43	0.48	0.55	0.64	0.76	1.11

PO2	MOD/FSW
1.30	120
1.35	126
1.40	132
1.45	138
1.50	144
1.55	150
1.60	156

34 % O2

	ACTUAL DEPTH FSW								
	40	50	60	70	80	90	100	110	120
EAD	28	36	45	53	61	70	78	86	95
PO2	0.75	0.86	0.96	1.06	1.16	1.27	1.37	1.47	1.58
OTU MIN	0.57	0.75	0.93	1.10	1.27	1.43	1.58	1.74	1.89
% CNS O2	0.20	0.25	0.30	0.38	0.45	0.52	0.63	0.78	1.30

PO2	MOD/FSW
1.30	93
1.35	98
1.40	103
1.45	108
1.50	113
1.55	117
1.60	122

26 % O2

	ACTUAL DEPTH FSW													
	40	50	60	70	80	90	100	110	120	130	140	150	160	170
EAD	35	45	54	63	73	82	92	101	110	120	129	138	148	157
PO2	0.58	0.65	0.73	0.81	0.89	0.97	1.05	1.13	1.21	1.28	1.36	1.44	1.52	1.60
OTU MIN	0.21	0.38	0.53	0.68	0.81	0.95	1.08	1.21	1.33	1.45	1.57	1.69	1.81	1.92
% CNS O2	0.00	0.16	0.19	0.23	0.27	0.31	0.36	0.43	0.48	0.54	0.62	0.72	0.93	1.72

PO2	MOD/FSW
1.30	132
1.35	138
1.40	145
1.45	151
1.50	157
1.55	164
1.60	170

36 % O2

	ACTUAL DEPTH FSW							
	40	50	60	70	80	90	100	110
EAD	26	34	42	50	59	67	75	83
PO2	0.80	0.91	1.01	1.12	1.23	1.34	1.45	1.56
OTU MIN	0.65	0.84	1.02	1.20	1.37	1.54	1.70	1.87
% CNS O2	0.22	0.28	0.34	0.43	0.50	0.60	0.74	1.19

PO2	MOD/FSW
1.30	86
1.35	91
1.40	95
1.45	100
1.50	105
1.55	109
1.60	114

24 % O2

	ACTUAL DEPTH FSW														
	40	50	60	70	80	90	100	110	120	130	140	150	160	170	180
EAD	37	47	56	66	76	85	95	105	114	124	133	143	153	162	172
PO2	0.53	0.60	0.68	0.75	0.82	0.89	0.97	1.04	1.11	1.19	1.26	1.33	1.40	1.48	1.55
OTU MIN	0.10	0.27	0.42	0.56	0.69	0.82	0.95	1.07	1.18	1.30	1.41	1.52	1.63	1.74	1.85
% CNS O2	0.00	0.14	0.16	0.19	0.23	0.27	0.31	0.36	0.42	0.46	0.51	0.58	0.67	0.78	1.04

PO2	MOD/FSW
1.30	146
1.35	153
1.40	160
1.45	166
1.50	173
1.55	180
1.60	187

38 % O2

	ACTUAL DEPTH FSW						
	40	50	60	70	80	90	100
EAD	24	32	40	48	56	64	71
PO2	0.84	0.96	1.07	1.19	1.30	1.42	1.53
OTU MIN	0.73	0.93	1.12	1.30	1.48	1.65	1.82
% CNS O2	0.24	0.30	0.39	0.46	0.56	0.68	0.98

PO2	MOD/FSW
1.30	80
1.35	84
1.40	89
1.45	93
1.50	97
1.55	102
1.60	106

PRODUCED BY TOM MOUNT/MARK OWENS

⚠ Warning: DO NOT attempt to use these tables unless you are fully trained & certified in the use of gas mixtures other than air, or are under the supervision of a gas mixtures other than air instructor. Proper use of these tables will reduce the risk of decompression sickness & oxygen toxicity, but no table or computer can eliminate those risks.

Table 8 B

IANTD EAD/MOD TABLES

40 % O2

ACTUAL DEPTH FSW	40	50	60	70	80	90	100
EAD	22	30	38	45	53	60	68
PO2	0.88	1.01	1.13	1.25	1.37	1.49	1.61
OTU MIN	0.80	1.01	1.21	1.40	1.58	1.76	1.94
% CNS O2	0.26	0.33	0.43	0.51	0.62	0.81	2.50

PO2	MOD/FSW
1.30	74
1.35	78
1.40	82
1.45	87
1.50	91
1.55	95
1.60	99

60 % O2

ACTUAL DEPTH FSW	10	20	30	40	50
EAD	0	0	0	4	9
PO2	0.78	0.96	1.15	1.33	1.51
OTU MIN	0.62	0.94	1.24	1.52	1.79
% CNS O2	0.21	0.31	0.44	0.57	0.83

PO2	MOD/FSW
1.30	39
1.35	41
1.40	44
1.45	47
1.50	50
1.55	52
1.60	55

80 % O2

FSW	10	20	30
EAD	0	0	0
PO2	1.04	1.28	1.53
OTU MIN	1.07	1.45	1.82
% CNS O2	0.36	0.54	0.93

PO2	MOD/FSW
1.30	21
1.35	23
1.40	25
1.45	27
1.50	29
1.55	31
1.60	33

45 % O2

ACTUAL DEPTH FSW	10	20	30	40	50	60	80
EAD	0	4	11	18	25	32	46
PO2	0.59	0.72	0.86	1.00	1.13	1.27	1.54
OTU MIN	0.23	0.51	0.76	0.99	1.21	1.43	1.84
% CNS O2	0.00	0.18	0.25	0.33	0.43	0.52	1.04

PO2	MOD/FSW
1.30	62
1.35	66
1.40	70
1.45	73
1.50	77
1.55	81
1.60	84

65 % O2

ACTUAL DEPTH FSW	10	20	30	40
EAD	0	0	0	0
PO2	0.85	1.04	1.24	1.44
OTU MIN	0.74	1.07	1.39	1.69
% CNS O2	0.24	0.36	0.51	0.71

PO2	MOD/FSW
1.30	33
1.35	36
1.40	38
1.45	41
1.50	43
1.55	46
1.60	48

85 % O2

FSW	10	20
EAD	0	0
PO2	1.11	1.37
OTU MIN	1.18	1.58
% CNS O2	0.42	0.62

PO2	MOD/FSW
1.30	17
1.35	19
1.40	21
1.45	23
1.50	25
1.55	27
1.60	29

90 % O2

FSW	10	20
EAD	0	0
PO2	1.17	1.45
OTU MIN	1.28	1.70
% CNS O2	0.46	0.72

PO2	MOD/FSW
1.30	15
1.35	17
1.40	18
1.45	20
1.50	22
1.55	24
1.60	26

50 % O2

ACTUAL DEPTH FSW	10	20	30	40	50	60
EAD	0	1	7	13	20	26
PO2	0.65	0.80	0.95	1.11	1.26	1.41
OTU MIN	0.37	0.66	0.92	1.17	1.41	1.64
% CNS O2	0.16	0.22	0.30	0.42	0.51	0.67

PO2	MOD/FSW
1.30	53
1.35	56
1.40	59
1.45	63
1.50	66
1.55	69
1.60	73

70 % O2

ACTUAL DEPTH FSW	10	20	30	40
EAD	0	0	0	0
PO2	0.91	1.12	1.34	1.55
OTU MIN	0.85	1.20	1.53	1.85
% CNS O2	0.28	0.43	0.58	1.04

PO2	MOD/FSW
1.30	28
1.35	31
1.40	33
1.45	35
1.50	38
1.55	40
1.60	42

95 % O2

FSW	10	20
EAD	0	0
PO2	1.24	1.53
OTU MIN	1.38	1.82
% CNS O2	0.50	0.93

PO2	MOD/FSW
1.30	12
1.35	14
1.40	16
1.45	17
1.50	19
1.55	21
1.60	23

100 % O2

FSW	10	20
EAD	0	0
PO2	1.30	1.61
OTU MIN	1.48	1.93
% CNS O2	0.56	2.22

PO2	MOD/FSW
1.30	10
1.35	12
1.40	13
1.45	15
1.50	17
1.55	18
1.60	20

55 % O2

ACTUAL DEPTH FSW	10	20	30	40	50	60
EAD	0	0	3	9	14	20
PO2	0.72	0.88	1.05	1.22	1.38	1.55
OTU MIN	0.50	0.80	1.08	1.35	1.60	1.85
% CNS O2	0.18	0.26	0.37	0.48	0.64	1.11

PO2	MOD/FSW
1.30	45
1.35	48
1.40	51
1.45	54
1.50	57
1.55	60
1.60	63

75 % O2

FSW	10	20	30
EAD	0	0	0
PO2	0.98	1.20	1.43
OTU MIN	0.96	1.33	1.68
% CNS O2	0.31	0.48	0.71

PO2	MOD/FSW
1.30	24
1.35	26
1.40	29
1.45	31
1.50	33
1.55	35
1.60	37

PRODUCED BY TOM MOUNT/MARK OWENS

⚠ **Warning: DO NOT attempt to use these tables unless you are fully trained & certified in the use of gas mixtures other than air, or are under the supervision of a gas mixtures other than air instructor. Proper use of these tables will reduce the risk of decompression sickness & oxygen toxicity, but no table or computer can eliminate those risks.**

Table 9

IANTD GAS MANAGEMENT CHART - U.S. VERSION

PSIG/Min to SAC (Cu.Ft./Min)

TANK PRESSURE AND SIZE																
PSIG →	2475	2640	2640	2640	2640	2640	3000	3000	3190	3190	3190	3500	3500	3500	3500	4400
Cu.Ft. →	70	45	95	104	108	121	70	80	95	120	140	65	80	100	120	190
PSI/min																
6	0.17	0.10	0.22	0.24	0.25	0.28	0.14	0.16	0.18	0.23	0.26	0.11	0.14	0.17	0.21	0.26
7	0.20	0.12	0.25	0.28	0.29	0.32	0.16	0.19	0.21	0.26	0.31	0.13	0.16	0.20	0.24	0.30
8	0.23	0.14	0.29	0.32	0.33	0.37	0.19	0.21	0.24	0.30	0.35	0.15	0.18	0.23	0.27	0.35
9	0.25	0.15	0.32	0.35	0.37	0.41	0.21	0.24	0.27	0.34	0.39	0.17	0.21	0.26	0.31	0.39
10	0.28	0.17	0.36	0.39	0.41	0.46	0.23	0.27	0.30	0.38	0.44	0.19	0.23	0.29	0.34	0.43
11	0.31	0.19	0.40	0.43	0.45	0.50	0.26	0.29	0.33	0.41	0.48	0.20	0.25	0.31	0.38	0.48
12	0.34	0.20	0.43	0.47	0.49	0.55	0.28	0.32	0.36	0.45	0.53	0.22	0.27	0.34	0.41	0.52
13	0.37	0.22	0.47	0.51	0.53	0.60	0.30	0.35	0.39	0.49	0.57	0.24	0.30	0.37	0.45	0.56
14	0.40	0.24	0.50	0.55	0.57	0.64	0.33	0.37	0.42	0.53	0.61	0.26	0.32	0.40	0.48	0.60
15	0.42	0.26	0.54	0.59	0.61	0.69	0.35	0.40	0.45	0.56	0.66	0.28	0.34	0.43	0.51	0.65
16	0.45	0.27	0.58	0.63	0.65	0.73	0.37	0.43	0.48	0.60	0.70	0.30	0.37	0.46	0.55	0.69
17	0.48	0.29	0.61	0.67	0.70	0.78	0.40	0.45	0.51	0.64	0.75	0.32	0.39	0.49	0.58	0.73
18	0.51	0.31	0.65	0.71	0.74	0.83	0.42	0.48	0.54	0.68	0.79	0.33	0.41	0.51	0.62	0.78
19	0.54	0.32	0.68	0.75	0.78	0.87	0.44	0.51	0.57	0.71	0.83	0.35	0.43	0.54	0.65	0.82
20	0.57	0.34	0.72	0.79	0.82	0.92	0.47	0.53	0.60	0.75	0.88	0.37	0.46	0.57	0.69	0.86
21	0.59	0.36	0.76	0.83	0.86	0.96	0.49	0.56	0.63	0.79	0.92	0.39	0.48	0.60	0.72	0.91
22	0.62	0.38	0.79	0.87	0.90	1.01	0.51	0.59	0.66	0.83	0.97	0.41	0.50	0.63	0.75	0.95
23	0.65	0.39	0.83	0.91	0.94	1.05	0.54	0.61	0.68	0.87	1.01	0.43	0.53	0.66	0.79	0.99
24	0.68	0.41	0.86	0.95	0.98	1.10	0.56	0.64	0.71	0.90	1.05	0.45	0.55	0.69	0.82	1.04
25	0.71	0.43	0.90	0.98	1.02	1.15	0.58	0.67	0.74	0.94	1.10	0.46	0.57	0.71	0.86	1.08
26	0.74	0.44	0.94	1.02	1.06	1.19	0.61	0.69	0.77	0.98	1.14	0.48	0.59	0.74	0.89	1.12
27	0.76	0.46	0.97	1.06	1.10	1.24	0.63	0.72	0.80	1.02	1.18	0.50	0.62	0.77	0.93	1.17
28	0.79	0.48	1.01	1.10	1.15	1.28	0.65	0.75	0.83	1.05	1.23	0.52	0.64	0.80	0.96	1.21
29	0.82	0.49	1.04	1.14	1.19	1.33	0.68	0.77	0.86	1.09	1.27	0.54	0.66	0.83	0.99	1.25
30	0.85	0.51	1.08	1.18	1.23	1.38	0.70	0.80	0.89	1.13	1.32	0.56	0.69	0.86	1.03	1.30
31	0.88	0.53	1.12	1.22	1.27	1.42	0.72	0.83	0.92	1.17	1.36	0.58	0.71	0.89	1.06	1.34
32	0.91	0.55	1.15	1.26	1.31	1.47	0.75	0.85	0.95	1.20	1.40	0.59	0.73	0.91	1.10	1.38
33	0.93	0.56	1.19	1.30	1.35	1.51	0.77	0.88	0.98	1.24	1.45	0.61	0.75	0.94	1.13	1.43
34	0.96	0.58	1.22	1.34	1.39	1.56	0.79	0.91	1.01	1.28	1.49	0.63	0.78	0.97	1.17	1.47
35	0.99	0.60	1.26	1.38	1.43	1.60	0.82	0.93	1.04	1.32	1.54	0.65	0.80	1.00	1.20	1.51
36	1.02	0.61	1.30	1.42	1.47	1.65	0.84	0.96	1.07	1.35	1.58	0.67	0.82	1.03	1.23	1.55
37	1.05	0.63	1.33	1.46	1.51	1.70	0.86	0.99	1.10	1.39	1.62	0.69	0.85	1.06	1.27	1.60
38	1.07	0.65	1.37	1.50	1.55	1.74	0.89	1.01	1.13	1.43	1.67	0.71	0.87	1.09	1.30	1.64
39	1.10	0.66	1.40	1.54	1.60	1.79	0.91	1.04	1.16	1.47	1.71	0.72	0.89	1.11	1.34	1.68
40	1.13	0.68	1.44	1.58	1.64	1.83	0.93	1.07	1.19	1.50	1.76	0.74	0.91	1.14	1.37	1.73

Produced by: Mount/Owens/Taylor

To determine your SAC in Cubic Feet per Minute, first find the correct tank size across the top.

EXAMPLE: Tank is 80 Cubic Feet at 3000 PSIG.

Then find your consumption rate in PSI/Min in the left column. **EXAMPLE: 20 PSI/Min**

The number where the column and row intersect is your SAC in Cubic Feet per Minute. **EXAMPLE: 0.53**

⚠ Warning: DO NOT attempt to use these tables unless you are fully trained & certified in the use of gas mixtures other than air, or are under the supervision of a gas mixtures other than air instructor. Proper use of these tables will reduce the risk of decompression sickness & oxygen toxicity, but no table or computer can eliminate those risks.

Table 10

IANTD GAS MANAGEMENT CHART

IMPERIAL-US VERSION GAS USED PER MINUTE IN PSIG

GAS USED PER MINUTE IN PSIG																		
SAC →	6	8	10	12	14	16	18	20	22	24	26	28	30	32	34	36	38	40
FSW ↓																		
10	8	10	13	16	18	21	23	26	29	31	34	36	39	42	44	47	50	52
20	10	13	16	19	22	26	29	32	35	39	42	45	48	51	55	58	61	64
30	11	15	19	23	27	31	34	38	42	46	50	53	57	61	65	69	73	76
40	13	18	22	27	31	35	40	44	49	53	58	62	66	71	75	80	84	88
50	15	20	25	30	35	40	45	50	55	60	65	70	75	80	86	91	96	101
60	17	23	28	34	39	45	51	56	62	68	73	79	85	90	96	101	107	113
70	19	25	31	37	44	50	56	62	69	75	81	87	94	100	106	112	119	125
80	21	27	34	41	48	55	62	68	75	82	89	96	103	110	116	123	130	137
90	22	30	37	45	52	60	67	75	82	89	97	104	112	119	127	134	142	149
100	24	32	40	48	56	64	73	81	89	97	105	113	121	129	137	145	153	161
110	26	35	43	52	61	69	78	87	95	104	113	121	130	139	147	156	165	173
120	28	37	46	56	65	74	83	93	102	111	121	130	139	148	158	167	176	185
130	30	40	49	59	69	79	89	99	109	119	128	138	148	158	168	178	188	198
140	31	42	52	63	73	84	94	105	115	126	136	147	157	168	178	189	199	210
150	33	44	55	67	78	89	100	111	122	133	144	155	166	177	189	200	211	222
160	35	47	58	70	82	94	105	117	129	140	152	164	175	187	199	211	222	234
170	37	49	62	74	86	98	111	123	135	148	160	172	185	197	209	221	234	246
180	39	52	65	77	90	103	116	129	142	155	168	181	194	207	219	232	245	258
190	41	54	68	81	95	108	122	135	149	162	176	189	203	216	230	243	257	270
200	42	56	71	85	99	113	127	141	155	169	184	198	212	226	240	254	268	282
210	44	59	74	88	103	118	133	147	162	177	191	206	221	236	250	265	280	295
220	46	61	77	92	107	123	138	153	169	184	199	215	230	245	261	276	291	307
230	48	64	80	96	112	128	143	159	175	191	207	223	239	255	271	287	303	319
240	50	66	83	99	116	132	149	165	182	199	215	232	248	265	281	298	314	331
250	51	69	86	103	120	137	154	172	189	206	223	240	257	274	292	309	326	343
260	53	71	89	107	124	142	160	178	195	213	231	249	266	284	302	320	337	355
270	55	73	92	110	129	147	165	184	202	220	239	257	275	294	312	331	349	367
280	57	76	95	114	133	152	171	190	209	228	247	266	285	304	322	341	360	379
290	59	78	98	117	137	157	176	196	215	235	254	274	294	313	333	352	372	392
300	61	81	101	121	141	161	182	202	222	242	262	283	303	323	343	363	383	404

If using a cylinder where the psig/bar per minute is known, gas calculations may be completed from Table 10. For instance, a diver breathes at a SAC rate of 10 psig (.66 bar) per minute. If the dive is planned to 300 feet (91 meters), the diver will use 101 psig (6.1 bar) per minute. This means that on a 20 minute dive the diver would use 2020 psig (122 bar).

Table 11

IANTD GAS MANAGEMENT CHART
SAC / FSW Table

	SURFACE AIR CONSUMPTION IN CUBIC FEET PER MINUTE																
FSW	0.35	0.40	0.45	0.50	0.55	0.60	0.65	0.70	0.75	0.80	0.85	0.90	0.95	1.00	1.05	1.10	1.15
10	0.5	0.5	0.6	0.7	0.7	0.8	0.8	0.9	1.0	1.0	1.1	1.2	1.2	1.3	1.4	1.4	1.5
15	0.5	0.6	0.7	0.7	0.8	0.9	0.9	1.0	1.1	1.2	1.2	1.3	1.4	1.5	1.5	1.6	1.7
20	0.6	0.6	0.7	0.8	0.9	1.0	1.0	1.1	1.2	1.3	1.4	1.4	1.5	1.6	1.7	1.8	1.8
30	0.7	0.8	0.9	1.0	1.1	1.1	1.2	1.3	1.4	1.5	1.6	1.7	1.8	1.9	2.0	2.1	2.2
40	0.8	0.9	1.0	1.1	1.2	1.3	1.4	1.5	1.7	1.8	1.9	2.0	2.1	2.2	2.3	2.4	2.5
50	0.9	1.0	1.1	1.3	1.4	1.5	1.6	1.8	1.9	2.0	2.1	2.3	2.4	2.5	2.6	2.8	2.9
60	1.0	1.1	1.3	1.4	1.6	1.7	1.8	2.0	2.1	2.3	2.4	2.5	2.7	2.8	3.0	3.1	3.2
70	1.1	1.2	1.4	1.6	1.7	1.9	2.0	2.2	2.3	2.5	2.7	2.8	3.0	3.1	3.3	3.4	3.6
80	1.2	1.4	1.5	1.7	1.9	2.1	2.2	2.4	2.6	2.7	2.9	3.1	3.3	3.4	3.6	3.8	3.9
90	1.3	1.5	1.7	1.9	2.1	2.2	2.4	2.6	2.8	3.0	3.2	3.4	3.5	3.7	3.9	4.1	4.3
100	1.4	1.6	1.8	2.0	2.2	2.4	2.6	2.8	3.0	3.2	3.4	3.6	3.8	4.0	4.2	4.4	4.6
110	1.5	1.7	2.0	2.2	2.4	2.6	2.8	3.0	3.3	3.5	3.7	3.9	4.1	4.3	4.6	4.8	5.0
120	1.6	1.9	2.1	2.3	2.6	2.8	3.0	3.2	3.5	3.7	3.9	4.2	4.4	4.6	4.9	5.1	5.3
130	1.7	2.0	2.2	2.5	2.7	3.0	3.2	3.5	3.7	4.0	4.2	4.4	4.7	4.9	5.2	5.4	5.7
140	1.8	2.1	2.4	2.6	2.9	3.1	3.4	3.7	3.9	4.2	4.5	4.7	5.0	5.2	5.5	5.8	6.0
150	1.9	2.2	2.5	2.8	3.1	3.3	3.6	3.9	4.2	4.4	4.7	5.0	5.3	5.5	5.8	6.1	6.4
160	2.0	2.3	2.6	2.9	3.2	3.5	3.8	4.1	4.4	4.7	5.0	5.3	5.6	5.8	6.1	6.4	6.7
170	2.2	2.5	2.8	3.1	3.4	3.7	4.0	4.3	4.6	4.9	5.2	5.5	5.8	6.2	6.5	6.8	7.1
180	2.3	2.6	2.9	3.2	3.6	3.9	4.2	4.5	4.8	5.2	5.5	5.8	6.1	6.5	6.8	7.1	7.4
190	2.4	2.7	3.0	3.4	3.7	4.1	4.4	4.7	5.1	5.4	5.7	6.1	6.4	6.8	7.1	7.4	7.8
200	2.5	2.8	3.2	3.5	3.9	4.2	4.6	4.9	5.3	5.6	6.0	6.4	6.7	7.1	7.4	7.8	8.1
210	2.6	2.9	3.3	3.7	4.1	4.4	4.8	5.2	5.5	5.9	6.3	6.6	7.0	7.4	7.7	8.1	8.5
220	2.7	3.1	3.5	3.8	4.2	4.6	5.0	5.4	5.8	6.1	6.5	6.9	7.3	7.7	8.1	8.4	8.8
230	2.8	3.2	3.6	4.0	4.4	4.8	5.2	5.6	6.0	6.4	6.8	7.2	7.6	8.0	8.4	8.8	9.2
240	2.9	3.3	3.7	4.1	4.6	5.0	5.4	5.8	6.2	6.6	7.0	7.4	7.9	8.3	8.7	9.1	9.5
250	3.0	3.4	3.9	4.3	4.7	5.1	5.6	6.0	6.4	6.9	7.3	7.7	8.1	8.6	9.0	9.4	9.9
260	3.1	3.6	4.0	4.4	4.9	5.3	5.8	6.2	6.7	7.1	7.5	8.0	8.4	8.9	9.3	9.8	10.2
270	3.2	3.7	4.1	4.6	5.1	5.5	6.0	6.4	6.9	1.0	0.9	8.3	8.7	9.2	9.6	10.1	10.6
280	3.3	3.8	4.3	4.7	5.2	5.7	6.2	6.6	7.1	7.6	8.1	8.5	9.0	9.5	10.0	10.4	10.9
290	3.4	3.9	4.4	4.9	5.4	5.9	6.4	6.9	7.3	7.8	8.3	8.8	9.3	9.8	10.3	10.8	11.3
300	3.5	4.0	4.5	5.0	5.6	6.1	6.6	7.1	7.6	8.1	8.6	9.1	9.6	10.1	10.6	11.1	11.6
310	3.6	4.2	4.7	5.2	5.7	6.2	6.8	7.3	7.8	8.3	8.8	9.4	9.9	10.4	10.9	11.4	12.0
320	3.7	4.3	4.8	5.3	5.9	6.4	7.0	7.5	8.0	8.6	9.1	9.6	10.2	10.7	11.2	11.8	12.3
330	3.9	4.4	5.0	5.5	6.1	6.6	7.2	7.7	0.8	8.8	9.4	9.9	10.5	11.0	11.6	12.1	12.7
340	4.0	4.5	5.1	5.7	6.2	6.8	7.3	7.9	8.5	9.0	9.6	10.2	10.7	11.3	11.9	12.4	13.0
350	4.1	4.6	5.2	5.8	6.4	7.0	7.5	8.1	8.7	9.3	9.9	10.4	11.0	11.6	12.2	12.8	13.3

Locate your Surface Air Consumption (SAC) across the top row.
Example: 0.65 (SAC) Cubic Feet per Minute
Go down the column under the 0.65 until you get to your depth location row from the far left column
Example: 200 FSW
This gives you the SAC for one minute at this depth.
Example: 4.6 Cubic Feet per Minute per Minute.

⚠ Warning: DO NOT attempt to use these tables unless you are fully trained & certified in the use of gas mixtures other than air, or are under the supervision of a gas mixtures other than air instructor. Proper use of these tables will reduce the risk of decompression sickness & oxygen toxicity, but no table or computer can eliminate those risks.

TABLE 12

IANTD GAS MANAGEMENT - IMPERIAL - VERSION
PSIG / CUBIC FOOT CONVERSION TABLE

	PSIG	100	500	1000	1500	2000	2500	3000	3500	4000
CYLINDER SIZE	2475/70	2.80	14.10	28.30	42.40	56.60	70.70	84.80	99.00	113.10
	2640/46	1.70	8.70	17.40	26.10	34.80	43.60	52.30	61.00	69.70
	2640/66	2.50	12.50	25.00	37.50	50.00	62.50	75.00	87.50	100.00
	2640/85	3.20	16.10	32.20	48.30	64.40	80.50	96.60	112.70	128.80
	2640/98	3.70	18.60	37.10	55.70	74.20	92.80	111.40	129.90	148.50
	2640/104	3.90	19.70	39.40	59.10	78.80	98.50	118.20	137.90	157.60
	2640/112	4.20	21.20	42.40	63.60	84.80	106.10	127.30	148.50	169.70
	2640/125	4.60	22.90	45.80	68.80	91.70	114.60	137.50	160.40	183.30
	2640/131	5.00	24.80	49.60	74.40	99.20	124.00	148.90	173.70	198.50
	3000/70	2.30	11.70	23.30	35.00	46.70	58.30	70.00	81.70	93.30
	3000/80	2.70	13.30	26.70	40.00	53.30	66.70	80.00	93.30	106.70
	3190/95	3.00	14.90	29.80	44.70	59.60	74.50	89.30	104.20	119.10
	3190/120	3.80	18.80	37.60	56.40	75.20	94.00	112.90	131.70	150.50
	3190/140	4.40	21.90	43.90	65.80	87.80	109.70	131.70	153.60	175.50
	3500/65	1.90	9.30	18.60	27.90	37.10	46.40	55.70	65.00	74.30
	3500/80	2.30	11.40	22.90	34.30	45.70	57.10	68.60	80.00	91.40
	3500/100	2.90	14.30	28.60	42.90	57.10	71.40	85.70	100.00	114.30
	3500/120	3.40	17.10	34.30	51.40	68.60	85.70	102.90	120.00	137.10

Produced by: Mount/Owens/Taylor/Townsend

The column on the left shows PSIG for various sizes of cylinders. To determine the amount of gas in a cylinder, first locate the cylinder size from the column on the left. **Example: 3500 PSIG/100 cubic feet.** Then read the gauge pressure: **Example: 2700 PSIG**. Go to the column marked "2500 PSIG" and follow this column down to the row marked "3500/100". This represents the cubic feet for that quantity of gas. **Example: 71.4**. Now find the column marked "100 PSIG". This gives you 2.9 cubic feet. You then must multiply this number by 2. **Example: (2700 - 2500) = 200 (200/100 = 2) 2.9 x 2 = 5.8**

Add these two numbers to get the total gas in cubic feet in the cylinder. **Example: 71.4 + 5.8 = 77.2 cubic feet.**

Note: This is for a single cylinder. If you are using doubles, you must also double the cubic feet. The above example would then be 154.4 cubic feet.

⚠ **Warning: DO NOT attempt to use these tables unless you are fully trained & certified in the use of gas mixtures other than air, or are under the supervision of a gas mixtures other than air instructor. Proper use of these tables will reduce the risk of decompression sickness & oxygen toxicity, but no table or computer can eliminate those risks.**

Table 13

IANTD GAS MANAGEMENT CHART - U.S. VERSION

SAC RATIO FACTOR (SRF)

	<<<<<<<<<<<<<< CUBIC FEET >>>>>>>>>>>>>>																
↑		1.15	1.10	1.05	1.00	0.95	0.90	0.85	0.80	0.75	0.70	0.65	0.60	0.55	0.50	0.45	0.40	0.35
↑	1.15	0.67																
↑	1.10	0.67	0.67															
↑	1.05	0.68	0.67	0.67														
C	1.00	0.68	0.68	0.67	0.67													
U	0.95	0.69	0.68	0.68	0.67	0.67												
B	0.90	0.69	0.69	0.68	0.68	0.67	0.67											
I	0.85	0.70	0.70	0.69	0.69	0.68	0.67	0.67										
C	0.80	0.71	0.70	0.70	0.69	0.69	0.68	0.67	0.67									
	0.75	0.72	0.71	0.71	0.70	0.69	0.69	0.68	0.67	0.67								
F	0.70	0.73	0.72	0.71	0.71	0.70	0.70	0.69	0.68	0.67	0.67							
E	0.65	0.73	0.73	0.72	0.72	0.71	0.70	0.70	0.69	0.68	0.67	0.67						
E	0.60	0.74	0.74	0.73	0.73	0.72	0.71	0.71	0.70	0.69	0.68	0.68	0.68					
T	0.55	0.76	0.75	0.74	0.74	0.73	0.73	0.72	0.71	0.70	0.69	0.69	0.68	0.67				
↓	0.50	0.77	0.76	0.76	0.75	0.74	0.74	0.73	0.72	0.71	0.71	0.70	0.69	0.68	0.67			
↓	0.45	0.78	0.78	0.77	0.76	0.76	0.75	0.74	0.74	0.73	0.72	0.71	0.70	0.69	0.68	0.67		
↓	0.40	0.79	0.79	0.78	0.78	0.77	0.76	0.76	0.75	0.74	0.73	0.72	0.71	0.70	0.69	0.68	0.67	
↓	0.35	0.81	0.81	0.80	0.79	0.79	0.78	0.77	0.77	0.76	0.75	0.74	0.73	0.72	0.71	0.70	0.68	0.67

Produced by: Mount/Owens/Taylor ♠ Copyright: IANTD/IAND, Inc./Repetitive Diver, Inc.

The SRF Table modifies the Rule of Thirds to represent true turn pressures for divers with different SAC rates. If you have a higher SAC rate than your buddy, the Rule of Thirds works fine. When you have consumed 33% of your gas, it's time to turn the dive. However, if your buddy has a higher SAC than you, this would not allow enough gas. In this situation, to find the proper turn pressure, locate your SAC along the **left column. EXAMPLE: 0.43 round your SAC down to 0.40 to provide the proper match points.**

Now go across the **top row** until you are under the column of your dive buddy's SAC.
EXAMPLE: 0.81 round the buddies higher SAC rate up to 0.85 to provide gas matching data.

The number where these two SACs intersect is the SRF. **EXAMPLE: 0.76**

You then multiply your cylinder pressure by the SRF number and this gives your turn pressure. You can also look up the turn pressure on the Turn Pressure Table.
EXAMPLE: You have 2700 PSIG in your cylinder. 2700 x 0.76 = 2052 PSIG

Strictly following the Rule of Thirds you would normally turn the dive at 1800 PSIG, which would not leave enough gas to exit.
You must turn at 2052 PSIG or rounded to 2100 PSIG.

IANTD GAS MANAGEMENT CHART – IMPERIAL-US VERSION

Turn Pressure

SRF → / PSIG ↓	0.67	0.68	0.69	0.70	0.71	0.72	0.73	0.74	0.75	0.76	0.77	0.78	0.79	0.80	0.81
2000	1340	1360	1380	1400	1420	1440	1460	1480	1500	1520	1540	1560	1580	1600	1620
2100	1407	1428	1449	1470	1491	1512	1533	1554	1575	1596	1617	1638	1659	1680	1701
2200	1474	1496	1518	1540	1562	1584	1606	1628	1650	1672	1694	1716	1738	1760	1782
2300	1541	1564	1587	1610	1633	1656	1679	1702	1725	1748	1771	1794	1817	1840	1863
2400	1608	1632	1656	1680	1704	1728	1752	1776	1800	1824	1848	1872	1896	1920	1944
2500	1675	1700	1725	1750	1775	1800	1825	1850	1875	1900	1925	1950	1975	2000	2025
2600	1742	1768	1794	1820	1846	1872	1898	1924	1950	1976	2002	2028	2054	2080	2106
2700	1809	1836	1863	1890	1917	1944	1971	1998	2025	2052	2079	2106	2133	2160	2187
2800	1876	1904	1932	1960	1988	2016	2044	2072	2100	2128	2156	2184	2212	2240	2268
2900	1943	1972	2001	2030	2059	2088	2117	2146	2175	2204	2233	2262	2291	2320	2349
3000	2010	2040	2070	2100	2130	2160	2190	2220	2250	2280	2310	2340	2370	2400	2430
3100	2077	2108	2139	2170	2201	2232	2263	2294	2325	2356	2387	2418	2449	2480	2511
3200	2144	2176	2208	2240	2272	2304	2336	2368	2400	2432	2464	2496	2528	2560	2592
3300	2211	2244	2277	2310	2343	2376	2409	2442	2475	2508	2541	2574	2607	2640	2673
3400	2278	2312	2346	2380	2414	2448	2482	2516	2550	2584	2618	2652	2686	2720	2754
3500	2345	2380	2415	2450	2485	2520	2555	2590	2625	2660	2695	2730	2765	2800	2835
3600	2412	2448	2484	2520	2556	2592	2628	2664	2700	2736	2772	2808	2844	2880	2916
3700	2479	2516	2553	2590	2627	2664	2701	2738	2775	2812	2849	2886	2923	2960	2997
3800	2546	2584	2622	2660	2698	2736	2774	2812	2850	2888	2926	2964	3002	3040	3078
3900	2613	2652	2691	2730	2769	2808	2847	2886	2925	2964	3003	3042	3081	3120	3159
4000	2680	2720	2760	2800	2840	2880	2920	2960	3000	3040	3080	3120	3160	3200	3240

To locate your turn pressure, first find your SRF from the IANTD SRF Table 13.

EXAMPLE: 0.76

Follow this column down until you are across from your tank pressure in the left column.

EXAMPLE: 2700 PSIG

The point of intersection is the turn pressure for this dive.

EXAMPLE: 2052 PSIG

⚠ **Warning: DO NOT attempt to use these tables unless you are fully trained & certified in the use of gas mixtures other than air, or are under the supervision of a gas mixtures other than air instructor. Proper use of these tables will reduce the risk of decompression sickness & oxygen toxicity, but no table or computer can eliminate those risks.**

Table 15

IANTD GAS MANAGEMENT CHART – IMPERIAL-US VERSION

MINUTES ALLOWED UNTIL TURN

PSIG USED ↓	GAS AVAILABLE UNTIL TURN IN PSIG												
	400	500	600	700	800	900	1000	1100	1200	1300	1400	1500	1600
15	27	33	40	47	53	60	67	73	80	87	93	100	107
30	13	17	20	23	27	30	33	37	40	43	47	50	53
45	99	11	13	16	18	20	22	24	27	29	31	33	36
60	7	8	10	12	13	15	17	18	20	22	23	25	27
75	5	7	8	9	11	12	13	15	16	17	19	20	21
90	4	6	7	8	9	10	11	12	13	14	16	17	18
105	4	5	6	7	8	9	10	10	11	12	13	14	15
120	3	4	5	6	7	8	8	9	10	11	12	13	13
135	3	4	4	5	6	7	7	8	9	10	10	11	12
150	3	3	4	5	5	6	7	7	8	9	9	10	11
165	2	3	4	4	5	5	6	7	7	8	8	9	10
180	2	3	3	4	4	5	6	6	7	7	8	8	9
195	2	3	3	4	4	5	5	6	6	7	7	8	8
210	2	2	3	3	4	4	5	5	6	6	7	7	8
225	2	2	3	3	4	4	4	5	5	6	6	7	7
240	2	2	3	3	3	4	4	5	5	5	6	6	7
255	2	2	2	3	3	4	4	4	5	5	5	6	6
270	1	2	2	3	3	3	4	4	4	5	5	6	6
285	1	2	2	2	3	3	4	4	4	5	5	5	6
300	1	2	2	2	3	3	3	4	4	4	5	5	5
315	1	2	2	2	3	3	3	3	4	4	4	5	5
330	1	2	2	2	2	3	3	3	4	4	4	5	5
345	1	1	2	2	2	3	3	3	3	4	4	4	5
360	1	1	2	2	2	3	3	3	3	4	4	4	4
375	1	1	2	2	2	2	3	3	3	3	4	4	4
390	1	1	2	2	2	2	3	3	3	3	4	4	4
400	1	1	2	2	2	2	3	3	3	3	4	4	4

"PSIG USED" IS PSIG CONSUMED PER MINUTE DURING THE DIVE.

Table 16

IANTD GAS MANAGEMENT CHART – IMPERIAL-US VERSION

DISTANCE TRAVELED IN FEET

MINUTES TO TURN ↓	DISTANCED TRAVELED IN FEET							
1	25	50	75	100	125	150	175	200
2	50	100	150	200	250	300	360	400
3	75	150	225	300	375	450	525	600
4	100	200	30	400	500	600	700	800
5	125	250	375	500	625	750	875	1000
6	150	300	450	600	750	900	1050	1200
7	175	350	525	700	875	1050	1225	1400
8	200	400	600	800	1000	1200	1400	1600
9	225	450	675	900	1125	1350	1575	1800
10	250	500	750	1000	1250	1500	1750	2000
11	275	560	625	1100	1375	1650	1925	2200
12	300	600	900	1200	1500	1800	2100	2400
13	325	660	975	1300	1625	1950	2275	2600
14	350	700	1050	1400	1750	2100	2450	2900
15	375	750	1125	1500	1875	2250	2625	3000
16	400	800	1200	1600	2000	2400	2800	3200
17	425	850	1275	1700	2125	2550	2975	3400
18	450	900	1350	1800	2250	2700	3150	3600
19	475	950	1425	1900	2375	2850	3325	3800
20	500	1000	1500	2000	2500	3000	3500	4000
23	575	1150	1725	2300	2875	3450	4025	4600
24	600	1200	1800	2400	3000	3600	4200	4800
25	625	1250	1875	2500	3125	3750	4375	5000
27	675	1350	2025	2700	3375	4050	4725	5400
29	725	1450	2175	2900	3625	4350	5075	5800
30	750	1500	2250	3000	3750	4500	5250	6000
31	775	1550	2325	3100	3875	4650	5425	6200
33	825	1650	2475	3300	4125	4950	5775	6600
36	900	1800	2700	3600	4500	5400	6300	7200
37	925	1850	2775	3700	4625	5550	6475	7400
40	1000	2000	3000	4000	5000	6000	7000	8000
43	1075	2150	3225	4300	5375	6450	7525	8800
47	1175	2350	3525	4700	5875	7050	8225	9400
50	1250	2500	3750	5000	6250	7500	8750	10000
53	1325	2650	3975	5300	6625	7950	9275	10600
60	1500	3000	4500	6000	7500	9000	10500	12000
67	1675	3350	5025	6700	8375	10050	11725	13400
73	1825	3650	5475	7300	9125	10950	12775	14600
80	2000	4000	6000	8000	10000	12000	14000	16000
87	2175	4350	6525	8700	10875	13050	15225	17400
93	2325	4650	6975	9300	11625	13950	16275	18600
107	2675	5350	8025	10700	13375	16050	18725	21400

⚠ Warning: DO NOT attempt to use these tables unless you are fully trained & certified in the use of gas mixtures other than air, or are under the supervision of a gas mixtures other than air instructor. Proper use of these tables will reduce the risk of decompression sickness & oxygen toxicity, but no table or computer can eliminate those risks.

Table 17

IANTD/IAND, INC. GAS DENSITY TABLE

(values are approximate)

PERCENT OF GASES IN THE MIX								
Oxygen	0%	0%	100%	34%	15%	14%	16%	21%
Nitrogen	0%	100%	0%	66%	40%	53%	60%	0%
Helium	100%	0%	0%	0%	45%	33%	24%	79%
Air								
fsw	fsw	fsw	fsw	fsw	fsw	fsw	fsw	fsw
10	1	10	11	10	6	7	8	3
20	3	19	22	20	12	14	16	7
30	4	29	33	30	18	21	24	10
40	6	39	44	41	25	29	32	14
50	7	48	55	51	31	36	40	17
60	8	58	66	61	37	43	47	20
70	10	68	77	71	43	50	55	24
80	11	77	88	81	49	57	63	27
90	12	87	99	91	55	64	71	31
100	14	97	111	101	61	71	79	34
110	15	106	122	112	68	78	87	38
120	17	116	133	122	74	86	95	41
130	18	126	144	132	80	93	103	44
140	19	135	155	142	86	100	111	48
150	21	145	166	152	92	107	119	51
160	22	155	177	162	98	114	126	55
170	23	164	188	172	104	121	134	58
180	25	174	199	183	111	128	142	61
190	26	184	210	193	117	135	150	65
200	28	193	221	203	123	143	158	68
210	29	203	232	213	129	150	166	72
220	30	213	243	223	135	157	174	75
230	32	222	254	233	141	164	182	78
240	33	232	265	243	148	171	190	82
250	35	242	276	253	154	178	198	85
260	36	251	287	264	160	185	205	89
270	37	261	298	274	166	192	213	92
280	39	271	309	284	172	200	221	95
290	40	280	320	294	178	207	229	99
300	41	290	332	304	184	214	237	102

- **Note:** Although the approximate Equivalent Air Depth Density is given for all gases tabulated, the user should not attempt to use any gas mixture outside the appropriate Maximum Operating Depth. The densities are given strictly for reference information.

- This table gives approximate Equivalent Air Depth Densities for a given gas mixture at some bottom depth. As an example: A 16-24 Trimix breathed at 270 fsw would have a density approximately equal to air at 213 fsw.

Chart 1

IANTD/IAND, INC. CNS REPETITIVE CHART

START PERCENT	SURFACE INTERVAL (S.I.) 30 MINS	60 MINS	90 MINS	2 HRS	3 HRS	4 HRS	5 HRS	6 HRS
100	83	66	49	41	24	16	11	7
95	79	63	46	38	22	15	10	7
90	75	59	44	37	22	15	10	7
85	71	56	42	35	21	14	9	6
80	66	53	39	32	19	13	9	6
75	62	49	37	31	18	12	8	5
70	58	46	34	28	17	11	7	5
65	54	43	32	27	16	11	7	5
60	50	40	29	24	14	9	6	4
55	46	36	27	22	13	9	6	4
50	41	33	24	20	12	8	5	3
45	37	30	22	18	11	7	5	3
40	33	26	20	17	10	7	5	3
35	29	23	17	14	8	5	3	2
30	25	20	15	12	7	5	3	2
25	21	16	12	10	6	4	3	2
20	17	13	10	8	5	3	2	1
15	12	10	7	6	3	2	1	1
10	8	7	5	4	2	1	1	1
	RESIDUAL PERCENT CNS O_2 CLOCK							

To read the CNS repetitive CNS % chart, begin at the top left column with 100%. Read to the right and after 30 minutes Surface Interval, you will read down the column to see that the diver still has 83% of the CNS O_2 clock loaded, while after 6 hrs. S.I., only 7% of the CNS O_2 clock will remain.

⚠ Warning: DO NOT attempt to use these tables unless you are fully trained & certified in the use of gas mixtures other than air, or are under the supervision of a gas mixtures other than air instructor. Proper use of these tables will reduce the risk of decompression sickness & oxygen toxicity, but no table or computer can eliminate those risks.

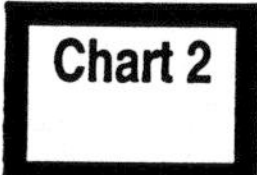

Nitrox Top Up Chart

IMPERIAL-US Version

[psi]

Oxygen %	Pressure of fill (PSIG)																				
	400	600	800	1000	1200	1400	1600	1800	2000	2200	2400	2600	2800	3000	3200	3400	3600	3800	4000	4200	4400
21%	0	0	0	0	0	0	0	0	0	0	0	0	0	0	0	0	0	0	0	0	0
22%	5	8	10	13	15	18	20	23	25	28	30	33	35	38	41	43	46	48	51	53	53
23%	10	15	20	25	30	35	41	46	51	56	61	66	71	76	81	86	91	96	101	106	111
24%	20	23	30	38	46	53	61	68	76	84	91	99	106	114	122	129	137	144	152	159	167
25%	20	30	41	51	61	71	81	91	101	111	122	132	142	152	162	172	182	192	203	213	223
26%	25	38	51	63	76	89	101	114	127	139	152	165	177	190	203	215	228	241	253	266	278
27%	30	46	61	76	91	106	122	137	152	167	182	197	213	228	243	258	273	289	304	319	334
28%	35	53	71	89	106	124	142	159	177	195	213	230	248	266	284	301	319	337	354	372	390
29%	41	61	81	101	122	142	162	182	203	223	243	263	284	304	324	344	365	385	405	425	446
30%	46	68	91	114	137	159	182	205	228	251	273	296	319	342	365	387	410	433	456	478	501
31%	51	76	101	127	152	177	203	228	253	278	304	329	354	380	405	430	456	481	506	532	557
32%	56	84	111	139	167	195	223	251	278	306	334	362	390	418	446	473	501	529	557	585	613
33%	61	91	122	152	182	213	243	273	304	334	365	395	425	456	486	516	547	577	608	638	668
34%	66	99	132	165	197	230	263	296	329	362	395	428	461	494	527	559	592	625	658	691	724
35%	71	106	142	177	213	248	284	319	354	390	425	461	496	532	567	603	638	673	709	744	780
36%	76	114	152	190	228	266	304	342	380	418	456	494	532	570	608	646	684	722	759	797	835
37%	81	122	162	203	243	284	324	365	405	446	486	527	567	608	648	689	729	770	810	851	891
38%	86	129	172	215	258	301	344	387	430	473	516	559	603	646	689	732	775	818	861	904	947
39%	91	137	182	228	273	319	365	410	456	501	547	5920	638	684	729	775	820	866	911	957	1003
40%	96	144	192	241	289	337	385	433	481	529	577	625	673	722	770	818	866	914	962	1010	1058

Rules:

1. Having dived the cylinder (note mix prior to dive) gauge the pressure. Using the table, move down the current gauge pressure and across the mix. This will give a number.
2. Go to the new mix required and the new fill pressure. This will give you another number.
3. Take the first number from the second. This is the pure O_2 to add to the part of the used cylinder. Now fill with air to the pressure used in step 2.
4. If the answer is negative, then more gas must be drained to make the answer 0 (zero) or positive. Then fill with air or air and oxygen respectively.
5. To estimate how much gas to remove from the first fill, go to the first mix and fill number, find a number along the same row Less Than or Equal To the second mix and fill number. Move up to the fill pressure. This must be the pressure in the cylinder prior to topping.

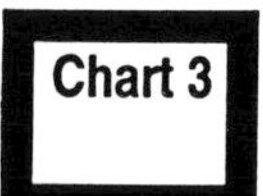

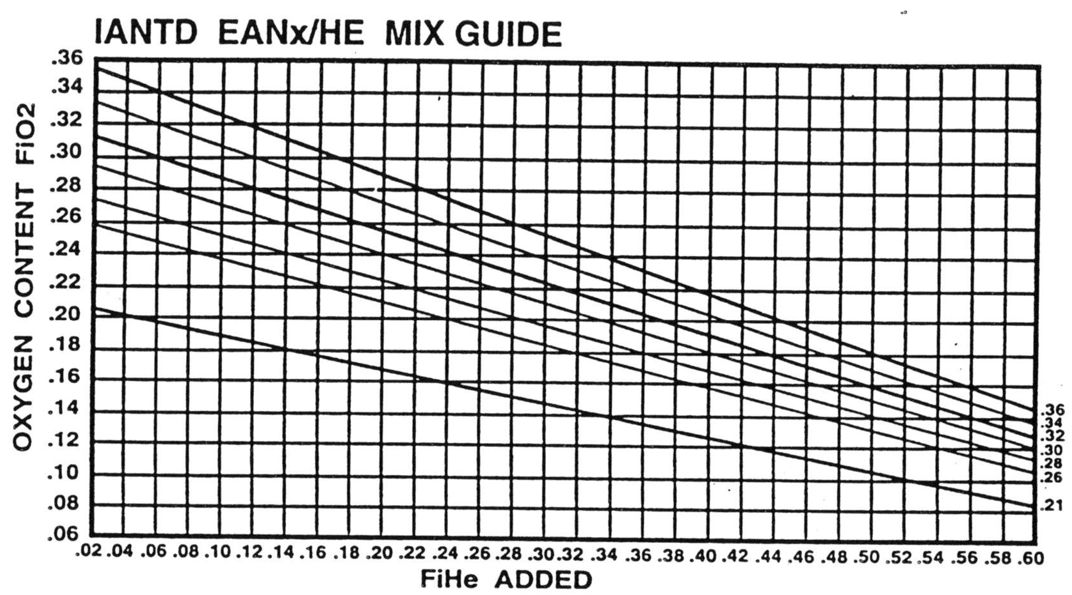

Chart 4

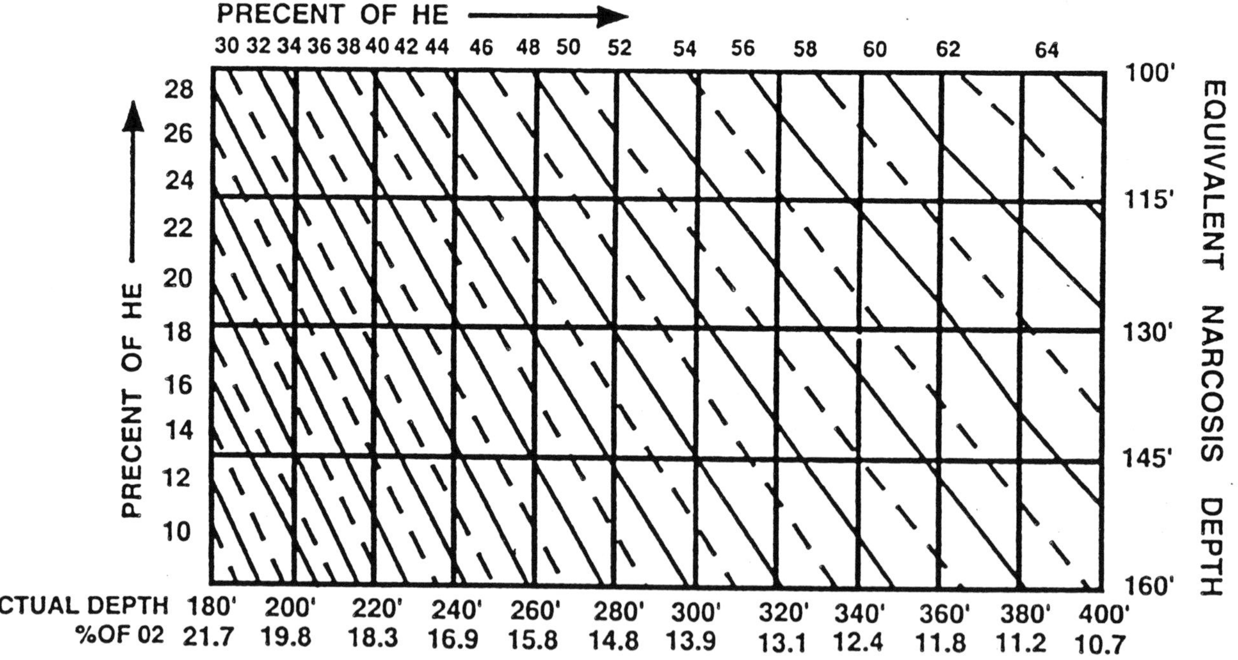

PRODUCED BY TOM MOUNT/MARK OWENS

⚠ Warning: DO NOT attempt to use these tables unless you are fully trained & certified in the use of gas mixtures other than air, or are under the supervision of a gas mixtures other than air instructor. Proper use of these tables will reduce the risk of decompression sickness & oxygen toxicity, but no table or computer can eliminate those risks.

IANTD/IAND, Inc. PO_2 TABLE - Metric

Table 1 M

	Oxygen Content																														
MSW	0.21	0.22	0.23	0.24	0.25	0.26	0.27	0.28	0.29	0.30	0.31	0.32	0.33	0.34	0.35	0.36	0.37	0.38	0.39	0.40	0.45	0.50	0.55	0.60	0.65	0.70	0.75	0.80	0.85	0.90	0.95	1.00
3	0.27	0.29	0.30	0.31	0.33	0.34	0.35	0.36	0.38	0.39	0.40	0.42	0.43	0.44	0.46	0.47	0.48	0.49	0.51	0.52	0.59	0.65	0.72	0.78	0.85	0.91	0.98	1.04	1.11	1.17	1.24	1.30
4.5	0.30	0.32	0.33	0.35	0.36	0.38	0.39	0.41	0.42	0.44	0.45	0.46	0.48	0.49	0.51	0.52	0.54	0.55	0.57	0.58	0.65	0.73	0.80	0.87	0.94	1.02	1.09	1.16	1.23	1.31	1.38	1.45
6	0.34	0.35	0.37	0.38	0.40	0.42	0.43	0.45	0.46	0.48	0.50	0.51	0.53	0.54	0.56	0.58	0.59	0.61	0.62	0.64	0.72	0.80	0.88	0.96	1.04	1.12	1.20	1.28	1.36	1.44	1.52	1.60
9	0.40	0.42	0.44	0.46	0.48	0.49	0.51	0.53	0.55	0.57	0.59	0.61	0.63	0.65	0.67	0.68	0.70	0.72	0.74	0.76	0.86	0.95	1.05	1.14	1.24	1.33	1.43	1.52	1.62			
12	0.46	0.48	0.51	0.53	0.55	0.57	0.59	0.62	0.64	0.66	0.68	0.70	0.73	0.75	0.77	0.79	0.81	0.84	0.86	0.88	0.99	1.10	1.21	1.32	1.43	1.54	1.65					
15	0.53	0.55	0.58	0.60	0.63	0.65	0.68	0.70	0.73	0.75	0.78	0.80	0.83	0.85	0.88	0.90	0.93	0.95	0.98	1.00	1.13	1.25	1.38	1.50	1.63							
18	0.59	0.62	0.64	0.67	0.70	0.73	0.76	0.78	0.81	0.84	0.87	0.90	0.92	0.95	0.98	1.01	1.04	1.06	1.09	1.12	1.26	1.40	1.54	1.68								
21	0.65	0.68	0.71	0.74	0.78	0.81	0.84	0.87	0.90	0.93	0.96	0.99	1.02	1.05	1.09	1.12	1.15	1.18	1.21	1.24	1.40	1.55										
24	0.71	0.75	0.78	0.82	0.85	0.88	0.92	0.95	0.99	1.02	1.05	1.09	1.12	1.16	1.19	1.22	1.26	1.29	1.33	1.36	1.53											
27	0.78	0.81	0.85	0.89	0.93	0.96	1.00	1.04	1.07	1.11	1.15	1.18	1.22	1.26	1.30	1.33	1.37	1.41	1.44	1.48	1.67											
30	0.84	0.88	0.92	0.96	1.00	1.04	1.08	1.12	1.16	1.20	1.24	1.28	1.32	1.36	1.40	1.44	1.48	1.52	1.56	1.60												
33	0.90	0.95	0.99	1.03	1.08	1.12	1.16	1.20	1.25	1.29	1.33	1.38	1.42	1.46	1.51	1.55	1.59	1.63	1.68													
36	0.97	1.01	1.06	1.10	1.15	1.20	1.24	1.29	1.33	1.38	1.43	1.47	1.52	1.56	1.61	1.66																
39	1.03	1.08	1.13	1.18	1.23	1.27	1.32	1.37	1.42	1.47	1.52	1.57	1.62	1.67																		
42	1.09	1.14	1.20	1.25	1.30	1.35	1.40	1.46	1.51	1.56	1.61	1.66																				
45	1.16	1.21	1.27	1.32	1.38	1.43	1.49	1.54	1.60	1.65																						
48	1.22	1.28	1.33	1.39	1.45	1.51	1.57	1.62																								
51	1.28	1.34	1.40	1.46	1.53	1.59	1.65																									
54	1.34	1.41	1.47	1.54	1.60	1.66																										
57	1.41	1.47	1.54	1.61																												
60	1.47	1.54	1.61																													
63	1.53	1.61																														

Produced by: Tom Mount / Mark Owens / Don Townsend

1. Find the depth on the left side of Table.
2. Go across horizontally until you are in the column of the mix you are using.
3. Read the PO_2 indicated.

Example: 33 MSW using EAN 28 = 1.20 PO_2

Note: This table may be used for determining both the TOD and MOD values for a given dive.
To use the IANTD/IAND, Inc. OTU / CNS O_2 Tracking Table with this Table, simply round the PO_2 obtained to the nearest 0.5.
YOU MUST ALWAYS ROUND TO THE NEXT HIGHEST PO_2

⚠ Warning: DO NOT attempt to use these tables unless you are fully trained & certified in the use of gas mixtures other than air, or are under the supervision of a gas mixtures other than air instructor. Proper use of these tables will reduce the risk of decompression sickness & oxygen toxicity, but no table or computer can eliminate those risks.

Table 2 M

IANTD HYPOXIC PO_2 TABLE - METRIC

	Oxygen Percent												
MSW	0.20	0.19	0.18	0.17	0.16	0.15	0.14	0.13	0.12	0.11	0.10	0.09	0.08
3	0.26	0.25	0.23	0.22	0.21	0.20	0.18	0.17	0.16	0.14	0.13	0.12	0.10
4.5	0.29	0.28	0.26	0.25	0.23	0.22	0.20	0.19	0.17	0.16	0.15	0.13	0.12
6	0.32	0.30	0.29	0.27	0.26	0.24	0.22	0.21	0.19	0.18	0.16	0.14	0.13
9	0.38	0.36	0.34	0.32	0.30	0.29	0.27	0.25	0.23	0.21	0.19	0.17	0.15
12	0.44	0.42	0.40	0.37	0.35	0.33	0.31	0.29	0.26	0.24	0.22	0.20	0.18
15	0.50	0.48	0.45	0.43	0.40	0.38	0.35	0.33	0.30	0.28	0.25	0.23	0.20
18	0.56	0.53	0.50	0.48	0.45	0.42	0.39	0.36	0.34	0.31	0.28	0.25	0.22
21	0.62	0.59	0.56	0.53	0.50	0.47	0.43	0.40	0.37	0.34	0.31	0.28	0.25
24	0.68	0.65	0.61	0.58	0.54	0.51	0.48	0.44	0.41	0.37	0.34	0.31	0.27
27	0.74	0.70	0.67	0.63	0.59	0.56	0.52	0.48	0.44	0.41	0.37	0.33	0.30
30	0.80	0.76	0.72	0.68	0.64	0.60	0.56	0.52	0.48	0.44	0.40	0.36	0.32
33	0.86	0.82	0.77	0.73	0.69	0.65	0.60	0.56	0.52	0.47	0.43	0.39	0.34
36	0.92	0.87	0.83	0.78	0.74	0.69	0.64	0.60	0.55	0.51	0.46	0.41	0.37
39	0.98	0.93	0.88	0.83	0.78	0.74	0.69	0.64	0.59	0.54	0.49	0.44	0.39
42	1.04	0.99	0.94	0.88	0.83	0.78	0.73	0.68	0.62	0.57	0.52	0.47	0.42
45	1.10	1.05	0.99	0.94	0.88	0.83	0.77	0.72	0.66	0.61	0.55	0.50	0.44
48	1.16	1.10	1.04	0.99	0.93	0.87	0.81	0.75	0.70	0.64	0.58	0.52	0.46
51	1.22	1.16	1.10	1.04	0.98	0.92	0.85	0.79	0.73	0.67	0.61	0.55	0.49
54	1.28	1.22	1.15	1.09	1.02	0.96	0.90	0.83	0.77	0.70	0.64	0.58	0.51
57	1.34	1.27	1.21	1.14	1.07	1.01	0.94	0.87	0.80	0.74	0.67	0.60	0.54
60	1.40	1.33	1.26	1.19	1.12	1.05	0.98	0.91	0.84	0.77	0.70	0.63	0.56
63	1.46	1.39	1.31	1.24	1.17	1.10	1.02	0.95	0.88	0.80	0.73	0.66	0.58
66	1.52	1.44	1.37	1.29	1.22	1.14	1.06	0.99	0.91	0.84	0.76	0.68	0.61
69	1.58	1.50	1.42	1.34	1.26	1.19	1.11	1.03	0.95	0.87	0.79	0.71	0.63
72	1.64	1.56	1.48	1.39	1.31	1.23	1.15	1.07	0.98	0.90	0.82	0.74	0.66
75		1.62	1.53	1.45	1.36	1.28	1.19	1.11	1.02	0.94	0.85	0.77	0.68
78			1.58	1.50	1.41	1.32	1.23	1.14	1.06	0.97	0.88	0.79	0.70
81			1.64	1.55	1.46	1.37	1.27	1.18	1.09	1.00	0.91	0.82	0.73
84				1.60	1.50	1.41	1.32	1.22	1.13	1.03	0.94	0.85	0.75
87					1.55	1.46	1.36	1.26	1.16	1.07	0.97	0.87	0.78
90					1.60	1.50	1.40	1.30	1.20	1.10	1.00	0.90	0.80
93						1.55	1.44	1.34	1.24	1.13	1.03	0.93	0.82
96						1.59	1.48	1.38	1.27	1.17	1.06	0.95	0.85
99							1.53	1.42	1.31	1.20	1.09	0.98	0.87
102							1.57	1.46	1.34	1.23	1.12	1.01	0.90
105							1.61	1.50	1.38	1.27	1.15	1.04	0.92
108								1.53	1.42	1.30	1.18	1.06	0.94
111								1.57	1.45	1.33	1.21	1.09	0.97
114								1.61	1.49	1.36	1.24	1.12	0.99
117									1.52	1.40	1.27	1.14	1.02
120									1.56	1.43	1.30	1.17	1.04
123									1.60	1.46	1.33	1.20	1.06
126										1.50	1.36	1.22	1.09
129										1.53	1.39	1.25	1.11
132										1.56	1.42	1.28	1.14
135										1.60	1.45	1.31	1.16
138											1.48	1.33	1.18
141											1.51	1.36	1.21
144											1.54	1.39	1.23
147											1.57	1.41	1.26
150											1.60	1.44	1.28

⚠ Warning: DO NOT attempt to use these tables unless you are fully trained & certified in the use of gas mixtures other than air, or are under the supervision of a gas mixtures other than air instructor. Proper use of these tables will reduce the risk of decompression sickness & oxygen toxicity, but no table or computer can eliminate those risks.

IANTD CNS% PER MINUTE BY PO_2 CHART

PO_2	CNS% MIN.	PO_2	CNS% MIN.	PO_2	CNS% MIN.
0.60	0.14	1.02	0.35	1.42	0.68
0.62	0.14	1.04	0.36	1.44	0.71
0.64	0.15	1.06	0.38	1.46	0.74
0.66	0.16	1.08	0.40	1.48	0.78
0.68	0.17	1.10	0.42	1.50	0.83
0.70	0.18	1.12	0.43	1.52	0.93
0.72	0.18	1.14	0.43	1.54	1.04
0.74	0.19	1.16	0.44	1.56	1.19
0.76	0.20	1.18	0.46	1.58	1.47
0.78	0.21	1.20	0.47	1.60	2.22
0.80	0.22	1.22	0.48	1.62	5.00
0.82	0.23	1.24	0.51	1.65	6.25
0.84	0.24	1.26	0.52	1.67	7.69
0.86	0.25	1.28	0.54	1.70	10.00
0.88	0.26	1.30	0.56	1.72	12.50
0.90	0.28	1.32	0.57	1.74	20.00
0.92	0.29	1.34	0.60	1.77	25.00
0.94	0.30	1.36	0.62	1.78	31.25
0.96	0.31	1.38	0.63	1.80	50.00
0.98	0.32	1.40	0.65	1.82	100.00
1.00	0.33				

The above Table 3 is valuable on longer dives where exact CNS% values must be computed to insure a safe exposure. In the following text, you will be presented with a table that is expressed in 0.05 ata increments and is easier on which to calculate dives. For the majority of technical dives, and for all examples in the remainder of this text, Table 5 will be used. The additional advantage of Table 5 is that it combines information from both Table 3 and Table 4.

Table 4 M

SINGLE DIVE	
PO_2 (ATA)	OTU per MINUTE
0.50	00
0.55	0.15
0.60	0.27
0.65	0.37
0.70	0.47
0.75	0.56
0.80	0.65
0.85	0.74
0.90	0.83
0.95	0.92
1.00	1.00
1.05	1.08
1.10	1.16
1.15	1.24
1.20	1.32
1.25	1.40
1.30	1.48
1.35	1.55
1.40	1.63
1.45	1.70
1.50	1.78
1.55	1.85
1.60	1.92
1.65	2.00
1.70	2.07
1.75	2.14
1.80	2.21
1.85	2.28
1.90	2.35
1.95	2.42
2.00	2.49

MULTIPLE DAY ALLOTMENT OF OTUs		
EXPOSURE DAYS	AVERAGE DOSE	TOTAL DOSE
1	850	850
2	700	1400
3	620	1860
4	420	2100
5	380	2300
6	350	2520
7	330	2660
8	310	2800
9	300	2970
10	300	3100
11	300	3300
12	300	3600
13	300	3900
14	300	4200
15-30	300	AS REQUIRED

Note! An important point of the Repex Table is it tracks multi-day whole body oxygen exposure limits.

For additional safety, IANTD has designed tables to track the oxygen risk exposure. The values used in the tables have been converted into a linear representation making them slightly more conservative than if the raw values reflected in Table 3 are used. Refer to Table 5 for calculating CNS % and OTU accumulation on a given dive.
Example of OTU and CNS% tracking and planning using IANTD Table 5. OTUs are tracked in units. CNS O_2 is tracked in percent of the clock.

If PO_2 is not exact, use the next higher PO_2 on the chart. Slight differences may occur in rounding depending on column used in chart.

EXAMPLE: Total dive time is 80 minutes at 1.3 PO_2

60 minutes column used	33.33% CNS O_2	88.63 OTUs
20 minutes column used	11.11% CNS O_2	29.54 OTUs
Total for dive:	*44.44% CNS O_2*	*118.17 OTUs or if the*
1 minute column is used:	**44.80% CNS O_2**	**118.40 OTUs**

⚠ **Warning: DO NOT attempt to use these tables unless you are fully trained & certified in the use of gas mixtures other than air, or are under the supervision of a gas mixtures other than air instructor. Proper use of these tables will reduce the risk of decompression sickness & oxygen toxicity, but no table or computer can eliminate those risks.**

IANTD/IAND, INC. OTU / CNS TRACKING TABLE

Table 5 M

PO_2	1 In OTU - CNS O_2	5 Min OTU - CNS O_2	10 Min OTU - CNS O_2	20 Min OTU - CNS O_2	30 Min OTU - CNS O_2	40 Min OTU - CNS O_2	50 Min OTU - CNS O_2	60 Min OTU - CNS O_2
0.60	0.26 - 0.14	1.31 - 0.69	2.63 - 1.39	5.26 - 2.78	7.89 - 4.17	10.52 - 5.56	13.15 - 6.94	15.78 - 8.33
0.65	0.37 - 0.16	1.84 - 0.78	3.68 - 1.55	7.36 - 3.10	11.04 - 4.65	14.73 - 6.20	18.41 - 7.75	22.09 - 9.30
0.70	0.47 - 0.18	2.34 - 0.88	4.67 - 1.75	9.35 - 3.51	14.02 - 5.26	18.70 - 7.02	23.37 - 8.77	28.05 -10.53
0.75	0.56 - 0.20	2.81 - 0.98	5.63 - 1.96	11.25 - 3.92	16.88 - 5.88	22.50 - 7.84	28.13 - 9.80	33.75 -11.76
0.80	0.65 - 0.22	3.27 - 1.11	6.54 - 2.22	13.09 - 4.44	19.63 - 6.67	26.18 - 8.89	32.72 -11.11	39.27 -13.33
0.85	0.74 - 0.25	3.72 - 1.23	7.44 - 2.47	14.88 - 4.94	22.31 - 7.41	29.75 - 9.87	37.19 -12.34	44.63 -14.81
0.90	0.83 - 0.28	4.15 - 1.39	8.31 - 2.78	16.62 - 5.56	24.93 - 8.33	33.24 -11.11	41.55 -13.89	49.86 -16.67
0.95	0.92 - 0.31	4.58 - 1.57	9.16 - 3.14	18.33 - 6.27	27.49 - 9.41	36.65 -12.54	45.81 -15.68	54.98 -18.81
1.00	1.00 - 0.33	5.00 - 1.67	10.00 - 3.33	20.00 - 6.67	30.00 -10.00	40.00 -13.33	50.00 -16.67	60.00 -20.00
1.05	1.08 - 0.37	5.41 - 1.85	10.82 - 3.70	21.65 - 7.41	32.47 -11.11	43.29 -14.81	54.12 -18.52	64.94 -22.22
1.10	1.16 - 0.42	5.82 - 2.08	11.63 - 4.17	23.27 - 8.33	34.90 -12.50	46.54 -16.67	58.17 -20.83	69.80 -25.00
1.15	1.24 - 0.44	6.22 - 2.19	12.43 - 4.39	24.87 - 8.77	37.30 -13.16	49.73 -17.55	62.16 -21.93	74.60 -26.32
1.20	1.32 - 0.48	6.61 - 2.38	13.22 - 4.76	26.44 - 9.52	39.67 -14.29	52.89 -19.05	66.11 -23.81	79.33 -28.57
1.25	1.40 - 0.51	7.00 - 2.56	14.00 - 5.13	28.00 -10.26	42.00 -15.39	56.00 -20.51	70.00 -25.64	84.01 -30.77
1.30	1.48 - 0.56	7.39 - 2.78	14.77 - 5.56	29.54 -11.11	44.31 -16.67	59.09 -22.22	73.86 -27.78	88.63 -33.33
1.35	1.55 - 0.61	7.77 - 3.03	15.53 - 6.06	31.07 -12.12	46.60 -18.18	62.13 -24.24	77.67 -30.30	93.20 -36.36
1.40	1.63 - 0.65	8.14 - 3.33	16.29 - 6.67	32.58 -13.33	48.86 -20.00	65.15 -26.67	81.44 -33.33	97.73 -40.00
1.45	1.70 - 0.72	8.52 - 3.62	17.04 - 7.25	34.07 -14.49	51.11 -21.74	68.14 -28.99	85.18 -36.23	102.2 -43.48
1.50	1.78 - 0.83	8.89 - 4.17	17.78 - 8.33	35.55 -16.67	53.33 -25.00	71.11 -33.33	88.88 -41.67	106.7 -50.00
1.55	1.85 - 1.11	9.26 - 5.56	18.51 -11.11	37.02 -22.22	55.53 -33.34	74.05 -44.45	92.56 -55.56	111.1 -66.67
1.60	1.92 - 2.22	9.62 - 11.11	19.24 -22.22	38.48 -44.44	57.72 -66.67	76.96 -88.89	96.20 -111.1	115.4 -133.3

Produced by: Tom Mount / Mark Owens ♠Copyright 1993-2000: IAND, Inc. / Repetitive Diver, Inc.

⚠ Warning: DO NOT attempt to use these tables unless you are fully trained & certified in the use of gas mixtures other than air, or are under the supervision of a gas mixtures other than air instructor. Proper use of these tables will reduce the risk of decompression sickness & oxygen toxicity, but no table or computer can eliminate those risks.

Table 6M may be used as a quick reference for END values on a known mix. If a Trimix 14 45 is used at 82 meters, by finding the mix and going down the page to 82 meters the END will be 36 meters.

Equivalent Nitrogen Depths For Trimixtures

% Oxygen →	16%	14%	12%	15%	13%	12%
% Helium →	24%	33%	40%	45%	50%	63%
MSW	MSW	MSW	MSW	MSW	MSW	MSW
55	39	33	29	23	20	10
58	41	35	31	24	21	11
61	44	37	33	26	23	12
64	46	39	35	27	24	13
67	48	42	37	29	26	14
70	51	43	39	30	27	15
73	53	46	40	32	29	16
76	55	48	42	33	30	17
79	60	50	44	35	32	18
82	60	52	46	36	33	19
85	62	54	48	38	35	20
88	65	56	50	40	36	21
91	67	58	51	41	37	22
94	69	60	53	43	39	23
97	71	62	55	44	40	24
100	74	64	57	46	42	25
103	76	66	59	47	43	26
107	79	68	61	49	44	27
110	81	70	63	51	46	28
113	83	72	65	52	47	29
116	86	74	66	54	49	30
119	88	76	68	55	50	31
122	90	78	70	57	52	32

Produced by: Mount / Owens / Townsend

Note: Please be advised that the PO_2 of some of the mixes at certain depths will exceed 1.6 ATA. This chart is intended to show Equivalent Narcosis Depths only.

⚠ Warning: DO NOT attempt to use these tables unless you are fully trained & certified in the use of gas mixtures other than air, or are under the supervision of a gas mixtures other than air instructor. Proper use of these tables will reduce the risk of decompression sickness & oxygen toxicity, but no table or computer can eliminate those risks.

Planning Information for Simplified Mixes

(PO_2 = 1.4 ATA)

MAXIMUM OPERATING DEPTH (MOD) FOR TRIMIXTURES IN METERS

INITIAL O_2% →	21%		26%		30%		32%		34%		36%	
END (MSW) →	57		40		31		28		24		21	
	Mix		Mix		Mix		Mix		Mix		Mix	
He %	O_2 %	MOD	O_2 %	MOD	O_2 %	MOD	O_2 %	MOD	O_2 %	MOD	O_2 %	MOD
2	21	58	25	45	29	38	31	35	33	32	35	30
4	20	60	25	46	29	39	31	35	33	33	35	31
6	20	61	24	47	28	40	30	37	32	34	34	32
8	19	63	24	49	28	41	29	38	31	35	33	32
10	19	64	23	50	27	42	29	39	31	36	32	33
12	18	66	23	51	26	43	28	40	30	37	32	34
14	18	68	22	53	26	44	28	41	29	38	31	35
16	18	70	22	54	25	46	27	42	29	39	30	36
18	17	71	21	56	25	47	26	43	28	40	30	38
20	17	74	21	57	24	49	26	45	27	42	29	39
22	16	76	20	59	23	50	25	46	27	43	28	40
24	16	78	20	61	23	52	24	48	26	44	27	41
26	16	80	19	63	22	53	24	49	25	46	27	42
28	15	83	19	65	22	58	23	51	24	47	26	44
30	15	85	18	67	21	57	22	53	24	49	25	46
32	14	89	18	69	20	59	22	54	23	51	24	47
34	14	91	17	72	20	61	21	57	22	53	24	49
36	13	95	17	74	19	63	20	59	22	54	23	51
38	13	98	16	77	19	65	20	61	21	57	22	53
40	13	102	16	80	18	68	19	63	20	59	22	55
42	12	105	15	83	17	71	19	66	20	61	21	57
44	12	110	15	86	17	74	18	68	19	64	20	60
46	11	114	14	90	16	77	17	71	18	67	19	62
48	11	119	14	94	16	80	17	75	18	69	19	65
50	11	124	13	98	15	83	16	78	17	73	18	68
52	10	129	12	103	14	88	15	82	16	76	17	71
54	10	136	12	108	14	92	15	86	16	80	17	75
56	9	142	11	113	13	97	14	90	15	84	16	79
58	9	150	11	119	13	102	13	94	14	89	15	83
60	8	158	10	125	12	107	13	100	14	93	14	88

Produced by: Mount / Owens / Blunt

Metric Version By Pettennude

Table 8 M

IANTD METRIC EAD / MOD TABLES

40 % O2

	ACTUAL DEPTH MSW						
	12	15	18	21	24	27	30
EAD	6.7	9.0	11.3	13.5	15.8	18.1	20.4
PO2	0.88	1.00	1.12	1.24	1.36	1.48	1.60
OTU PER MIN	0.80	1.00	1.20	1.38	1.57	1.75	1.92
% CNS	0.26	0.33	0.42	0.50	0.62	0.79	2.22

PO2	MOD Mtr
1.30	22.5
1.35	23.8
1.40	25.0
1.45	26.3
1.50	27.5
1.55	28.8
1.60	30.0

60 % O2

	DEPTH MSW				
	3	6	9	12	15
EAD	0	0	0	1.1	2.7
PO2	0.78	0.96	1.14	1.32	1.50
OTU PER MIN	0.62	0.93	1.23	1.51	1.78
% CNS	0.21	0.30	0.43	0.57	0.83

PO2	MOD Mtr
1.30	11.7
1.35	12.5
1.40	13.3
1.45	14.2
1.50	15.0
1.55	15.8
1.60	16.7

80 % O2

	MSW		
	3	6	9
EAD	0	0	0
PO2	1.04	1.28	1.52
OTU PER MIN	1.07	1.45	1.81
% CNS	0.36	0.54	0.93

PO2	MOD Mtr
1.30	6.3
1.35	6.9
1.40	7.5
1.45	8.1
1.50	8.8
1.55	9.4
1.60	10.0

45 % O2

	ACTUAL DEPTH MSW							
	3	6	9	12	15	18	21	24
EAD	0	1.1	3.2	5.3	7.4	9.5	11.6	13.7
PO2	0.59	0.72	0.86	0.99	1.13	1.26	1.40	1.53
OTU PER MIN	0.23	0.51	0.75	0.98	1.20	1.42	1.62	1.82
% CNS	0.00	0.18	0.25	0.32	0.43	0.51	0.67	0.99

PO2	MOD Mtr
1.30	18.9
1.35	20.0
1.40	21.1
1.45	22.2
1.50	23.3
1.55	24.4
1.60	25.6

65 % O2

	DEPTH MSW			
	3	6	9	12
EAD	0	0	0	0
PO2	0.85	1.04	1.24	1.43
OTU PER MIN	0.73	1.07	1.38	1.67
% CNS	0.24	0.36	0.50	0.71

PO2	MOD Mtr
1.30	10.0
1.35	10.8
1.40	11.5
1.45	12.3
1.50	13.1
1.55	13.8
1.60	14.6

85 % O2

	MSW	
	3	6
EAD	0	0
PO2	1.11	1.36
OTU PER MIN	1.17	1.57
% CNS	0.42	0.62

PO2	MOD Mtr
1.30	5.3
1.35	5.9
1.40	6.5
1.45	7.1
1.50	7.6
1.55	8.2
1.60	8.8

50 % O2

	ACTUAL DEPTH MSW						
	3	6	9	12	15	18	21
EAD	0	0.1	2.0	3.9	5.8	7.7	9.6
PO2	0.65	0.80	0.95	1.10	1.25	1.40	1.55
OTU PER MIN	0.37	0.65	0.92	1.16	1.40	1.63	1.85
% CNS	0.16	0.22	0.30	0.42	0.51	0.67	1.11

PO2	MOD Mtr
1.30	16.0
1.35	17.0
1.40	18.0
1.45	19.0
1.50	20.0
1.55	21.0
1.60	22.0

70 % O2

	DEPTH MSW			
	3	6	9	12
EAD	0	0	0	0
PO2	0.91	1.12	1.33	1.54
OTU PER MIN	0.85	1.20	1.52	1.84
% CNS	0.28	0.42	0.58	1.04

PO2	MOD Mtr
1.30	8.6
1.35	9.3
1.40	10.0
1.45	10.7
1.50	11.4
1.55	12.1
1.60	12.9

90 % O2

	MSW	
	3	6
EAD	0	0
PO2	1.17	1.44
OTU PER MIN	1.27	1.69
% CNS	0.45	0.72

PO2	MOD Mtr
1.30	4.4
1.35	5.0
1.40	5.6
1.45	6.1
1.50	6.7
1.55	7.2
1.60	7.8

55 % O2

	ACTUAL DEPTH MSW					
	3	6	9	12	15	18
EAD	0	0	0.8	2.5	4.2	5.9
PO2	0.72	0.88	1.05	1.21	1.38	1.54
OTU PER MIN	0.50	0.80	1.07	1.34	1.59	1.84
% CNS	0.18	0.26	0.36	0.48	0.64	1.04

PO2	MOD Mtr
1.30	13.6
1.35	14.5
1.40	15.5
1.45	16.4
1.50	17.3
1.55	18.2
1.60	19.1

75 % O2

	MSW		
	3	6	9
EAD	0	0	0
PO2	0.98	1.20	1.43
OTU PER MIN	0.96	1.32	1.67
% CNS	0.31	0.48	0.71

PO2	MOD Mtr
1.30	7.3
1.35	8.0
1.40	8.7
1.45	9.3
1.50	10.0
1.55	10.7
1.60	11.3

95 % O2

	MSW	
	3	6
EAD	0	0
PO2	1.24	1.52
OTU PER MIN	1.38	1.81
% CNS	0.50	0.93

PO2	MOD Mtr
1.30	3.7
1.35	4.2
1.40	4.7
1.45	5.3
1.50	5.8
1.55	6.3
1.60	6.8

100% O2

	MSW	
	3	6
EAD	0	0
PO2	1.30	1.60
OTU PER MIN	1.48	1.92
% CNS	0.56	2.22

PO2	MOD Mtr
1.30	3.0
1.35	3.5
1.40	4.0
1.45	4.5
1.50	5.0
1.55	5.5
1.60	6.0

PRODUCED BY TOM MOUNT, MARK OWENS, AND CLAYTON BOHM

⚠ **Warning: DO NOT attempt to use these tables unless you are fully trained & certified in the use of gas mixtures other than air, or are under the supervision of a gas mixtures other than air instructor. Proper use of these tables will reduce the risk of decompression sickness & oxygen toxicity, but no table or computer can eliminate those risks.**

Table 8 B M

IANTD METRIC EAD / MOD TABLES

24 % O2

	ACTUAL DEPTH MSW														
	12	15	18	21	24	27	30	33	36	39	42	45	48	51	54
EAD	11.2	14.1	16.9	19.6	22.7	25.6	28.5	31.4	34.3	37.1	40.0	42.9	45.8	48.7	51.6
PO2	0.53	0.60	0.67	0.74	0.82	0.89	0.96	1.03	1.10	1.18	1.25	1.32	1.39	1.46	1.54
OTU PER MIN	0.09	0.26	0.41	0.55	0.68	0.81	0.93	1.05	1.17	1.28	1.40	1.51	1.62	1.72	1.83
% CNS	0.00	0.14	0.16	0.20	0.23	0.27	0.30	0.35	0.42	0.46	0.51	0.57	0.65	0.75	1.04

PO2	MOD Mtr
1.30	44.2
1.35	46.3
1.40	48.3
1.45	50.4
1.50	52.5
1.55	54.6
1.60	56.7

26 % O2

	ACTUAL DEPTH MSW													
	12	15	18	21	24	27	30	33	36	39	42	45	48	51
EAD	10.6	13.4	16.2	19.0	21.8	24.7	27.5	30.3	33.1	35.9	38.7	41.5	44.3	47.1
PO2	0.57	0.65	0.73	0.81	0.88	0.96	1.04	1.12	1.20	1.27	1.35	1.43	1.51	1.59
OTU PER MIN	0.20	0.37	0.52	0.67	0.80	0.94	1.07	1.19	1.32	1.44	1.56	1.67	1.79	1.90
% CNS	0.00	0.16	0.19	0.23	0.26	0.30	0.36	0.42	0.48	0.52	0.60	0.71	0.92	2.00

PO2	MOD Mtr
1.30	40.0
1.35	41.9
1.40	43.8
1.45	45.8
1.50	47.7
1.55	49.6
1.60	51.5

28 % O2

	ACTUAL DEPTH MSW											
	12	15	18	21	24	27	30	33	36	39	42	45
EAD	10.1	12.8	15.5	18.3	21.0	23.7	26.5	29.2	31.9	34.7	37.4	40.1
PO2	0.62	0.70	0.78	0.87	0.95	1.04	1.12	1.20	1.29	1.37	1.46	1.54
OTU PER MIN	0.30	0.47	0.63	0.78	0.92	1.06	1.20	1.33	1.46	1.59	1.71	1.84
% CNS	0.14	0.18	0.21	0.26	0.30	0.36	0.42	0.48	0.55	0.62	0.75	1.04

PO2	MOD Mtr
1.30	36.4
1.35	38.2
1.40	40.0
1.45	41.8
1.50	43.6
1.55	45.4
1.60	47.1

30 % O2

	ACTUAL DEPTH MSW										
	12	15	18	21	24	27	30	33	36	39	42
EAD	9.5	12.2	14.8	17.5	20.1	22.8	25.4	28.1	30.8	33.4	36.1
PO2	0.66	0.75	0.84	0.93	1.02	1.11	1.20	1.29	1.38	1.47	1.56
OTU PER MIN	0.39	0.56	0.73	0.88	1.03	1.18	1.32	1.46	1.60	1.73	1.87
% CNS	0.16	0.20	0.24	0.29	0.34	0.42	0.48	0.55	0.64	0.76	1.2

PO2	MOD Mtr
1.30	33.3
1.35	35.0
1.40	36.7
1.45	38.3
1.50	40.0
1.55	41.7
1.60	43.3

38 % O2

	ACTUAL DEPTH MSW						
	12	15	18	21	24	27	30
EAD	7.3	9.6	12.0	14.3	16.7	19.0	21.4
PO2	0.84	0.95	1.06	1.18	1.29	1.41	1.52
OTU PER MIN	0.72	0.92	1.11	1.29	1.46	1.64	1.81
% CNS	0.24	0.30	0.37	0.46	0.55	0.67	0.93

PO2	MOD Mtr
1.30	24.2
1.35	25.5
1.40	26.8
1.45	28.2
1.50	29.5
1.55	30.8
1.60	32.1

36 % O2

	ACTUAL DEPTH MSW							
	12	15	18	21	24	27	30	33
EAD	7.8	10.3	12.7	15.1	17.5	20.0	22.4	24.8
PO2	0.79	0.90	1.01	1.12	1.22	1.33	1.44	1.55
OTU PER MIN	0.64	0.83	1.01	1.19	1.36	1.53	1.69	1.85
% CNS	0.21	0.28	0.33	0.42	0.48	0.58	0.72	1.11

PO2	MOD Mtr
1.30	26.1
1.35	27.5
1.40	28.9
1.45	30.3
1.50	31.7
1.55	33.1
1.60	34.4

34 % O2

	ACTUAL DEPTH MSW								
	12	15	18	21	24	27	30	33	36
EAD	8.4	10.9	13.4	15.9	18.4	20.9	23.4	25.9	28.4
PO2	0.75	0.85	0.95	1.05	1.16	1.26	1.36	1.46	1.56
OTU PER MIN	0.56	0.74	0.92	1.09	1.25	1.41	1.57	1.72	1.87
% CNS	0.20	0.24	0.30	0.36	0.44	0.51	0.62	0.75	1.20

PO2	MOD Mtr
1.30	28.2
1.35	29.7
1.40	31.2
1.45	32.6
1.50	34.1
1.55	35.6
1.60	37.1

32 % O2

	ACTUAL DEPTH MSW									
	12	15	18	21	24	27	30	33	36	39
EAD	8.9	11.5	14.1	16.7	19.3	21.8	24.4	27.0	29.6	32.2
PO2	0.70	0.80	0.90	0.99	1.09	1.18	1.28	1.38	1.47	1.57
OTU PER MIN	0.48	0.65	0.82	0.99	1.14	1.30	1.45	1.59	1.74	1.88
% CNS	0.16	0.22	0.28	0.32	0.41	0.46	0.54	0.64	0.76	1.30

PO2	MOD Mtr
1.30	30.6
1.35	32.2
1.40	33.8
1.45	35.3
1.50	36.9
1.55	38.4
1.60	40.0

PRODUCED BY TOM MOUNT, MARK OWENS, AND CLAYTON BOHM

⚠ Warning: DO NOT attempt to use these tables unless you are fully trained & certified in the use of gas mixtures other than air, or are under the supervision of a gas mixtures other than air instructor. Proper use of these tables will reduce the risk of decompression sickness & oxygen toxicity, but no table or computer can eliminate those risks.

Table
9 M

IANTD GAS MANAGEMENT CHART - METRIC VERSION

BAR/Min to SAC (FREE LITERS/MIN)

TANK PRESSURE AND SIZE																
BAR →	168	180	180	180	180	180	204	204	220	220	220	240	240	240	240	300
LITER →	70 *	7	15	16	17	19	70 *	10	12	15	18	65 *	10	13	15	18
BAR/MIN																
.41	4.81	2.83	6.23	6.80	7.08	7.93	3.96	4.53	5.10	6.51	7.36	3.12	3.96	4.81	5.95	7.36
.48	5.66	3.40	7.08	7.93	8.21	9.06	4.53	5.38	5.95	7.36	8.78	3.68	4.53	5.66	6.80	8.50
.54	6.51	3.96	8.21	9.06	9.35	10.48	5.38	5.95	6.80	8.50	9.91	4.25	5.10	6.51	7.65	9.91
.61	7.08	4.25	9.06	9.91	10.48	11.61	5.95	6.80	7.65	9.63	11.04	4.81	5.95	7.36	8.78	11.04
.68	7.93	4.81	10.20	11.04	11.61	13.03	6.51	7.65	8.50	10.76	12.46	5.38	6.51	8.21	9.63	12.18
.75	8.79	5.38	11.33	12.18	12.74	14.16	7.36	8.21	9.35	11.61	13.59	5.66	7.08	8.78	10.76	13.59
.82	9.63	5.66	12.18	13.31	13.88	15.58	7.93	9.06	10.20	12.74	15.01	6.23	7.65	9.63	11.61	14.73
.88	10.48	6.23	13.31	14.44	15.01	16.99	8.50	9.91	11.05	13.88	16.14	6.80	8.50	10.48	12.74	15.86
.95	11.33	6.80	14.16	15.58	16.14	18.12	9.35	10.48	11.89	15.01	17.28	7.36	9.06	11.33	13.59	16.99
1.02	11.89	7.36	15.29	16.71	17.28	19.54	9.91	11.33	12.74	15.86	18.69	7.93	9.63	12.18	14.44	18.41
1.09	12.74	7.65	16.45	17.84	18.41	20.67	10.48	12.18	13.59	16.99	19.82	8.50	10.48	13.03	15.58	19.54
1.16	13.59	8.21	17.28	18.97	19.82	22.09	11.33	12.74	14.44	18.12	21.24	9.06	11.04	13.88	16.43	20.67
1.22	14.44	8.78	18.41	20.11	20.00	23.51	11.89	13.59	15.29	19.26	22.37	9.35	11.61	14.44	17.56	22.09
1.29	15.29	9.06	19.26	21.24	22.09	24.64	12.46	14.44	16.14	20.11	23.51	9.91	12.18	15.29	18.41	23.22
1.36	16.14	9.63	20.39	22.38	23.22	26.05	13.31	15.01	16.99	21.24	24.92	10.48	13.03	16.14	19.54	24.36
1.43	16.71	10.20	21.52	23.51	24.36	27.19	13.88	15.86	17.84	22.37	26.05	11.04	13.59	16.99	20.39	25.77
1.50	17.56	10.76	22.37	24.64	25.49	28.60	14.44	16.71	18.69	23.51	27.47	11.61	14.16	17.84	21.24	26.90
1.56	18.41	11.04	23.51	25.77	26.62	29.74	15.29	17.28	19.26	24.64	28.60	12.18	15.01	18.69	22.38	28.04
1.63	19.26	11.61	24.36	26.90	27.75	31.15	15.86	18.12	20.11	25.49	29.74	12.74	15.58	19.54	23.22	29.45
1.70	20.11	12.18	25.49	27.75	28.89	32.56	16.43	18.97	20.96	26.62	31.15	13.03	16.14	20.11	24.36	30.59
1.77	20.96	12.46	26.62	28.89	30.02	33.70	17.28	19.54	21.81	27.75	32.28	13.59	16.71	20.96	25.20	31.72
1.84	21.52	13.03	27.47	30.02	31.15	35.12	17.84	20.39	22.66	28.89	33.42	14.16	17.56	21.81	26.34	33.13
1.90	22.37	13.59	28.60	31.15	32.57	36.25	18.41	21.24	23.51	29.74	34.83	14.73	18.12	22.66	27.19	34.27
1.97	23.22	13.88	29.45	32.28	33.70	37.67	19.26	21.81	24.36	30.87	35.97	15.29	18.69	23.51	28.04	35.40
2.04	24.07	14.44	30.59	33.42	34.83	39.08	19.82	22.66	25.20	32.00	37.38	15.86	19.54	24.36	29.17	36.82
2.11	24.92	15.01	31.72	34.55	35.97	40.21	20.39	23.51	26.05	33.13	38.52	16.43	20.11	25.20	30.02	37.95
2.18	25.77	15.58	32.57	35.68	37.10	41.63	21.24	24.07	26.90	33.98	39.65	16.71	20.67	25.77	31.15	39.08
2.24	26.34	15.86	33.70	36.82	38.23	42.76	21.80	24.92	27.75	35.12	41.06	17.28	21.24	26.62	32.00	40.50
2.31	27.19	16.43	34.55	37.95	39.36	44.18	22.37	25.77	28.60	36.25	42.20	17.84	22.09	27.47	33.13	41.63
2.38	28.04	16.99	35.68	39.08	40.50	45.31	23.22	26.34	29.45	37.38	43.61	18.41	22.66	28.32	33.98	42.76
2.45	28.89	17.28	36.82	40.21	41.63	46.73	23.79	27.19	30.30	38.23	44.75	18.97	23.22	29.17	34.84	43.90
2.52	29.74	17.84	37.67	41.35	42.76	48.14	24.36	28.04	31.15	39.36	45.88	19.54	24.07	30.02	35.97	45.31
2.5	30.30	18.41	38.80	42.48	43.90	49.28	25.20	28.60	32.00	40.50	47.29	20.11	24.63	30.87	36.82	46.44
2.65	31.15	18.69	39.65	43.61	45.31	50.69	25.77	29.45	32.85	41.63	48.43	20.39	25.20	31.44	37.95	47.58
2.72	32.00	19.26	40.78	44.75	46.44	51.83	26.34	30.30	33.70	42.48	49.84	20.96	25.77	32.28	38.80	48.99

*** METRIC EQUIVALENTS FOR THESE TANK SIZES ARE CURRENTLY UNAVAILABLE.**

Produced by: Mount/Owens/Taylor ♣ Metric Conversion by Pettennude ♣ Copyright 1996: IANTD/IAND, Inc./Repetitive Diver, Inc.

To determine your SAC in Free Liters per Minute, first find the correct tank size across the top. **EXAMPLE: Tank is 7 Liters at 180 BAR**

Then find your consumption rate in BAR/Min in the left column. **EXAMPLE: 2.72 BAR/Min**

The number where the column and row intersect is your SAC in Free Liters per Minute. **EXAMPLE: 19.26.**

⚠ **Warning: DO NOT attempt to use these tables unless you are fully trained & certified in the use of gas mixtures other than air, or are under the supervision of a gas mixtures other than air instructor. Proper use of these tables will reduce the risk of decompression sickness & oxygen toxicity, but no table or computer can eliminate those risks.**

Table 10 M

IANTD GAS MANAGEMENT CHART - METRIC VERSION

GAS USED PER MINUTE IN BAR

GAS USED PER MINUTE IN BAR																		
SAC →	0.4	0.5	0.6	0.7	0.8	0.9	1.0	1.1	1.2	1.3	1.4	1.5	1.6	1.7	1.8	1.9	2.0	2.1
MSW ↓																		
3	0.5	0.7	0.8	0.9	1.0	1.2	1.3	1.4	1.6	1.7	1.8	2.0	2.1	2.2	2.3	2.5	2.6	2.7
6	0.6	0.8	1.0	1.1	1.3	1.4	1.6	1.8	1.9	2.1	2.2	2.4	2.6	2.7	2.9	3.1	3.2	3.4
9	0.8	1.0	1.1	1.3	1.5	1.7	1.9	2.1	2.3	2.5	2.7	2.9	3.1	3.2	3.4	3.6	3.8	4.0
12	0.9	1.1	1.3	1.5	1.8	2.0	2.2	2.4	2.7	2.9	3.1	3.3	3.5	3.8	4.0	4.2	4.4	4.6
15	1.0	1.3	1.5	1.8	2.0	2.3	2.5	2.8	3.0	3.3	3.5	3.8	4.0	4.3	4.5	4.8	5.0	5.3
18	1.1	1.4	1.7	2.0	2.3	2.5	2.8	3.1	3.4	3.7	3.9	4.2	4.5	4.8	5.1	5.4	5.6	5.9
21	1.2	1.6	1.9	2.2	2.5	2.8	3.1	3.4	3.7	4.1	4.4	4.7	5.0	5.3	5.6	5.9	6.2	6.6
24	1.4	1.7	2.1	2.4	2.7	3.1	3.4	3.8	4.1	4.5	4.8	5.1	5.5	5.8	6.2	6.5	6.8	7.2
27	1.5	1.9	2.2	2.6	3.0	3.4	3.7	4.1	4.5	4.8	5.2	5.6	6.0	6.3	6.7	7.1	7.5	7.8
30	1.6	2.0	2.4	2.8	3.2	3.6	4.0	4.4	4.8	5.2	5.6	6.0	6.4	6.9	7.3	7.7	8.1	8.5
34	1.7	2.2	2.6	3.0	3.5	3.9	4.3	4.8	5.2	5.6	6.1	6.5	6.9	7.4	7.8	8.2	8.7	9.1
37	1.9	2.3	2.8	3.2	3.7	4.2	4.6	5.1	5.6	6.0	6.5	7.0	7.4	7.9	8.3	8.8	9.3	9.7
40	2.0	2.5	3.0	3.5	4.0	4.4	4.9	5.4	5.9	6.4	6.9	7.4	7.9	8.4	8.9	9.4	9.9	10.4
43	2.1	2.6	3.1	3.7	4.2	4.7	5.2	5.8	6.3	6.8	7.3	7.9	8.4	8.9	9.4	10.0	10.5	11.0
46	2.2	2.8	3.3	3.9	4.4	5.0	5.5	6.1	6.7	7.2	7.8	8.3	8.9	9.4	10.0	10.5	11.1	11.6
49	2.3	2.9	3.5	4.1	4.7	5.3	5.8	6.4	7.0	7.6	8.2	8.8	9.4	9.9	10.5	11.1	11.7	12.3
52	2.5	3.1	3.7	4.3	4.9	5.5	6.2	6.8	7.4	8.0	8.6	9.2	9.8	10.5	11.1	11.7	12.3	12.9
55	2.6	3.2	3.9	4.5	5.2	5.8	6.5	7.1	7.7	8.4	9.0	9.7	10.3	11.0	11.6	12.3	12.9	13.6
58	2.7	3.4	4.1	4.7	5.4	6.1	6.8	7.4	8.1	8.8	9.5	10.1	10.8	11.5	12.2	12.8	13.5	14.2
61	2.8	3.5	4.2	4.9	5.6	6.4	7.1	7.8	8.5	9.2	9.9	10.6	11.3	12.0	12.7	13.4	14.1	14.8
64	2.9	3.7	4.4	5.2	5.9	6.6	7.4	8.1	8.8	9.6	10.3	11.0	11.8	12.5	13.3	14.0	14.7	15.5
67	3.1	3.8	4.6	5.4	6.1	6.9	7.7	8.4	9.2	10.0	10.7	11.5	12.3	13.0	13.8	14.6	15.3	16.1
70	3.2	4.0	4.8	5.6	6.4	7.2	8.0	8.8	9.6	10.4	11.2	12.0	12.8	13.5	14.3	15.1	15.9	16.7
73	3.3	4.1	5.0	5.8	6.6	7.4	8.3	9.1	9.9	10.8	11.6	12.4	13.2	14.1	14.9	15.7	16.5	17.4
76	3.4	4.3	5.1	6.0	6.9	7.7	8.6	9.4	10.3	11.1	12.0	12.9	13.7	14.6	15.4	16.3	17.2	18.0
79	3.6	4.4	5.3	6.2	7.1	8.0	8.9	9.8	10.7	11.5	12.4	13.3	14.2	15.1	16.0	16.9	17.8	18.6
82	3.7	4.6	5.5	6.4	7.3	8.3	9.2	10.1	11.0	11.9	12.9	13.8	14.7	15.6	16.5	17.4	18.4	19.3
85	3.8	4.7	5.7	6.6	7.6	8.5	9.5	10.4	11.4	12.3	13.3	14.2	15.2	16.1	17.1	18.0	19.0	19.9
88	3.9	4.9	5.9	6.9	7.8	8.8	9.8	10.8	11.7	12.7	13.7	14.7	15.7	16.6	17.6	18.6	19.6	20.6
91	4.0	5.0	6.1	7.1	8.1	9.1	10.1	11.1	12.1	13.1	14.1	15.1	16.1	17.2	18.2	19.2	20.2	21.2

Table 11 may be used when planning the total volume of gas needed for a dive. This can be applied individually or to the group. By knowing ones gas consumption in free liters per minute, a total gas need calculation is made. For instance, the planned depth is 40 meters. The diver uses 16.99 (17) free liters per minute at the surface. Go down the table and you will discover that 84.96 free liters per minute of exposure are needed. For decompression purposes, each gas and stop depth gas supply need can be determined in the same manner. Remember to add the Rule of Thirds safety reserve to the total volume. This table is especially beneficial when planning Trimix dives due to the multiple gas switches and the duration of the dives.

Table 11 M

IANTD GAS MANAGEMENT CHART - METRIC VERSION
SAC / MSW Table

	SURFACE AIR CONSUMPTION IN FREE LITERS PER MINUTE																	
MSW	10	11	12	13	14	15	16	17	18	19	20	21	22	23	24	25	26	27	28
3	13	14	16	17	18	20	21	22	23	25	26	27	29	30	31	33	34	35	36
4.5	14.5	16.0	17.4	18.9	20.3	21.8	23.2	24.7	26.1	27.6	29.0	30.5	31.9	33.4	34.8	36.3	37.7	39.2	40.6
6	16	18	19	27	22	24	26	27	29	30	32	34	35	37	38	40	42	43	45
9	19	21	23	25	27	29	30	32	34	36	38	40	42	44	46	48	49	51	53
12	22	24	26	29	31	33	35	37	40	42	44	46	48	51	53	55	57	59	62
15	25	28	30	33	35	38	40	43	45	48	50	53	55	58	60	63	65	68	70
18	28	31	34	36	39	42	45	48	50	53	56	59	62	64	67	70	73	76	78
21	31	34	37	40	43	47	50	53	56	59	62	65	68	71	74	78	81	84	87
24	34	37	41	44	48	51	54	58	61	65	68	71	75	78	82	85	88	92	95
27	37	41	44	48	52	56	59	63	67	70	74	78	81	85	89	93	96	100	104
30	40	44	48	52	56	60	64	68	72	76	80	84	88	92	96	100	104	108	112
33	43	47	52	56	60	65	69	73	77	82	86	90	95	99	103	108	112	116	120
36	46	51	55	60	64	69	74	78	83	87	92	97	101	106	110	115	120	124	129
39	49	54	59	64	69	74	78	83	88	93	98	103	108	113	118	123	127	132	137
42	52	57	62	68	73	78	83	88	94	99	104	109	114	120	125	130	135	140	146
45	55	61	66	72	77	83	88	94	99	105	110	116	121	127	132	138	143	149	154
48	58	64	70	75	81	87	93	99	104	110	116	122	128	133	139	145	151	157	162
51	61	67	73	79	85	92	98	104	110	116	122	128	134	140	146	153	159	165	171
54	64	70	77	83	90	96	102	109	115	122	128	134	141	147	154	160	166	173	179
57	67	74	80	87	94	101	107	114	121	127	134	141	147	154	161	168	174	181	188
60	70	77	84	91	98	105	112	119	126	133	140	147	154	161	168	175	182	189	196
63	73	80	88	95	102	110	117	124	131	139	146	153	161	168	175	183	190	197	204
66	76	84	91	99	106	114	122	129	137	144	152	160	167	175	182	190	198	205	213
69	79	87	95	103	111	119	126	134	142	150	158	166	174	182	190	198	205	213	221
72	82	90	98	107	115	123	131	16	148	156	164	172	180	189	197	205	213	221	230
75	85	94	102	111	119	128	136	145	153	162	170	179	187	196	204	213	221	230	238
78	88	97	106	114	123	132	141	150	158	167	176	185	194	202	211	220	229	238	246
81	91	100	109	118	127	137	146	155	164	173	182	191	200	209	218	228	237	246	255
84	94	103	113	122	132	141	150	160	169	179	188	197	207	216	226	235	244	254	263
87	97	107	116	126	136	146	155	165	175	184	194	204	213	223	233	243	252	262	272
90	100	110	120	130	140	150	160	170	180	190	200	210	220	230	240	250	260	270	280
93	103	113	124	134	144	155	165	175	185	196	206	216	227	237	247	258	268	278	288
96	106	117	127	138	148	159	170	288	191	201	212	223	233	244	254	265	276	286	297
99	109	120	131	142	153	164	174	185	196	207	218	229	240	251	262	273	283	294	305
102	112	123	134	146	157	168	179	190	202	213	224	235	246	258	269	280	291	302	314
105	115	127	138	150	161	173	184	196	207	219	230	242	253	265	276	288	299	311	322

Produced by: Mount/Owens/Taylor/Townsend Copyright IAND, Inc./Repetitive Diver, Inc. 1998-2000

Locate your Surface Air Consumption (SAC) across the top row.
Example: 18 (SAC) Free Liters per Minute
Go down the column under the 18 until you get to your depth location row from the far left column
Example: 61 MSW
This gives you the SAC for one minute at this depth.
Example: 128 Free Liters per Minute

⚠ Warning: DO NOT attempt to use these tables unless you are fully trained & certified in the use of gas mixtures other than air, or are under the supervision of a gas mixtures other than air instructor. Proper use of these tables will reduce the risk of decompression sickness & oxygen toxicity, but no table or computer can eliminate those risks.

IANTD/IAND, Inc. GAS MANAGEMENT CHART - METRIC VERSION

BAR/FREE LITER Conversion Table

BAR & TANK SIZE	7 BAR	34 BAR	68 BAR	102 BAR	136 BAR	170 BAR	204 BAR	238 BAR	272 BAR
170 / 70fT³*	82	396	793	1189	1586	1982	2379	2775	3172
180 / 7 LITERS	49	238	476	714	952	1190	1428	1666	1904
180 / 15 LITERS	105	510	1020	1530	2040	2550	3060	3570	4080
180 / 16 LITERS	112	544	1088	1632	2176	2720	3264	3808	4352
180 / 17 LITERS	119	578	1156	1734	2312	2890	3468	4046	4624
180 / 19 LITERS	133	646	1292	1938	2584	3230	3876	4522	5168
204 / 70 FT³*	68	330	661	991	1322	1652	1983	2313	2644
204 / 10 LITERS	70	340	680	1020	1360	1700	2040	2380	2720
220 / 12 LITERS	84	408	816	1224	1632	2040	2448	2856	3264
220 / 15 LITERS	105	510	1020	1530	2040	2550	3060	3570	4080
220 / 18 LITERS	126	612	1224	1836	2448	3060	3672	4284	4896
240 / 65 FT³*	54	261	522	782	1043	1304	1565	1825	2086
240 / 10 LITERS	70	340	680	1020	1360	1700	2040	2380	2720
240 / 13 LITERS	91	442	884	1326	1768	2210	2652	3094	3536
240 / 15 LITERS	105	510	1020	1530	2040	2550	3060	3570	4080
300 / 18 LITERS	126	612	1224	1836	2448	3060	3672	4284	4896

Produced by: Mount/Owens/Taylor ♣ Metric Conversion by Denlay ♣ Copyright: IANTD/IAND, Inc./Repetitive Diver, Inc.

- **THESE TANK SIZES ARE IN CUBIC FEET. METRIC SIZE DATA IS UNAVAILABLE.**

Column one on the left shows the pressure rating for various cylinders. Column one on the right lists various size cylinders.

To determine the amount of gas in your cylinder, locate your cylinder size. For example, "220 18 " is an 18 liter tank rated for a capacity of 220 Bar.

The remaining columns show the amount of free liters in your tank for a given Bar. For example, if you continue to follow the line for the 18 liter tank to "7 Bar", you'll see the tank contains 126 free liters of gas.

To determine the amount of gas for pressures not shown, simply add columns together. For example, an 18 liter tank with a gauge pressure of 109 Bar contains 1962 free liters of gas. This was determined by adding 126 free liters from the column under 7 Bar and 1836 free liters from the 102 Bar column.

For twin tank configurations, double the free liters.

⚠ **Warning: DO NOT attempt to use these tables unless you are fully trained & certified in the use of gas mixtures other than air, or are under the supervision of a gas mixtures other than air instructor. Proper use of these tables will reduce the risk of decompression sickness & oxygen toxicity, but no table or computer can eliminate those risks.**

IANTD GAS MANAGEMENT CHART - METRIC VERSION

SAC RATIO FACTOR (SRF)

<<<<<<<<<<<<< FREE LITERS >>>>>>>>>>>>>>

↑		32.57	31.15	29.74	28.32	26.90	25.49	24.07	22.66	21.24	19.82	18.40	16.99	15.58	14.16	12.74	11.33	9.91
↑	32.57	0.67																
F	31.15	0.67	0.67															
R	29.74	0.68	0.67	0.67														
E	28.32	0.68	0.68	0.67	0.67													
E	26.90	0.69	0.68	0.68	0.67	0.67												
	25.49	0.69	0.69	0.68	0.68	0.67	0.67											
L	24.07	0.70	0.70	0.69	0.69	0.68	0.67	0.67										
I	22.66	0.71	0.70	0.70	0.69	0.69	0.68	0.67	0.67									
T	21.24	0.72	0.71	0.71	0.70	0.69	0.69	0.68	0.67	0.67								
E	19.82	0.73	0.72	0.71	0.71	0.70	0.70	0.69	0.68	0.67	0.67							
R	18.40	0.73	0.73	0.72	0.72	0.71	0.70	0.70	0.69	0.68	0.67	0.67						
S	16.99	0.74	0.74	0.73	0.73	0.72	0.71	0.71	0.70	0.69	0.68	0.68	0.68					
↓	15.58	0.76	0.75	0.74	0.74	0.73	0.73	0.72	0.71	0.70	0.69	0.69	0.68	0.67				
↓	14.16	0.77	0.76	0.76	0.75	0.74	0.74	0.73	0.72	0.71	0.71	0.70	0.69	0.68	0.67			
↓	12.74	0.78	0.78	0.77	0.76	0.76	0.75	0.74	0.74	0.73	0.72	0.71	0.70	0.69	0.68	0.67		
↓	11.33	0.79	0.79	0.78	0.78	0.77	0.76	0.76	0.75	0.74	0.73	0.72	0.71	0.70	0.69	0.68	0.67	
↓	9.91	0.81	0.81	0.80	0.79	0.79	0.78	0.77	0.77	0.76	0.75	0.74	0.73	0.72	0.71	0.70	0.68	0.67

Produced by: Mount/Owens/Taylor • Metric Conversion By Pettennude • Copyright: IANTD/IAND, Inc./Repetitive Diver, Inc.

The SRF Table modifies the Rule of Thirds to represent true turn pressures for divers with different SAC rates. If you have a higher SAC rate than your buddy, the Rule of Thirds works fine. When you have consumed 33% of your gas, it's time to turn the dive. However, if your buddy has a higher SAC than you, this would not allow enough gas. In this situation, to find the proper turn pressure, locate your SAC along the **left column. EXAMPLE: 9.91**

Now go across the **top row** until you are under the column of your dive buddy's SAC. **EXAMPLE: 11.33**

The number where these two SACs intersect is the SRF. **EXAMPLE: 0.68**

You then multiply your cylinder pressure by the SRF number and this gives your turn pressure. You can also simply look up the turn pressure on the Turn Pressure Table. **EXAMPLE: you have 184 Bar in your cylinder 184 Bar x .68 = 125 Bar**

Strictly following the Rule of Thirds you would normally turn the dive at 121 Bar, which would not leave enough gas to exit. **You must turn at 125 Bar.**

Table
14 M

IANTD/IAND, Inc. GAS MANAGEMENT CHART - METRIC VERSION

Turn Pressure

SRF→ / BAR ↓	0.67	0.68	0.69	0.70	0.71	0.72	0.73	0.74	0.75	0.76	0.77	0.78	0.79	0.80	0.81
136	91	92	94	95	96	98	99	101	102	103	105	106	107	109	110
143	96	97	99	100	101	103	104	106	107	109	110	111	113	114	116
150	100	102	103	105	106	108	109	111	112	114	115	117	118	120	121
156	105	106	108	110	111	113	114	116	117	119	120	122	124	125	127
163	109	111	113	114	116	118	119	121	122	124	126	127	129	131	132
170	114	116	117	119	121	122	124	126	128	129	131	133	134	136	138
177	119	120	122	124	126	127	129	131	133	134	136	138	140	141	143
184	123	125	127	129	130	132	134	136	138	140	141	143	145	147	149
190	128	130	131	133	135	137	139	141	143	145	147	149	150	152	154
197	132	134	136	138	140	142	144	146	148	150	152	154	156	158	160
204	137	139	141	143	145	147	149	151	153	155	157	159	161	163	165
211	141	143	146	148	150	152	154	156	158	160	162	164	167	169	171
218	146	148	150	152	155	157	159	161	163	165	168	170	172	174	176
224	150	153	155	157	159	162	164	166	168	171	173	175	177	180	182
231	155	157	160	162	164	167	169	171	173	176	178	180	183	185	187
238	160	162	164	167	169	171	174	176	179	181	183	186	188	190	193
245	164	167	169	171	174	176	179	181	184	186	189	191	193	196	198
252	169	171	174	176	179	181	184	186	189	191	194	196	199	201	204
259	173	176	178	181	184	186	189	191	194	196	199	202	204	207	209
265	178	180	183	186	188	191	194	196	199	202	204	207	210	212	215
272	182	185	188	190	193	196	199	201	204	207	210	212	215	218	220

Produced by: Mount/Owens/Taylor ♣ Metric Conversion By Pettennude

To locate your turn pressure, first find your SRF from the IANTD SRF Table 13.

EXAMPLE: 0.74

Follow this column down until you are across from your tank pressure in the left column.

EXAMPLE: 184 Bar

The point of intersection is the turn pressure for this dive.

EXAMPLE: 136 Bar

⚠ Warning: DO NOT attempt to use these tables unless you are fully trained & certified in the use of gas mixtures other than air, or are under the supervision of a gas mixtures other than air instructor. Proper use of these tables will reduce the risk of decompression sickness & oxygen toxicity, but no table or computer can eliminate those risks.

IANTD/IAND, Inc. GAS MANAGEMENT CHART - METRIC VERSION

MINUTES ALLOWED UNTIL TURN

BAR USED ↓	GAS AVAILABLE UNTIL TURN IN BAR															
1	25	30	35	40	45	50	55	60	65	70	75	80	85	90	95	100
2	13	15	18	20	23	25	28	30	33	35	38	40	43	45	48	50
3	8	10	12	13	15	17	18	20	22	23	25	27	28	30	32	33
4	6	8	9	10	11	13	14	15	16	18	19	20	21	23	24	25
5	5	6	7	8	9	10	11	12	13	14	15	16	17	18	19	20
6	4	5	6	7	8	8	9	10	11	12	13	13	14	15	16	17
7	4	4	5	6	6	7	8	9	9	10	11	11	12	13	14	14
8	3	4	4	5	6	6	7	8	8	9	9	10	11	11	12	13
9	3	3	4	4	5	6	6	7	7	8	8	9	9	10	11	11
10	3	3	4	4	5	5	6	6	7	7	8	8	9	9	10	10
11	2	3	3	4	4	5	5	5	6	6	7	7	8	8	9	9
12	2	3	3	3	4	4	5	5	5	6	6	7	7	8	8	8
13	2	2	3	3	3	4	4	5	5	5	6	6	7	7	7	8
14	2	2	3	3	3	4	4	4	5	5	5	6	6	6	7	7
15	2	2	2	3	3	3	4	4	4	5	5	5	6	6	6	7
16	2	2	2	3	3	3	3	4	4	4	5	5	5	6	6	6
17	1	2	2	2	3	3	3	4	4	4	4	5	5	5	6	6
18	1	2	2	2	3	3	3	3	4	4	4	4	5	5	5	6
19	1	2	2	2	2	3	3	3	3	4	4	4	4	5	5	5
20	1	2	2	2	2	3	3	3	3	4	4	4	4	5	5	5
21	1	1	2	2	2	2	3	3	3	3	4	4	4	4	5	5
22	1	1	2	2	2	2	3	3	3	3	3	4	4	4	4	5
23	1	1	2	2	2	2	2	3	3	3	3	3	4	4	4	4
24	1	1	1	2	2	2	2	3	3	3	3	3	4	4	4	4
25	1	1	1	2	2	2	2	2	3	3	3	3	3	4	4	4

PRODUCED BY TOM MOUNT / MARK OWENS ♠

"BAR USED" IS BAR CONSUMED PER MINUTE DURING THE DIVE.

⚠ Warning: DO NOT attempt to use these tables unless you are fully trained & certified in the use of gas mixtures other than air, or are under the supervision of a gas mixtures other than air instructor. Proper use of these tables will reduce the risk of decompression sickness & oxygen toxicity, but no table or computer can eliminate those risks.

Table 16 M

IANTD/IAND, Inc. GAS MANAGEMENT CAVE CHART - METRIC VERSION

DISTANCE TRAVELED IN METERS

MINUTES TO TURN ↓	DISTANCED TRAVELED IN METERS							
	10	15	20	25	30	35	40	45
1	10	15	20	25	30	35	40	45
2	20	30	40	50	60	70	80	90
3	30	45	60	75	90	105	120	135
4	40	60	80	100	120	140	160	180
5	50	75	100	125	150	175	200	225
6	60	90	120	150	180	210	240	270
7	70	105	140	175	210	245	280	315
8	80	120	160	200	240	280	320	360
9	90	135	180	225	270	315	360	405
10	100	150	200	250	300	350	400	450
11	110	165	220	275	330	385	440	495
12	120	180	240	300	360	420	480	540
13	130	195	260	325	390	455	520	585
14	140	210	280	350	420	490	560	630
15	150	225	300	375	450	525	600	675
16	160	240	320	400	480	560	640	720
17	170	255	340	425	510	595	680	765
18	180	270	360	450	540	630	720	810
19	190	285	380	475	570	665	760	855
20	200	300	400	500	600	700	800	900
21	210	315	420	525	630	735	840	945
23	230	345	460	575	690	805	920	1035
24	240	360	480	600	720	840	960	1080
25	250	375	500	625	750	875	1000	1125
27	270	405	540	675	810	945	1080	1215
28	280	420	560	700	840	980	1120	1260
30	300	450	600	750	900	1050	1200	1350
32	320	480	640	800	960	1120	1280	1440
33	330	495	660	825	990	1155	1320	1485
35	350	525	700	875	1050	1225	1400	1575
38	380	570	760	950	1140	1330	1520	1710
40	400	600	800	1000	1200	1400	1600	1800
43	430	645	860	1075	1290	1505	1720	1935
45	450	675	900	1125	1350	1575	1800	2025
48	480	720	960	1200	1440	1680	1920	2160
50	500	750	1000	1250	1500	1750	2000	2250
55	550	825	1100	1375	1650	1925	2200	2475
60	600	900	1200	1500	1800	2100	2400	2700
65	650	975	1300	1625	1950	2275	2600	2925
70	700	1050	1400	1750	2100	2450	2800	3150

PRODUCED BY TOM MOUNT / MARK OWENS

⚠ Warning: DO NOT attempt to use these tables unless you are fully trained & certified in the use of gas mixtures other than air, or are under the supervision of a gas mixtures other than air instructor. Proper use of these tables will reduce the risk of decompression sickness & oxygen toxicity, but no table or computer can eliminate those risks.

IANTD/IAND, Inc. GAS DENSITY TABLE

(values are approximate)

PERCENT OF GASES IN THE MIX								
Oxygen	0%	0%	100%	34%	15%	14%	16%	21%
Nitrogen	0%	100%	0%	66%	40%	53%	60%	0%
Helium	100%	0%	0%	0%	45%	33%	24%	79%
Air								
msw	msw	msw	msw	msw	msw	msw	msw	msw
3	0.3	3	3	3	2	2	2	1
6	1	6	6	6	3	4	5	2
9	1	9	9	9	5	6	7	3
12	2	12	12	12	7	9	10	4
15	2	14	15	15	9	11	12	5
19	2	17	18	18	11	13	14	6
21	3	21	21	21	13	15	17	7
24	3	23	24	24	15	17	19	8
27	4	26	28	28	17	19	21	9
30	4	29	31	31	18	21	24	10
33	4	32	34	34	21	24	26	11
36	5	35	37	37	22	26	29	12
39	5	38	40	40	24	28	31	13
42	6	41	43	43	26	30	34	14
46	6	44	46	46	28	32	36	15
49	7	47	49	49	30	35	38	17
52	7	50	52	52	32	37	41	17
55	7	53	56	56	34	39	43	18
58	8	56	59	59	35	41	46	20
61	8	59	62	62	37	43	48	21
64	9	62	65	65	39	46	50	22
67	9	65	68	68	41	48	53	23
70	10	67	71	71	43	50	55	24
73	10	71	74	74	45	52	58	25
76	11	74	77	77	47	54	60	26
79	11	76	80	80	49	56	62	27
82	11	79	83	83	50	58	65	28
85	12	82	86	86	52	61	67	29
88	12	85	89	89	54	63	70	30
91	12	88	92	92	56	65	72	31

- **Note:** Although the approximate Equivalent Air Depth Density is given for all gases tabulated, the user should not attempt to use any gas mixture outside the appropriate Maximum Operating Depth. The densities are given strictly for reference information.

- This table gives approximate Equivalent Air Depth Densities for a given gas mixture at some bottom depth. As an example: A 16 24 Trimix breathed at 82 msw would have a density approximately equal to air at 65 msw.

Chart 1

IANTD/IAND, INC. CNS REPETITIVE CHART

START PERCENT	SURFACE INTERVAL (S.I.) 30 MINS	60 MINS	90 MINS	2 HRS	3 HRS	4 HRS	5 HRS	6 HRS
100	83	66	49	41	24	16	11	7
95	79	63	46	38	22	15	10	7
90	75	59	44	37	22	15	10	7
85	71	56	42	35	21	14	9	6
80	66	53	39	32	19	13	9	6
75	62	49	37	31	18	12	8	5
70	58	46	34	28	17	11	7	5
65	54	43	32	27	16	11	7	5
60	50	40	29	24	14	9	6	4
55	46	36	27	22	13	9	6	4
50	41	33	24	20	12	8	5	3
45	37	30	22	18	11	7	5	3
40	33	26	20	17	10	7	5	3
35	29	23	17	14	8	5	3	2
30	25	20	15	12	7	5	3	2
25	21	16	12	10	6	4	3	2
20	17	13	10	8	5	3	2	1
15	12	10	7	6	3	2	1	1
10	8	7	5	4	2	1	1	1
RESIDUAL PERCENT CNS O_2 CLOCK								

Produced by: Tom Mount / Mark Owens ♠ Copyright 1993-2000: IANTD/IAND, Inc. / Repetitive Diver, Inc.

To read the CNS repetitive CNS % chart, begin at the top left column with 100%. Read to the right and after 30 minutes Surface Interval, you will read down the column to see that the diver still has 83% of the CNS O_2 clock loaded, while after 6 hrs. S.I., only 7% of the CNS O_2 clock will remain.

Nitrox Top Up Chart METRIC Version

Oxygen %	Pressure of fill (bars)																					
	30	40	50	60	70	80	90	100	110	120	130	140	150	160	170	180	190	200	210	220	230	240	250
21%	0	0	0	0	0	0	0	0	0	0	0	0	0	0	0	0	0	0	0	0	0	0	0
22%	0	1	1	1	1	1	1	1	2	2	2	2	2	2	2	2	2	3	3	3	3	3	3
23%	1	1	1	2	2	2	2	3	3	3	3	4	4	4	4	5	5	5	5	6	6	6	6
24%	1	2	2	2	3	3	3	4	4	5	5	5	6	6	6	7	7	8	8	8	9	9	9
25%	2	2	3	3	4	4	5	5	6	6	7	7	8	8	9	9	10	10	11	11	12	12	13
26%	2	3	3	4	4	5	6	6	7	8	8	9	9	10	11	11	12	13	13	14	15	15	16
27%	2	3	4	5	5	6	7	8	8	9	10	11	11	12	13	14	14	15	16	17	17	18	19
28%	3	4	4	5	6	7	8	9	10	11	12	12	13	14	15	16	17	18	19	19	20	21	22
29%	3	4	5	6	7	8	9	10	11	12	13	14	15	16	17	18	19	20	21	22	23	24	25
30%	3	5	6	7	8	9	10	11	13	14	15	16	17	18	19	21	22	23	24	25	26	27	28
31%	4	5	6	8	9	10	11	13	14	15	16	18	19	20	22	23	24	25	27	28	29	30	32
32%	4	6	7	8	10	11	13	14	15	17	18	19	21	22	24	25	26	28	29	31	32	33	35
33%	5	6	8	9	11	12	14	15	17	18	20	21	23	24	26	27	29	30	32	33	35	36	38
34%	5	7	8	10	12	13	15	16	18	20	21	23	25	26	28	30	31	33	35	36	38	39	41
35%	5	7	9	11	12	14	16	18	19	21	23	25	27	28	30	32	34	35	37	39	41	43	44
36%	6	8	9	11	13	15	17	19	21	23	25	27	28	30	32	34	36	38	40	42	44	46	47
37%	6	8	10	12	14	16	18	20	22	24	26	28	30	32	34	36	38	41	43	45	47	49	51
38%	6	9	11	13	15	17	19	22	24	26	28	30	32	34	37	39	41	43	45	47	49	52	54
39%	7	9	11	14	16	18	21	23	25	27	30	32	34	36	39	41	43	46	48	50	52	55	57
40%	7	10	12	14	17	19	22	24	26	29	31	34	36	38	41	43	46	48	51	53	55	58	60

Rules:

1. Having dived the cylinder (note mix prior to dive) gauge the pressure. Using the table, move down the current gauge pressure and across the mix. This will give a number.
2. Go to the new mix required and the new fill pressure. This will give you another number.
3. Take the first number from the second. This is the pure O_2 to add to the part of the used cylinder. Now fill with air to the pressure used in step 2.
4. If the answer is negative. More gas must be drained to make the answer 0 or positive. Then fill with air or air and oxygen respectively.
5. To estimate how much gas to remove from the first fill, go to the first mix and fill number, find a number along the same row Less Than or Equal To the second mix and fill number. Move up to the fill pressure. This must be the pressure in the cylinder prior to topping.

Chart 3 M

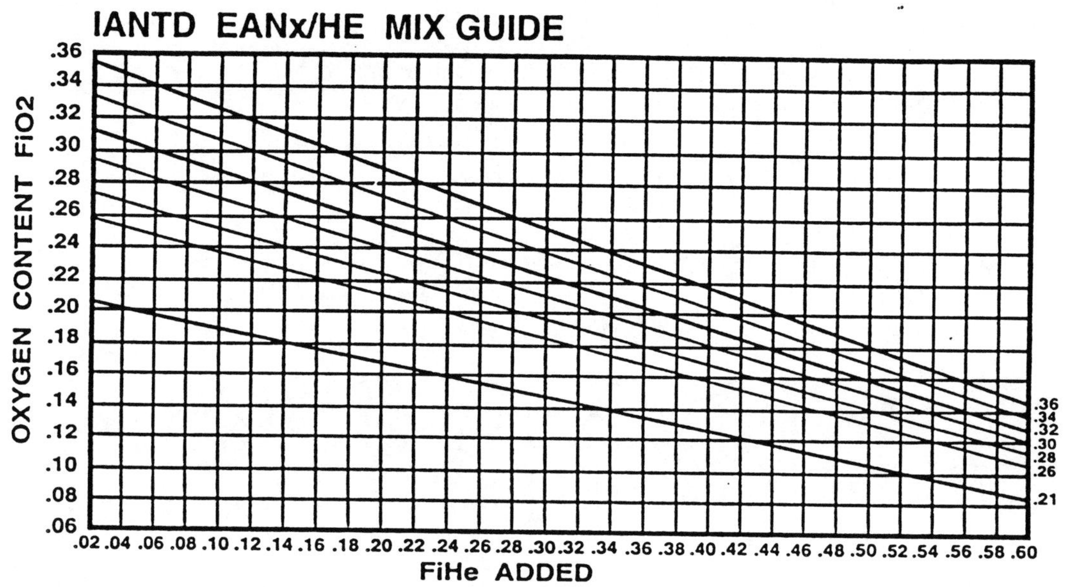

Chart 4 M

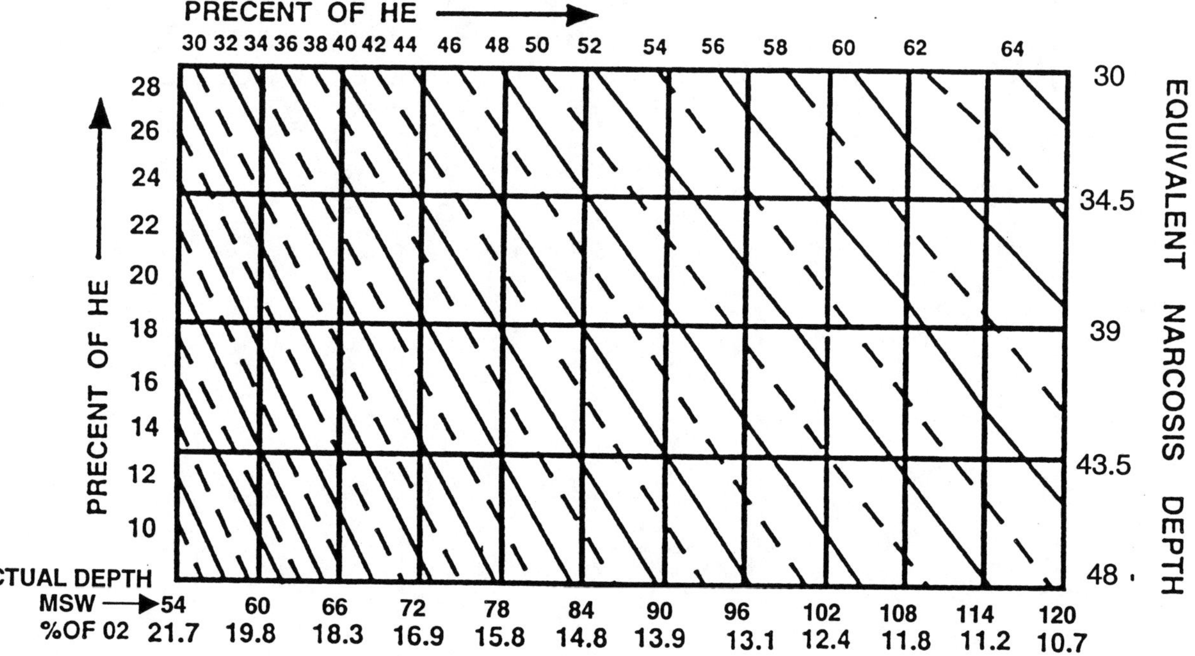

PRODUCED BY TOM MOUNT/MARK OWENS/DON TOWNSEND

⚠ Warning: DO NOT attempt to use these tables unless you are fully trained & certified in the use of gas mixtures other than air, or are under the supervision of a gas mixtures other than air instructor. Proper use of these tables will reduce the risk of decompression sickness & oxygen toxicity, but no table or computer can eliminate those risks.

IANTD
TABLE OF EQUIVALENT NARCOSIS DEPTHS FOR TRIMIX DIVING

ACTUAL DEPTH		EQUIVALENT NARCOSIS DEPTHS FOR 1.3 PO_2																	
		END 80 FSW 24 MSW		END 90 FSW 27 MSW		END 100 FSW 30 MSW		END 110 FSW 33 MSW		END 120 FSW 36 MSW		END 130 FSW 39 MSW		END 140 FSW 42 MSW		END 150 FSW 45 MSW		END 160 FSW 48 MSW	
FSW/MSW	Fi O_2	Fi HE	Fi N_2	Fi HE	Fi N_2	Fi HE	Fi N_2	Fi HE	Fi N_2	Fi HE	Fi N_2	Fi HE	Fi N_2	Fi HE	Fi N_2	Fi HE	Fi N_2	Fi HE	Fi N_2
210 / 63	0.18	0.46	0.37	0.42	0.40	0.39	0.43	0.36	0.46	0.33	0.50	0.29	0.53	0.26	0.56	0.23	0.59	0.20	0.63
220 / 66	0.17	0.48	0.35	0.45	0.38	0.42	0.42	0.38	0.45	0.35	0.48	0.32	0.51	0.29	0.54	0.26	0.57	0.23	0.60
230 / 69	0.16	0.50	0.34	0.47	0.37	0.44	0.40	0.41	0.43	0.38	0.46	0.35	0.49	0.32	0.52	0.29	0.55	0.26	0.58
240 / 72	0.16	0.52	0.33	0.49	0.36	0.46	0.38	0.43	0.41	0.40	0.44	0.37	0.47	0.34	0.50	0.31	0.53	0.28	0.56
250 / 75	0.15	0.53	0.32	0.51	0.34	0.48	0.37	0.45	0.40	0.42	0.43	0.39	0.46	0.37	0.48	0.34	0.51	0.31	0.54
260 / 78	0.15	0.55	0.30	0.52	0.33	0.49	0.36	0.47	0.39	0.44	0.41	0.41	0.44	0.39	0.47	0.36	0.49	0.33	0.52
270 / 81	0.14	0.56	0.29	0.54	0.32	0.51	0.35	0.49	0.37	0.46	0.40	0.43	0.42	0.41	0.45	0.38	0.48	0.36	0.50
280 / 84	0.14	0.58	0.29	0.55	0.31	0.53	0.34	0.50	0.36	0.48	0.39	0.45	0.41	0.43	0.44	0.40	0.46	0.38	0.49
290 / 87	0.13	0.59	0.28	0.57	0.30	0.54	0.33	0.52	0.35	0.49	0.37	0.47	0.40	0.44	0.42	0.42	0.45	0.40	0.47
300 / 91	0.13	0.60	0.27	0.58	0.29	0.56	0.32	0.53	0.34	0.51	0.36	0.48	0.39	0.46	0.41	0.44	0.43	0.41	0.46

Produced By Tom Mount, Mark Owens, and Clayton Bohm

⚠ Warning: DO NOT attempt to use these tables unless you are fully trained & certified in the use of gas mixtures other than air, or are under the supervision of a gas mixtures other than air instructor. Proper use of these tables will reduce the risk of decompression sickness & oxygen toxicity, but no table or computer can eliminate those risks.

IANTD
TABLE OF EQUIVALENT NARCOSIS DEPTHS FOR TRIMIX DIVING

ACTUAL DEPTH		EQUIVALENT NARCOSIS DEPTHS FOR 1.4 PO_2											
		END 70 FSW 21 MSW		END 80 FSW 24 MSW		END 90 FSW 27 MSW		END 100 FSW 30 MSW		END 110 FSW 33 MSW		END 120 FSW 36 MSW	
FSW/MSW	Fi O_2	Fi HE	Fi N_2	Fi HE	Fi N_2	Fi HE	Fi N_2	Fi HE	Fi N_2	Fi HE	Fi N_2	Fi HE	Fi N_2
150 / 45	0.25	0.30	0.44	0.26	0.49	0.22	0.53	0.17	0.57	0.13	0.62	0.09	0.66
160 / 48	0.24	0.34	0.42	0.30	0.46	0.26	0.50	0.22	0.54	0.18	0.59	0.13	0.63
170 / 51	0.23	0.37	0.40	0.33	0.44	0.29	0.48	0.25	0.52	0.22	0.56	0.18	0.60
180 / 54	0.22	0.40	0.38	0.36	0.42	0.33	0.46	0.29	0.49	0.25	0.53	0.22	0.57
190 / 57	0.21	0.43	0.36	0.39	0.40	0.36	0.44	0.32	0.47	0.29	0.51	0.25	0.54
200 / 60	0.20	0.45	0.35	0.42	0.38	0.38	0.42	0.35	0.45	0.32	0.48	0.28	0.52
210 / 63	0.19	0.48	0.33	0.44	0.37	0.41	0.40	0.38	0.43	0.34	0.46	0.31	0.50

ACTUAL DEPTH		EQUIVALENT NARCOSIS DEPTHS FOR 1.3 PO_2											
		END 70 FSW 21 MSW		END 80 FSW 24 MSW		END 90 FSW 27 MSW		END 100 FSW 30 MSW		END 110 FSW 33 MSW		END 120 FSW 36 MSW	
FSW/MSW	Fi O_2	Fi HE	Fi N_2	Fi HE	Fi N_2	Fi HE	Fi N_2	Fi HE	Fi N_2	Fi HE	Fi N_2	Fi HE	Fi N_2
150 / 45	0.23	0.32	0.44	0.28	0.49	0.23	0.53	0.19	0.57	0.15	0.62	0.11	0.66
160 / 48	0.22	0.36	0.42	0.32	0.46	0.27	0.50	0.23	0.54	0.19	0.59	0.15	0.63
170 / 51	0.21	0.39	0.40	0.35	0.44	0.31	0.48	0.27	0.52	0.23	0.56	0.19	0.60
180 / 54	0.20	0.42	0.38	0.38	0.42	0.34	0.46	0.31	0.49	0.27	0.53	0.23	0.57
190 / 57	0.19	0.44	0.36	0.41	0.40	0.37	0.44	0.34	0.47	0.30	0.51	0.27	0.54
200 / 60	0.18	0.47	0.35	0.43	0.38	0.40	0.42	0.36	0.45	0.33	0.48	0.30	0.52
210 / 63	0.18	0.49	0.33	0.46	0.37	0.42	0.40	0.39	0.43	0.36	0.46	0.33	0.50

Produced By Tom Mount, Mark Owens, and Clayton Bohm

⚠ **Warning: DO NOT attempt to use these tables unless you are fully trained & certified in the use of gas mixtures other than air, or are under the supervision of a gas mixtures other than air instructor. Proper use of these tables will reduce the risk of decompression sickness & oxygen toxicity, but no table or computer can eliminate those risks.**

IANTD AIR DIVING & DECOMPRESSION TABLES

(A) Planned depth · (B) BOTTOM TIMES · (C) SURFACE INTERVALS

(A) 40	50	60	70	80	90	100	110	120	130	140	Depth (Feet)			Repetitive Group			
12	15	18	21	24	27	30	33	36	39	42	Depth (Meters)						
125	75	51	35	25	20	17	14	12	10	9	No Decompression Limits (Minutes)			↓			
(B) 19	16	14	12	11	10	9	8	7	7	6					A	00:00 01:59	02:00
25	20	17	15	13	12	11	10	9	8	7				B	00:00 00:19	00:20 01:59	02:00
37	29	25	22	20	18	16	11	10	9	8			C	00:00 00:09	00:10 00:24	00:25 02:59	03:00
57	41	33	28	24	19	17	14	12	10	9		D	00:00 00:09	00:10 00:14	00:15 00:29	00:30 02:59	03:00
82	59	44	35	25	20						E	00:00 00:09	00:10 00:14	00:15 00:24	00:25 00:44	00:45 03:59	04:00
111	65	51								F	00:00 00:19	00:20 00:29	00:30 00:44	00:45 01:14	01:15 01:29	01:30 07:59	08:00
125	75								G	00:00 00:24	00:25 00:44	00:45 00:59	01:00 01:14	01:15 01:39	01:40 02:09	02:10 11:59	12:00
									H	00:50 01:04	01:05 01:34	01:35 02:09	02:10 02:59	03:00 03:59	04:00 05:39	05:40 23:59	24:00
									K	03:00 03:59	04:00 04:59	05:00 05:59	06:00 06:59	07:00 07:59	08:00 09:19	09:20 38:59	39:00
									L	06:00 06:59	07:00 08:29	08:30 09:59	10:00 11:59	12:00 13:59	14:00 16:29	16:30 47:59	48:00
(D) REPETITIVE GROUP AT END OF S.I.										G	F	E	D	C	B	A	

(E) REPETITIVE DIVE TABLES

G	F	E	D	C	B	A		DEPTH (F)	(M)
137	111	82	57	37	25	19	RNT	40	12
115	88	59	41	29	20	16	RNT	50	15
91	68	44	33	25	17	14	RNT	60	18
72	53	37	28	22	15	12	RNT	70	21
57	42	30	24	20	13	11	RNT	80	24
47	35	26	21	18	12	10	RNT	90	27
40	30	23	19	16	11	9	RNT	100	30
35	27	21	17	14	10	8	RNT	110	33
31	24	19	15	12	9	7	RNT	120	36
27	21	17	14	11	8	7	RNT	130	39
25	19	16	13	10	7	6	RNT	140	42
23	17	14	11	9	7	6	RNT	150	45
21	16	13	10	8	6	6	RNT	160	48
20	15	12	9	7	5	5	RNT	170	51
19	14	11	9	7	5	5	RNT	180	54
18	13	10	8	6	5	5	RNT	190	57

RESIDUAL NITROGEN TIME

These Tables Are For Air With Air As Deco Gas Or Accelerated Deco Using EAN 75% Oxygen Or Greater At 20 And 15 Foot Stops. The 15 Foot Stops MUST Be Taken At 15 Feet. These Tables Are Based On Buehlmann's ZHL-16 Algorithm For 0-1000 Feet Above Sea Level. They Were Produced Using Cybortronix DPA Software. The Repetitive Dive Groups Are Not Transferable To ANY Other Tables. A 3 Minute Safety Stop Is Required For All Dives. These Tables Do Not Account For Physical Condition Of Diver, Difficulty Of Dive, Water Temperature, Etc.

(A) Planned Depth
(B) Bottom Time In Depth Column
(C) Read Across To Find Surface Interval
(D) Locate RNT After S. I.
(E) Read Down To Planned Repetitive
    Dive Depth. Read RNT

⚠ Warning: DO NOT attempt to use these tables unless you are fully trained & certified in the use of gas mixtures other than air, or are under the supervision of a gas mixtures other than air instructor. Proper use of these tables will reduce the risk of decompression sickness & oxygen toxicity, but no table or computer can eliminate those risks.

IANTD AIR DECOMPRESSION TABLES WITH EAN 75% DECOMPRESSION

Depth m	Depth ft	Min	9 m / 30 ft	6 m / 20 ft	4.5 m / 15 ft	≥75% O_2 6 m / 20 ft	≥75% O_2 4.5 m / 15 ft	RG
12	40	150			1		1	G
15	50	90			5		3	G
		120			19		9	H
18	60	60			6		4	F
		70			11		6	G
		80			16		9	G
		90			24		12	H
		100			31		15	H
		110			37		18	H
		120			45		21	K
21	70	50			10		6	F
		60			17		9	G
		70			24		13	H
		80			35		17	H
		90			43		22	H
		100		1	52	1	24	H
		110		3	71	2	26	K
		120		5	87	3	33	K
24	80	40			11		6	F
		50			19		10	G
		60		1	28	1	14	G
		70		3	38	2	19	G
		80		5	46	4	22	H
		90	1	7	64	4	26	K
		100	3	9	84	5	31	K
		110	6	9	101	6	39	K
		120	8	12	114	7	45	L
27	90	30			9		6	F
		40			17		10	G
		50		3	26	2	14	G
		60	2	4	38	3	18	H
		70	4	6	47	4	23	H

Depth m	Depth ft	Min	15 m / 50 ft	12 m / 40 ft	9 m / 30 ft	6 m / 20 ft	4.5 m / 15 ft	≥75% O_2 6 m / 20 ft	≥75% O_2 4.5 m / 15 ft	RG
27	90	80			7	8	69	5	26	H
		90			10	9	92	6	34	K
		100			14	11	108	6	43	K
		110			17	14	129	8	49	K
		120		1	21	14	151	8	55	L
30	100	25					9		6	E
		30				1	12	1	7	F
		40			1	3	22	2	11	G
		50			4	4	35	3	16	H
		60			7	6	46	4	22	H
		70			11	8	68	5	26	H
		80		2	13	10	94	6	36	K
		90		4	16	13	112	8	44	K
		100		6	20	14	140	8	52	K
		110		9	24	14	171	8	60	L
33	110	25				1	11	1	7	F
		30			1	2	16	2	9	G
		40			4	4	27	3	14	G
		50			8	6	41	4	20	H
		60		3	10	8	61	5	26	K
		70		6	13	9	92	6	34	L
		80		9	16	13	113	8	44	L
		90		12	21	14	143	8	53	L
		100	2	14	25	14	181	8	63	L
36	120	20				1	9	1	6	E
		25			1	2	14	2	7	F
		30			3	3	18	2	11	G
		40		1	7	4	34	3	16	G
		50		4	10	6	48	4	24	H
		60		7	13	9	83	6	30	H
		70	2	10	16	12	110	7	43	L
		80	4	12	21	14	142	9	52	L
		90	7	15	25	15	184	9	63	L
		100	9	17	29	19	229	10	74	L

Depth m	Depth ft	Min	18 m / 60 ft	15 m / 50 ft	12 m / 40 ft	9 m / 30 ft	6 m / 20 ft	4.5 m / 15 ft	≥75% O_2 6 m / 20 ft	≥75% O_2 4.5 m / 15 ft	RG
39	130	15					1	6	1	4	F
		20				1	2	11	1	7	F
		25				3	2	17	2	9	G
		30			1	4	4	23	3	12	G
		40			4	7	6	41	4	19	H
		50		1	7	11	8	66	5	26	H
		60		4	9	16	10	102	6	39	K
		70		7	11	20	15	133	9	50	K
		80	1	9	15	25	15	178	9	62	L
42	140	15					2	7	1	5	E
		20				2	2	12	2	7	F
		25			1	4	3	18	2	11	G
		30			3	6	4	26	3	14	G
		40		2	6	9	6	46	4	23	G
		50		5	8	13	9	85	6	31	H
		60	1	7	11	17	14	116	8	46	K
		70	3	9	15	24	14	163	8	58	L
45	150	10						4		3	E
		15				1	2	8	1	5	E
		20			1	3	2	15	2	8	F
		25			3	4	4	22	3	11	G
		30		1	4	7	4	33	3	16	H
		40		4	7	10	7	55	5	25	H
		50	2	6	10	15	11	101	6	39	K
		60	5	8	13	22	14	142	8	53	K
48	160	10						5		4	E
		15				2	2	10	1	6	F
		20			2	4	2	17	2	9	F
		25		1	3	6	4	26	3	13	G
		30		3	4	8	5	39	3	19	H
		35		4	7	10	6	48	4	24	H
		40	2	5	7	12	9	73	6	27	H
		50	5	7	11	17	14	113	8	45	K

Depth m	Depth ft	Min	24 m / 80 ft	21 m / 70 ft	18 m / 60 ft	15 m / 50 ft	12 m / 40 ft	9 m / 30 ft	6 m / 20 ft	4.5 m / 15 ft	≥75% O_2 6 m / 20 ft	≥75% O_2 4.5 m / 15 ft	RG
51	170	10							1	5	1	3	E
		15					1	3	1	12	1	7	F
		20				1	2	4	3	19	2	11	G
		25				2	4	7	4	30	3	15	G
		30			1	3	6	8	6	43	4	21	H
		35			2	5	7	11	8	59	5	26	H
		40			4	6	9	14	9	89	6	33	K
		50		3	5	9	12	21	14	136	8	51	K
		60		5	8	11	17	28	14	201	8	69	L
54	180	10						1	1	6	1	4	E
		15					2	2	3	12	2	7	F
		20				2	3	4	4	22	3	11	G
		25			1	3	4	8	4	36	3	17	H
		30			2	4	7	9	6	48	4	24	H
		35		1	3	6	8	12	9	76	6	27	K
		40		2	5	6	10	16	11	102	6	40	K
		50		6	5	10	15	24	14	156	8	57	K
57	190	10						2	1	6	1	4	E
							3	3	2	14	2	8	F
		20				3	3	6	4	25	3	12	G
		25			2	4	5	7	6	40	4	19	H
		30		1	3	5	7	11	7	56	4	26	H
		35		2	5	6	9	14	9	90	6	33	K
60	200	10						2	2	7	1	5	E
		15				1	3	3	3	16	2	9	F
		20			1	3	4	6	4	28	3	14	G
		25		1	2	4	6	9	6	44	4	21	H
		30		2	4	6	7	12	9	70	5	27	K

ACCELERATED DECOMPRESSION
MUST BE
COMPLETED
ON 75% OR GREATER OXYGEN

⚠ **Warning: DO NOT attempt to use these tables unless you are fully trained & certified in the use of gas mixtures other than air, or are under the supervision of a gas mixtures other than air instructor. Proper use of these tables will reduce the risk of decompression sickness & oxygen toxicity, but no table or computer can eliminate those risks.**

IANTD EAN 26% DIVING & DECOMPRESSION TABLES

(A)

Depth (Feet)	40	50	60	70	80	90	100	110	120	130	140	Repetitive Group ↓								
Depth (Meters)	12	15	18	21	24	27	30	33	36	39	42									
No Decompression Limits (Minutes)	125	75	51	35	25	20	17	14	14	12	10									
(B) BOTTOM TIMES	19	16	14	12	11	10	9	8	8	7	7	A							00:00 01:59	02:00
	25	20	17	15	13	12	11	10	10	9	8	B						00:00 00:19	00:20 01:59	02:00
	37	29	25	22	20	18	16	11	11	10	9	C					00:00 00:09	00:10 00:24	00:25 02:59	03:00
	57	41	33	28	24	19	17	14	14	12	10	D				00:00 00:09	00:10 00:14	00:15 00:29	00:30 02:59	03:00
	82	59	44	35	25	20						E			00:00 00:09	00:10 00:14	00:15 00:24	00:25 00:44	00:45 03:59	04:00
	111	65	51									F		00:00 00:19	00:20 00:29	00:30 00:44	00:45 01:14	01:15 01:29	01:30 07:59	08:00
	125	75										G	00:00 00:24	00:25 00:44	00:45 00:59	01:00 01:14	01:15 01:39	01:40 02:09	02:10 11:59	12:00
												H	00:50 01:04	01:05 01:34	01:35 02:09	02:10 02:59	03:00 03:59	04:00 05:39	05:40 23:59	24:00
												K	03:00 03:59	04:00 04:59	05:00 05:59	06:00 06:59	07:00 07:59	08:00 09:19	09:20 38:59	39:00
												L	06:00 06:59	07:00 08:29	08:30 09:59	10:00 11:59	12:00 13:59	14:00 16:29	16:30 47:59	48:00
(D) REPETITIVE GROUP AT END OF S.I.													G	F	E	D	C	B	A	

SURFACE INTERVALS (C)

(E) REPETITIVE DIVE TABLES

G	F	E	D	C	B	A		DEPTH (F)	(M)
137	111	82	57	37	25	19	RNT	40	12
115	88	59	41	29	20	16	RNT	50	15
91	68	44	33	25	17	14	RNT	60	18
72	53	37	28	22	15	12	RNT	70	21
57	42	30	24	20	13	11	RNT	80	24
47	35	26	21	18	12	10	RNT	90	27
40	30	23	19	16	11	9	RNT	100	30
35	27	21	17	14	10	8	RNT	110	33
35	27	21	17	14	10	8	RNT	120	36
31	24	19	15	12	9	7	RNT	130	39
27	21	17	14	11	8	7	RNT	140	42
25	19	16	13	10	7	6	RNT	150	45
23	17	14	11	9	7	6	RNT	160	48

RESIDUAL NITROGEN TIME

These Tables Are For EAN 26% With EAN 26%As Deco Gas Or Accelerated Deco Using EAN 75% Oxygen Or Greater At 20 And 15 Foot Stops. The 15 Foot Stops MUST Be Taken At 15 Feet. These Tables Are Based On Buehlmann's ZHL-16 Algorithm For 0-1000 Feet Above Sea Level. They Were Produced Using Cybortronix DPA Software. The Repetitive Dive Groups Are Not Transferable To ANY Other Tables. A 3 Minute Safety Stop Is Required For All Dives. These Tables Do Not Account For Physical Condition Of Diver, Difficulty Of Dive, Water Temperature, Etc.

(A) Planned Depth
(B) Bottom Time In Depth Column
(C) Read Across To Find Surface Interval
(D) Locate RNT After S. I.
(E) Read Down To Planned Repetitive Dive Depth. Read RNT

⚠ Warning: DO NOT attempt to use these tables unless you are fully trained & certified in the use of gas mixtures other than air, or are under the supervision of a gas mixtures other than air instructor. Proper use of these tables will reduce the risk of decompression sickness & oxygen toxicity, but no table or computer can eliminate those risks.

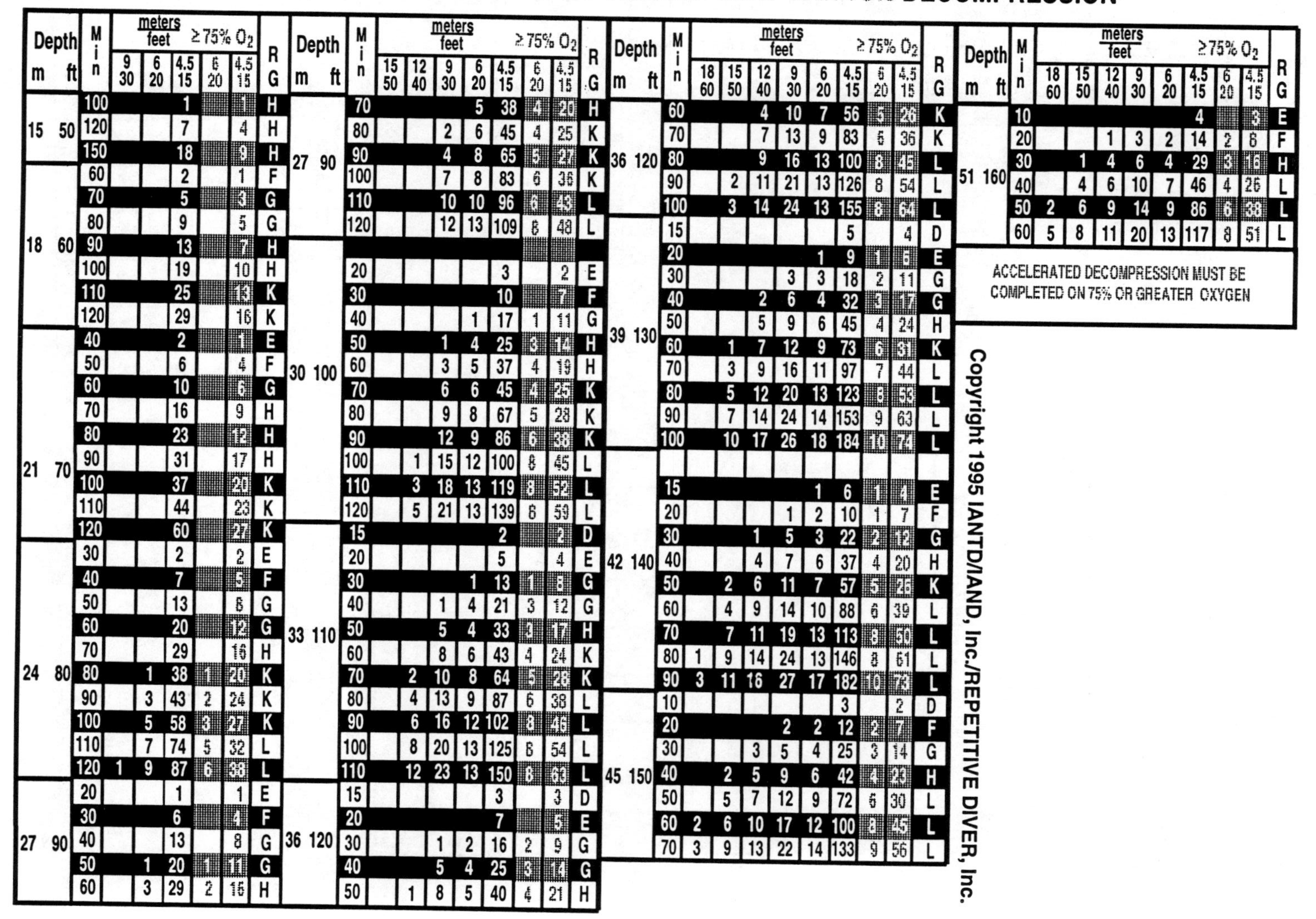

IANTD EAN 26% DECOMPRESSION TABLES WITH EAN 75% DECOMPRESSION

Depth m ft	Min	9 m / 30 ft	6 m / 20 ft	4.5 m / 15 ft	≥75% O2 6 m / 20 ft	≥75% O2 4.5 m / 15 ft	RG
15 50	100			1		1	H
	120			7		4	H
	150			18		9	H
18 60	60			2		1	F
	70			5		3	G
	80			9		5	G
	90			13		7	H
	100			19		10	H
	110			25		13	K
	120			29		16	K
21 70	40			2		1	E
	50			6		4	F
	60			10		6	G
	70			16		9	H
	80			23		12	H
	90			31		17	H
	100			37		20	K
	110			44		23	K
	120			60		27	K
24 80	30			2		2	E
	40			7		5	F
	50			13		8	G
	60			20		12	G
	70			29		16	H
	80		1	38	1	20	K
	90		3	43	2	24	K
	100		5	58	3	27	K
	110		7	74	5	32	L
	120	1	9	87	6	38	L
27 90	20			1		1	E
	30			6		4	F
	40			13		8	G
	50		1	20	1	11	G
	60		3	29	2	16	H

Depth m ft	Min	15 m / 50 ft	12 m / 40 ft	9 m / 30 ft	6 m / 20 ft	4.5 m / 15 ft	≥75% O2 6 m / 20 ft	≥75% O2 4.5 m / 15 ft	RG
27 90	70				5	38	4	20	H
	80			2	6	45	4	25	K
	90			4	8	65	5	27	K
	100			7	8	83	6	36	K
	110			10	10	96	6	43	L
	120			12	13	109	8	48	L
30 100	20					3		2	E
	30					10		7	F
	40				1	17	1	11	G
	50			1	4	25	3	14	H
	60			3	5	37	4	19	H
	70			6	6	45	4	25	K
	80			9	8	67	5	28	K
	90			12	9	86	6	38	K
	100		1	15	12	100	8	45	L
	110		3	18	13	119	8	52	L
	120		5	21	13	139	8	59	L
33 110	15					2		2	D
	20					5		4	E
	30				1	13	1	8	G
	40			1	4	21	3	12	G
	50			5	4	33	3	17	H
	60			8	6	43	4	24	K
	70		2	10	8	64	5	28	K
	80		4	13	9	87	6	38	L
	90		6	16	12	102	8	46	L
	100		8	20	13	125	8	54	L
	110		12	23	13	150	8	63	L
36 120	15					3		3	D
	20					7		5	E
	30			1	2	16	2	9	G
	40			5	4	25	3	14	G
	50		1	8	5	40	4	21	H

Depth m ft	Min	18 m / 60 ft	15 m / 50 ft	12 m / 40 ft	9 m / 30 ft	6 m / 20 ft	4.5 m / 15 ft	≥75% O2 6 m / 20 ft	≥75% O2 4.5 m / 15 ft	RG
36 120	60			4	10	7	56	5	26	K
	70			7	13	9	83	6	36	K
	80			9	16	13	100	8	45	L
	90		2	11	21	13	126	8	54	L
	100		3	14	24	13	155	8	64	L
39 130	15						5		4	D
	20					1	9	1	6	E
	30				3	3	18	2	11	G
	40			2	6	4	32	3	17	G
	50			5	9	6	45	4	24	H
	60		1	7	12	9	73	6	31	K
	70		3	9	16	11	97	7	44	L
	80		5	12	20	13	123	8	53	L
	90		7	14	24	14	153	9	63	L
	100		10	17	26	18	184	10	74	L
42 140	15					1	6	1	4	E
	20				1	2	10	1	7	F
	30			1	5	3	22	2	12	G
	40			4	7	6	37	4	20	H
	50		2	6	11	7	57	5	26	K
	60		4	9	14	10	88	6	39	L
	70		7	11	19	13	113	8	50	L
	80	1	9	14	24	13	146	8	61	L
	90	3	11	16	27	17	182	10	73	L
45 150	10						3		2	D
	20				2	2	12	2	7	F
	30			3	5	4	25	3	14	G
	40		2	5	9	6	42	4	23	H
	50		5	7	12	9	72	6	30	L
	60	2	6	10	17	12	100	8	45	L
	70	3	9	13	22	14	133	9	56	L

Depth m ft	Min	18 m / 60 ft	15 m / 50 ft	12 m / 40 ft	9 m / 30 ft	6 m / 20 ft	4.5 m / 15 ft	≥75% O2 6 m / 20 ft	≥75% O2 4.5 m / 15 ft	RG
51 160	10						4		3	E
	20			1	3	2	14	2	8	F
	30		1	4	6	4	29	3	16	H
	40		4	6	10	7	46	4	26	L
	50	2	6	9	14	9	86	6	38	L
	60	5	8	11	20	13	117	8	51	L

ACCELERATED DECOMPRESSION MUST BE COMPLETED ON 75% OR GREATER OXYGEN

⚠ Warning: DO NOT attempt to use these tables unless you are fully trained & certified in the use of gas mixtures other than air, or are under the supervision of a gas mixtures other than air instructor. Proper use of these tables will reduce the risk of decompression sickness & oxygen toxicity, but no table or computer can eliminate those risks.

IANTD EAN 28% DIVING & DECOMPRESSION TABLES

(A)

Depth (Feet)	40	50	60	70	80	90	100	110	120	130	140	Repetitive Group
Depth (Meters)	12	15	18	21	24	27	30	33	36	39	42	
No Decompression Limits (Minutes)	125	75	51	35	35	24	19	17	14	12	9	↓
(B) BOTTOM TIMES	19	16	14	12	12	11	10	9	8	7	7	A
	25	20	17	15	15	13	12	11	10	9	8	B
	37	29	25	22	22	20	18	16	14	12	9	C
	57	41	33	28	28	24	19	17				D
	82	59	44	35	35							E
	111	75	51									F
	125											G
												H
												K
												L

(C) SURFACE INTERVALS

Repetitive Group	G	F	E	D	C	B	A	
A							00:00 01:59	02:00
B						00:00 00:19	00:20 01:59	02:00
C					00:00 00:09	00:10 00:24	00:25 02:59	03:00
D				00:00 00:09	00:10 00:14	00:15 00:29	00:30 02:59	03:00
E			00:00 00:09	00:10 00:14	00:15 00:24	00:25 00:44	00:45 03:59	04:00
F		00:00 00:19	00:20 00:29	00:30 00:44	00:45 01:14	01:15 01:29	01:30 07:59	08:00
G	00:00 00:24	00:25 00:44	00:45 00:59	01:00 01:14	01:15 01:39	01:40 02:09	02:10 11:59	12:00
H	00:50 01:04	01:05 01:34	01:35 02:09	02:10 02:59	03:00 03:59	04:00 05:39	05:40 23:59	24:00
K	00:00 03:00	03:01 04:00	04:01 05:00	05:01 06:00	06:01 07:00	07:01 08:00	08:01 38:59	39:00
L	00:00 06:00	06:01 07:00	07:01 08:30	08:31 10:00	10:01 12:00	12:01 14:00	14:01 47:59	48:00

(D) REPETITIVE GROUP AT END OF S.I.

(E) REPETITIVE DIVE TABLES

G	F	E	D	C	B	A		DEPTH (F)	DEPTH (M)
137	111	82	57	37	25	19	RNT	40	12
115	88	59	41	29	20	16	RNT	50	15
91	68	44	33	25	17	14	RNT	60	18
72	53	37	28	22	15	12	RNT	70	21
72	53	37	28	22	15	12	RNT	80	24
57	42	30	24	20	13	11	RNT	90	27
47	35	26	21	18	12	10	RNT	100	30
40	30	23	19	16	11	9	RNT	110	33
35	27	21	17	14	10	8	RNT	120	36
31	24	19	15	12	9	7	RNT	130	39
27	21	17	14	11	8	7	RNT	140	42

RESIDUAL NITROGEN TIME

These Tables Are For EAN 28% With EAN 28% As Deco Gas. Or Accelerated Deco Using EAN 75% Oxygen Or Greater At 20 And 15 Foot Stops. The 15 Foot Stops MUST Be Taken At 15 Feet. These Tables Are Based On Buehlmann's ZHL-16 Algorithm For 0-1000 Feet Above Sea Level. They Were Produced Using Cybortronix DPA Software. The Repetitive Dive Groups Are Not Transferable To ANY Other Tables. A 3 Minute Safety Stop Is Required For All Dives. These Tables Do Not Account For Physical Condition Of Diver, Difficulty Of Dive, Water Temperature, Etc.

(A) Planned Depth
(B) Bottom Time In Depth Column
(C) Read Across To Find Surface Interval
(D) Locate RNT After S. I.
(E) Read Down To Planned Repetitive
Dive Depth. Read RNT

⚠ Warning: DO NOT attempt to use these tables unless you are fully trained & certified in the use of gas mixtures other than air, or are under the supervision of a gas mixtures other than air instructor. Proper use of these tables will reduce the risk of decompression sickness & oxygen toxicity, but no table or computer can eliminate those risks.

IANTD EANX 28% DECO. TABLES WITH EANX 75% ACCELERATED DECOMPRESSION

Depth m ft	Min	9 m / 30 ft	6 m / 20 ft	4.5 m / 15 ft	≥75% O_2 6 m / 20 ft	≥75% O_2 4.5 m / 15 ft	RG
15 50	120			3		2	H
	150			13		7	H
18 60	70			3		2	G
	80			6		4	G
	90			10		6	H
	100			15		8	H
21 70	40			1		1	E
	50			4		3	F
	60			8		5	G
	70			13		6	H
	80			19		11	H
	90			26		15	H
				33		18	K
24 80							
	40			6		4	F
	50			11		7	G
	60			18		10	G
	70			25		14	H
	80			34		19	H
	90		1	40	1	23	K
	100		3	49	2	26	K
	110		5	65	3	30	K
27 90							
	30			5		3	F
	40			11		7	F
	50			18		11	G
	60		2	25	1	15	G
	70		4	35	3	19	H
	80		6	42	4	23	H
	90	3	6	56	4	27	K
	100	4	8	73	6	32	K
	110	7	9	86	6	40	L
	120	9	11	97	7	48	L
	130	11	13	112	9	51	L

Depth m ft	Min	15 m / 50 ft	12 m / 40 ft	9 m / 30 ft	6 m / 20 ft	4.5 m / 15 ft	≥75% O_2 6 m / 20 ft	≥75% O_2 4.5 m / 15 ft	RG
30 100	20					2		2	E
	30					9		6	F
	40				1	16	1	10	G
	50				3	24	3	13	G
	60			2	4	34	3	19	H
	70			4	6	42	4	24	H
	80			7	7	58	5	27	K
	90			10	8	77	6	35	K
	100			13	11	90	7	43	K
	110		1	15	13	104	8	49	L
	120		2	19	13	123	9	54	L
	130		4	22	13	142	8	63	L
	140		6	24	13	165	8	71	L
33 110									
	20					4		3	E
	30				1	11	1	7	F
	40			1	3	19	2	11	G
	50			4	3	31	2	17	H
	60			6	6	40	4	22	H
	70			10	7	55	5	25	K
	80		2	12	9	76	6	35	K
	90		4	15	11	92	7	44	K
	100		6	18	13	110	8	51	L
	110		9	21	13	130	8	58	L
	120		11	24	13	155	8	68	L
36 120	15					3		2	D
	20					6		5	E
	30			1	2	14	1	9	G
	40			4	3	24	2	14	G
	50			7	5	36	4	19	H
	60		3	9	6	47	4	26	K
	70		5	12	8	73	6	32	K
	80		8	14	11	92	7	43	L
	90		10	18	13	111	9	51	L

Depth m ft	Min	18 m / 60 ft	15 m / 50 ft	12 m / 40 ft	9 m / 30 ft	6 m / 20 ft	4.5 m / 15 ft	≥75% O_2 6 m / 20 ft	≥75% O_2 4.5 m / 15 ft	RG
36 120	100		1	13	22	13	133	8	60	L
	110		3	14	25	13	162	8	70	L
39 130										
	20					1	8	1	5	E
	30				3	2	17	2	10	G
	40			1	6	4	28	3	16	G
	50			4	8	6	41	4	23	H
	60			6	11	8	63	6	27	K
	70		1	9	14	10	87	7	40	K
	80		3	10	18	13	107	9	49	L
	90		5	13	22	13	132	9	59	L
42 140	10						2		1	D
	20				1	1	10	1	7	F
	30				4	4	19	3	11	G
	40			3	7	5	34	4	18	H
	50		1	6	10	6	48	4	26	H
	60		3	8	13	9	78	6	36	K
	70		5	10	16	13	99	9	47	L
	80		8	13	21	13	127	9	56	L
45 150	10						3		2	D
	20				2	2	11	1	8	F
	30			2	5	4	22	3	13	G
	40		1	5	8	5	39	4	21	H

ACCELERATED DECOMPRESSION MUST BE COMPLETED ON 75% OR GREATER OXYGEN

⚠ Warning: DO NOT attempt to use these tables unless you are fully trained & certified in the use of gas mixtures other than air, or are under the supervision of a gas mixtures other than air instructor. Proper use of these tables will reduce the risk of decompression sickness & oxygen toxicity, but no table or computer can eliminate those risks.

IANTD EAN 30% DIVING & DECOMPRESSION TABLES

(A)

Depth (Feet)	40	50	60	70	80	90	100	110	120	130	140	Repetitive Group
Depth (Meters)	12	15	18	21	24	27	30	33	36	39	42	
No Decompression Limits (Minutes)	125	75	75	51	35	25	20	17	14	12	12	
(B) BOTTOM TIMES	19	16	16	14	12	11	10	9	8	7	7	A
	25	20	20	17	15	13	12	11	10	9	9	B
	37	29	29	25	22	20	18	16	11	10	10	C
	57	41	41	33	28	24	19	17	14	12	12	D
	82	59	59	44	35	25	20					E
	111	65	65	51								F
	125	75	75									G
												H
												K
												L

SURFACE INTERVALS (C)

Group	G	F	E	D	C	B	A	
A							00:00 01:59	02:00
B						00:00 00:19	00:20 01:59	02:00
C					00:00 00:09	00:10 00:24	00:25 02:59	03:00
D				00:00 00:09	00:10 00:14	00:15 00:29	00:30 02:59	03:00
E			00:00 00:09	00:10 00:14	00:15 00:24	00:25 00:44	00:45 03:59	04:00
F		00:00 00:19	00:20 00:29	00:30 00:44	00:45 01:14	01:15 01:29	01:30 07:59	08:00
G	00:00 00:24	00:25 00:44	00:45 00:59	01:00 01:14	01:15 01:39	01:40 02:09	02:10 11:59	12:00
H	00:50 01:04	01:05 01:34	01:35 02:09	02:10 02:59	03:00 03:59	04:00 05:39	05:40 23:59	24:00
K	03:00 03:59	04:00 04:59	05:00 05:59	06:00 06:59	07:00 07:59	08:00 09:19	09:20 38:59	39:00
L	06:00 06:59	07:00 08:29	08:30 09:59	10:00 11:59	12:00 13:59	14:00 16:29	16:30 47:59	48:00

(E) REPETITIVE DIVE TABLES — RESIDUAL NITROGEN TIME

REPETITIVE GROUP AT END OF S.I.	G	F	E	D	C	B	A		DEPTH (F)	(M)
	137	111	82	57	37	25	19	RNT	40	12
	115	88	59	41	29	20	16	RNT	50	15
	115	88	59	41	29	20	16	RNT	60	18
	91	68	44	33	25	17	14	RNT	70	21
	72	53	37	28	22	15	12	RNT	80	24
	57	42	30	24	20	13	11	RNT	90	27
	47	35	26	21	18	12	10	RNT	100	30
	40	30	23	19	16	11	9	RNT	110	33
	35	27	21	17	14	10	8	RNT	120	36
	31	24	19	15	12	9	7	RNT	130	39
	31	24	19	15	12	9	7	RNT	140	42

These Tables Are For EAN 30% With EAN 30% As Deco Gas. Or Accelerated Deco Using EAN 75% Oxygen Or Greater At 20 And 15 Foot Stops. The 15 Foot Stops MUST Be Taken At 15 Feet. These Tables Are Based On Buehlmann's ZHL-16 Algorithm For 0-1000 Feet Above Sea Level. They Were Produced Using Cybortronix DPA Software. The Repetitive Dive Groups Are Not Transferable To ANY Other Tables. A 3 Minute Safety Stop Is Required For All Dives. These Tables Do Not Account For Physical Condition Of Diver, Difficulty Of Dive, Water Temperature, Etc.

(A) Planned Depth
(B) Bottom Time In Depth Column
(C) Read Across To Find Surface Interval
(D) Locate RNT After S. I.
(E) Read Down To Planned Repetitive Dive Depth. Read RNT

⚠ Warning: DO NOT attempt to use these tables unless you are fully trained & certified in the use of gas mixtures other than air, or are under the supervision of a gas mixtures other than air instructor. Proper use of these tables will reduce the risk of decompression sickness & oxygen toxicity, but no table or computer can eliminate those risks.

IANTD EAN 30% DECOMPRESSION TABLES WITH EAN 75% DECOMPRESSION

Depth m	Depth ft	Min	Meters/Feet 6/20	Meters/Feet 4.5/15	O2 > 75% 6/20	O2 > 75% 4.5/15	RG
15	50	130		2		2	H
		150		8		5	H
18	60	80		4		3	G
		90		7		4	G
		100		10		6	H
		110		16		9	H
21	70						
		60		7		4	F
		70		11		6	G
		80		15		9	G
		90		22		13	H
		100		28		16	H
		110		33		19	K
		120		39		22	K
24	80						
		40		5		3	E
		50		9		6	F
		60		15		9	G
		70		21		13	H
		80		30		17	H
		90		37		22	H
		100	1	42	1	24	K
		110	3	56	2	27	K
		120	5	68	3	33	K
27	90	25		2		1	E
		30		4		3	F
		40		9		6	F
		50		16		10	G
		60	1	23	1	14	G

Depth m	Depth ft	Min	Meters/Feet 9/30	Meters/Feet 6/20	Meters/Feet 4.5/15	O2 ≥ 75% 6/20	O2 ≥ 75% 4.5/15	RG
27	90	70		2	32	2	18	H
		80		4	39	3	22	K
		90	1	5	48	4	26	K
		100	2	8	63	5	30	K
		110	4	8	78	6	37	L
		120	6	10	88	7	43	L
30	100	20			2		1	E
		30			8		5	F
		40			15		10	G
		50		2	22	2	13	G
		60	1	4	31	3	17	H
		70	5	6	39	4	22	H
		80	5	6	49	4	26	K
		90	7	8	68	6	32	K
		100	10	9	83	6	41	K
		110	13	12	93	8	46	L
		120	17	12	109	8	52	L
33	110							
		20			4		3	E
		30			11		8	F
		40		3	17	2	11	G
		50	3	3	27	2	16	H
		60	5	5	37	3	17	H
		70	8	6	46	4	26	K
		80	11	8	67	6	31	K

Depth m	Depth ft	Min	Meters/Feet 12/40	Meters/Feet 9/30	Meters/Feet 6/20	Meters/Feet 4.5/15	O2 ≥ 75% 6/20	O2 ≥ 75% 4.5/15	RG
33	110	90	2	14	9	84	6	41	K
		100	4	15	13	96	8	49	L
		110	6	19	13	115	8	55	L
		120	8	22	13	134	8	63	L
36	120	15				2		2	D
		20				6		4	E
		30			2	13	2	8	G
		40		3	3	22	2	13	G
		50		6	5	33	3	19	H
		60	1	9	5	43	4	25	K
		70	3	11	8	63	6	29	K
		80	6	13	10	83	7	40	L
		90	8	16	13	96	8	49	L
		100	11	20	13	118	8	56	L
39	130	15				4		3	D
		20			1	7	1	5	E
		30		2	2	16	2	10	G
		40		6	3	26	2	16	G
		50	3	7	6	38	4	22	H
		60	5	10	7	55	5	27	K
		70	8	13	9	78	6	38	L
42	140	15				5		4	D
		20			2	9	1	6	E
		30		4	3	17	2	11	G
		40	2	7	4	31	3	17	G

ACCELERATED DECOMPRESSION MUST BE COMPLETED USING 75% OR GREATER OXYGEN

⚠ Warning: DO NOT attempt to use these tables unless you are fully trained & certified in the use of gas mixtures other than air, or are under the supervision of a gas mixtures other than air instructor. Proper use of these tables will reduce the risk of decompression sickness & oxygen toxicity, but no table or computer can eliminate those risks.

IANTD EAN 32% DIVING & DECOMPRESSION TABLES

(A) Planned depth and (B) bottom times:

										Repetitive Group
(A)	40	50	60	70	80	90	100	110	120	Depth (Feet)
	12	15	18	21	24	27	30	33	36	Depth (Meters)
	154	125	75	51	35	25	20	20	17	No Decompression Limits (Minutes)
(B) BOTTOM TIMES	25	19	16	14	12	11	10	10	9	A
	37	25	20	17	15	13	12	12	11	B
	55	37	29	25	22	20	18	18	16	C
	81	57	41	33	28	24	19	19	17	D
	105	82	59	44	35	25	20	20		E
	130	111	65	51						F
	154	125	75							G
										H
										K
										L

SURFACE INTERVALS (C):

Repetitive Group	G	F	E	D	C	B	A	
A							00:00 01:59	02:00
B						00:00 00:19	00:20 01:59	02:00
C					00:00 00:09	00:10 00:24	00:25 02:59	03:00
D				00:00 00:09	00:10 00:14	00:15 00:29	00:30 02:59	03:00
E			00:00 00:09	00:10 00:14	00:15 00:24	00:25 00:44	00:45 03:59	04:00
F		00:00 00:19	00:20 00:29	00:30 00:44	00:45 01:14	01:15 01:29	01:30 07:59	08:00
G	00:00 00:24	00:25 00:44	00:45 00:59	01:00 01:14	01:15 01:39	01:40 02:09	02:10 11:59	12:00
H	00:50 01:04	01:05 01:34	01:35 02:09	02:10 02:59	03:00 03:59	04:00 05:39	05:40 23:59	24:00
K	03:00 03:59	04:00 04:59	05:00 05:59	06:00 06:59	07:00 07:59	08:00 09:19	09:20 38:59	39:00
L	06:00 06:59	07:00 08:29	08:30 09:59	10:00 11:59	12:00 13:59	14:00 16:29	16:30 47:59	48:00

(D) R. G. AT END OF S.I.

(E) REPETITIVE DIVE TABLES — RESIDUAL NITROGEN TIME

G	F	E	D	C	B	A		DEPTH (F)	(M)
154	130	105	81	55	37	25	RNT	40	12
137	111	82	57	37	25	19	RNT	50	15
115	88	59	41	29	20	16	RNT	60	18
91	68	44	33	25	17	14	RNT	70	21
72	53	37	28	22	15	12	RNT	80	24
57	42	30	24	20	13	11	RNT	90	27
47	35	26	21	18	12	10	RNT	100	30
47	35	26	21	18	12	10	RNT	110	33
40	30	23	19	16	11	9	RNT	120	36

These Tables Are For EAN 32% With EAN 32%As Deco Gas. Or Accelerated Deco Using EAN 75% Oxygen Or Greater At 20 And 15 Foot Stops. The 15 Foot Stops MUST Be Taken At 15 Feet. These Tables Are Based On Buehlmann's ZHL-16 Algorithm For 0-1000 Feet Above Sea Level. They Were Produced Using Cybortronix DPA Software. The Repetitive Dive Groups Are Not Transferable To ANY Other Tables. A 3 Minute Safety Stop Is Required For All Dives. These Tables Do Not Account For Physical Condition Of Diver, Difficulty Of Dive, Water Temperature, Etc.

(A) Planned Depth
(B) Bottom Time In Depth Column
(C) Read Across To Find Surface Interval
(D) Locate RNT After S. I,
(E) Read Down To Planned Repetitive Dive Depth Read RNT.

⚠ Warning: DO NOT attempt to use these tables unless you are fully trained & certified in the use of gas mixtures other than air, or are under the supervision of a gas mixtures other than air instructor. Proper use of these tables will reduce the risk of decompression sickness & oxygen toxicity, but no table or computer can eliminate those risks.

IANTD EAN 32% DECO. TABLES WITH EAN 75% ACCELERATED DECO

Depth m	Depth ft	Min	Meters/Feet 6/20	Meters/Feet 4.5/15	≥ 75% O2 6/20	≥ 75% O2 4.5/15	RG
15	50	150		4		2	G
18	60	80		2		1	G
		100		7		5	H
21	70	60		5		3	F
		70		8		5	G
		80		13		8	G
		90		18		10	H
		100		24		14	H
		110		29		17	K
		120		33		20	K
24	80	40		3		2	E
		50		7		5	F
		60		12		8	G
		70		18		11	H
		80		25		15	H
		90		32		20	H
		100		38		23	K
		110	1	47	1	25	K
		120	2	61	2	30	K
27	90	30		3		2	E
		40		8		5	F
		50		13		9	G
		60		21		13	G
		70	1	29	1	17	H
		80	3	35	2	21	H
		90	4	41	3	25	K
		100	7	55	5	27	K

Depth m	Depth ft	Min	Meters/Feet 9/30	Meters/Feet 6/20	Meters/Feet 4.5/15	≥ 75% O2 6/20	≥ 75% O2 4.5/15	RG
27	90	110	2	8	68	5	35	K
		120	4	8	80	6	41	K
		130	5	11	89	7	47	K
30	100	20			1		1	E
		25			3		3	F
		30			6		5	F
		40			13		9	G
		50		1	20	1	12	G
		60		3	28	3	16	H
		70	1	5	36	4	21	H
		80	3	6	42	4	25	H
		90	5	8	59	5	29	K
		100	8	8	74	6	37	K
		110	10	11	85	7	44	K
		120	13	12	96	8	50	L
33	110							
		20			3		2	E
		30			10		7	F
		40		2	16	1	11	G
		50	1	4	23	3	15	G
		60	4	4	34	3	20	H
		70	6	6	41	4	25	H
		80	9	8	58	5	29	K
		90	13	8	76	5	39	K

Depth m	Depth ft	Min	Meters/Feet 12/40	Meters/Feet 9/30	Meters/Feet 6/20	Meters/Feet 4.5/15	≥ 75% O2 6/20	≥ 75% O2 4.5/15	RG
33	110	100	2	14	11	88	8	45	K
		110	3	17	13	102	9	51	L
36	120	20				5		4	E
		30			1	12	1	8	F
		40		2	3	20	2	12	G
		50		5	4	30	3	17	H
		60		8	5	40	4	23	H
		70	2	10	7	55	5	27	K
		80	4	12	8	75	6	38	K
		90	6	15	11	88	8	46	K
		100	8	18	13	105	9	53	L
39	130	15				3		3	D
		20				7		5	E
		30		1	2	15	2	9	F
		40		5	3	23	2	15	G

ACCELERATED DECOMPRESSION MUST BE COMPLETED USING 75% OR GREATER OXYGEN

⚠ Warning: DO NOT attempt to use these tables unless you are fully trained & certified in the use of gas mixtures other than air, or are under the supervision of a gas mixtures other than air instructor. Proper use of these tables will reduce the risk of decompression sickness & oxygen toxicity, but no table or computer can eliminate those risks.

IANTD EAN 34% DIVING & DECOMPRESSION TABLES

(A) Planned depth, (B) Bottom times, Repetitive Group

Depth (Feet)	40	50	60	70	80	90	100	110	Repetitive Group
Depth (Meters)	12	15	18	21	27	27	30	33	
No Decompression Limits (Minutes)	154	125	75	51	35	35	25	20	
BOTTOM TIMES	25	19	16	14	12	12	11	10	A
	37	25	20	17	15	15	13	12	B
	55	37	29	25	22	22	20	18	C
	81	57	41	33	28	28	24	19	D
	105	82	59	44	35	35	25	20	E
	130	111	65	51					F
	154	125	75						G
									H
									K
									L

(C) SURFACE INTERVALS. (D) R.G. AT END OF S.I.:

Repetitive Group	G	F	E	D	C	B	A	
A							00:00 01:59	02:00
B						00:00 00:19	00:20 01:59	02:00
C					00:00 00:09	00:10 00:24	00:25 02:59	03:00
D				00:00 00:09	00:10 00:14	00:15 00:29	00:30 02:59	03:00
E			00:00 00:09	00:10 00:14	00:15 00:24	00:25 00:44	00:45 03:59	04:00
F		00:00 00:19	00:20 00:29	00:30 00:44	00:45 01:14	01:15 01:29	01:30 07:59	08:00
G	00:00 00:24	00:25 00:44	00:45 00:59	01:00 01:14	01:15 01:39	01:40 02:09	02:10 11:59	12:00
H	00:50 01:04	01:05 01:34	01:35 02:09	02:10 02:59	03:00 03:59	04:00 05:39	05:40 23:59	24:00
K	03:00 03:59	04:00 04:59	05:00 05:59	06:00 06:59	07:00 07:59	08:00 09:19	09:20 38:59	39:00
L	06:00 06:59	07:00 08:29	08:30 09:59	10:00 11:59	12:00 13:59	14:00 16:29	16:30 47:59	48:00

(E) REPETITIVE DIVE TABLES, RESIDUAL NITROGEN TIME:

G	F	E	D	C	B	A		DEPTH (F)	DEPTH (M)
154	130	105	81	55	37	25	RNT	40	12
137	111	82	57	37	25	19	RNT	50	15
115	88	59	41	29	20	16	RNT	60	18
91	68	44	33	25	17	14	RNT	70	21
72	53	37	28	22	15	12	RNT	80	24
72	53	37	28	22	15	12	RNT	90	27
57	42	30	24	20	13	11	RNT	100	30
47	35	26	21	18	12	10	RNT	110	33

These Tables Are For EAN 34% With EAN 34% As Deco Gas. Or Accelerated Deco Using EAN 75% Oxygen Or Greater At 20 And 15 Foot Stops. The 15 Foot Stops MUST Be Taken At 15 Feet. These Tables Are Based On Buehlmann's ZHL-16 Algorithm For 0-1000 Feet Above Sea Level. They Were Produced Using Cybortronix DPA Software. The Repetitive Dive Groups Are Not Transferable To ANY Other Tables. A 3 Minute Safety Stop Is Required For All Dives. These Tables Do Not Account For Physical Condition Of Diver, Difficulty Of Dive, Water Temperature, Etc.

(A) Planned Depth
(B) Bottom Time In Depth Column
(C) Read Across To Find Surface Interval
(D) Locate RNT After S. I.
(E) Read Down To Planned Repetitive Dive Depth Read RNT.

⚠ Warning: DO NOT attempt to use these tables unless you are fully trained & certified in the use of gas mixtures other than air, or are under the supervision of a gas mixtures other than air instructor. Proper use of these tables will reduce the risk of decompression sickness & oxygen toxicity, but no table or computer can eliminate those risks.

IANTD EAN 34% DECO. TABLES WITH EAN 75% ACCELERATED DECO.

Depth m ft	Min	Meters/Feet 6 / 20	Meters/Feet 4.5 / 15	O2 ≥ 75% 6 / 20	O2 ≥ 75% 4.5 / 15	RG
15 50	170		4		2	H
18 60	100		5		3	G
	110		7		5	H
	120		11		7	H
21 70	60		3		2	F
	70		6		4	G
	80		10		6	G
	90		14		9	H
	100		19		12	H
	110		24		15	H
	120		28		17	K
24 80	40		2		2	E
	50		6		4	F
	60		10		7	G
	70		15		10	H
	80		21		15	H
	90		28		17	H
	100		34		21	K
	110		39		24	K
	120		52		28	K
27 90	40		6		6	E
	50		12		8	F
	60		18		12	G
	70		26	1	16	H
	80	1	33	1	20	H

Depth m ft	Min	Meters/Feet 9 / 30	Meters/Feet 6 / 20	Meters/Feet 4.5 / 15	O2 ≥ 75% 6 / 20	O2 ≥ 75% 4.5 / 15	RG
27 90	90		3	38	2	24	H
	100		4	48	3	26	K
	110		7	60	5	31	K
	120	1	8	72	6	38	K
30 100	30			5		4	F
	40			11		8	F
	50			18		12	G
	60		2	25	2	15	G
	70		4	33	3	20	H
	80	2	5	39	4	24	K
	90	3	7	51	5	27	K
	100	5	8	66	6	34	K
	110	8	9	77	6	42	L
	120	10	11	87	8	47	L
33 110	30			8		6	F
	40		1	15	1	10	G
	50		4	21	3	14	G
	60	2	5	31	3	19	H
	70	5	5	38	4	23	H
	80	7	7	51	5	27	H
	90	10	8	67	6	35	K
	100	13	10	80	7	43	K

ACCELERATED DECOMPRESSION MUST BE COMPLETED ON 75% OR GREATER OXYGEN

⚠ **Warning: DO NOT attempt to use these tables unless you are fully trained & certified in the use of gas mixtures other than air, or are under the supervision of a gas mixtures other than air instructor. Proper use of these tables will reduce the risk of decompression sickness & oxygen toxicity, but no table or computer can eliminate those risks.**

IANTD *RUNTIME* TABLES FOR AIR WITH EAN 78% ACCELERATED DECO.

Depth m ft	Min	12 m / 40 ft	9 m / 30 ft	6 m / 20 ft	4.5 m / 15 ft	% CNS
		≥ 78% O2				
27 90	50			55	67	18
	60		63	66	82	24
	70		74	78	99	30
	80		85	90	115	34
	90		96	102	131	40
	100		108	115	151	48
	110		120	128	170	54
	120		131	140	188	61
	130		144	153	205	68
	140	144	157	166	225	72
	150	156	170	179	245	78
	160	167	182	192	263	84
	170	180	195	210	286	90
	180	193	208	225	308	97
	190	205	223	241	328	103
30 100	50		55	57	72	22
	60		66	70	90	27
	70		78	82	107	34
	80		90	95	123	41
	90	95	104	110	147	46
	100	106	117	124	168	53
	110	119	131	139	190	59
	120	131	145	153	210	67
	130	143	159	167	232	74
	140	157	173	183	254	80
	150	170	186	201	278	87
	160	183	200	218	301	95
	170	196	217	234	325	103

Depth m ft	Min	15 m / 50 ft	12 m / 40 ft	9 m / 30 ft	6 m / 20 ft	4.5 m / 15 ft	% CNS
				≥ 78% O2			
33 110	40			45	48	60	22
	50			57	60	78	30
	60		65	71	74	98	34
	70		77	84	89	116	39
	80		90	99	104	142	49
	90		102	112	120	165	58
	100		116	128	136	188	65
	110	114	129	143	151	212	73
	120	125	143	158	166	236	80
	130	137	159	174	188	254	89
	140	149	173	189	207	290	98
	150	161	187	208	225	316	108
36 120	30			35	37	47	19
	40			47	51	65	27
	50		56	61	66	87	32
	60		69	76	82	107	39
	70	74	83	91	98	134	49
	80	85	96	106	115	160	60
	90	98	111	124	133	185	68
	100	110	125	140	149	211	77
	110	122	142	157	168	239	86
	120	135	158	173	190	269	95
	130	148	172	192	210	295	106
39 130	30			37	39	50	21
	40		46	52	55	71	26
	50		60	67	71	95	34
	60	66	74	83	89	119	44
	70	78	88	99	107	149	55

Depth m ft	Min	21 m / 70 ft	18 m / 60 ft	15 m / 50 ft	12 m / 40 ft	9 m / 30 ft	6 m / 20 ft	4.5 m / 15 ft	% CNS
						≥ 78% O2			
39 130	80			91	105	118	126	178	64
	90		94	104	120	136	144	206	74
	100		106	118	138	156	165	237	83
	110		117	131	155	171	189	269	94
	120		129	146	171	194	211	301	108
42 140	30				36	40	42	54	23
	40			44	50	55	59	78	31
	50			57	65	72	77	103	41
	60			70	80	90	96	134	54
	70		75	83	97	109	117	166	65
	80		87	97	114	128	136	196	76
	90		99	112	133	148	159	230	88
	95		105	119	142	157	172	247	94
	100		111	126	151	167	184	265	101
45 150	20				25	27	29	37	16
	30				38	42	46	60	26
	40			47	53	59	64	86	35
	50		54	61	70	78	84	114	48
	60		67	75	87	97	106	151	63
	70		79	90	105	119	128	163	74
	75		86	97	114	129	138	201	82
	80	84	92	105	125	140	150	220	87
	85	90	99	113	135	150	164	238	93
48 160	20				26	29	31	39	16
	30			36	40	46	48	64	26
	40		45	50	57	65	69	94	38
	50		58	64	75	85	91	128	52
	60	64	71	80	94	107	115	165	67

⚠ Warning: DO NOT attempt to use these tables unless you are fully trained & certified in the use of gas mixtures other than air, or are under the supervision of a gas mixtures other than air instructor. Proper use of these tables will reduce the risk of decompression sickness & oxygen toxicity, but no table or computer can eliminate those risks.

IANTD *RUNTIME* TABLES FOR AIR WITH EAN 78% ACCELERATED DECO. (continued)

Depth m ft	Min	Meters Feet 24 80	21 70	18 60	15 50	12 40	> 78 % O2 9 30	6 20	4.5 15	% CNS
48 160	60		64	71	80	94	107	115	165	67
	65		70	78	88	104	119	127	183	73
	70		76	85	96	113	129	137	202	80
	75		82	92	105	125	141	151	222	87
	80		88	98	113	136	152	167	243	94
51 170	15					21	23	24	30	14
	20					28	31	32	42	19
	25				31	36	40	42	56	25
	30				38	44	49	52	70	31
	35			41	45	53	59	63	86	37
	40			47	53	62	69	74	101	43
	45			54	60	71	80	85	120	52
	50		55	61	69	81	91	99	141	62
	55		62	68	77	92	104	112	162	69
	60		68	75	85	102	116	124	180	75
	65		74	83	94	113	128	136	201	83
	70	74	81	90	103	125	140	151	223	91
	75	80	88	97	112	137	152	168	246	100
54 180	15					21	23	25	31	16
	20				26	29	32	35	45	21
	25				33	37	42	45	60	28
	30			36	40	47	52	57	77	35
	35			42	49	55	62	68	93	43
	40		45	50	57	66	74	81	111	53
	45		51	57	65	76	86	94	134	62
	50		58	64	74	87	99	108	156	70
	55	60	65	72	83	98	112	121	176	80
	60	64	71	80	92	110	125	134	199	88

Depth m ft	Min	Meters Feet 27 90	24 80	21 70	18 60	15 50	12 40	≥ 78 % O2 9 30	6 20	4.5 15	% CNS
54 180	65		72	78	87	102	123	138	150	222	95
	70		78	85	95	111	135	150	168	246	106
57 190	15						22	25	27	34	16
	20					27	30	34	37	48	23
	25				31	35	39	45	48	64	31
	30				38	43	49	56	60	82	37
	35			41	45	51	59	67	73	99	45
	40			47	53	59	70	80	86	123	56
	45		50	54	61	69	82	94	102	147	66
	50		56	61	69	78	94	108	116	169	74
	55		63	68	77	88	105	121	129	191	84
	60		69	75	85	99	119	135	146	217	93
	65	70	75	83	94	109	133	149	166	244	103
60 200	15					21	24	27	28	36	20
	20				26	28	33	37	39	52	28
	25				33	36	43	48	51	70	36
	30			37	40	45	53	60	64	88	44
	35			43	48	54	64	72	78	108	55
	40		46	50	56	64	76	86	93	135	67
	45		52	58	64	74	89	101	109	159	77
	50		59	65	73	83	101	115	123	182	88
	55	60	65	72	81	94	115	130	139	209	97
	60	67	72	80	90	105	130	146	161	239	108

Run Times are computed as the departure time from each stop, using Cybortronics DPA Software. Decompression Run Times in Green Columns must be completed using EAN 78%. Increased FiO2 will increase CNS O2 figures. To obtain repetitive group, Please see IANTD Accelerated Decompression Tables for Air.

⚠ Warning: DO NOT attempt to use these tables unless you are fully trained & certified in the use of gas mixtures other than air, or are under the supervision of a gas mixtures other than air instructor. Proper use of these tables will reduce the risk of decompression sickness & oxygen toxicity, but no table or computer can eliminate those risks.

IANTD *RUNTIME* TABLES FOR EAN 25% WITH EAN 78% ACCELERATED DECO.

Depth m ft	Min	Meters / Feet 12 / 40	≥ 78% O2 9 / 30	6 / 20	4.5 / 15	% CNS
27 90	70			76	95	30
	80		83	88	111	37
	90		94	100	125	41
	100		105	112	144	49
	110		117	124	162	57
	120		128	136	180	62
	130		140	149	197	69
	140		152	161	214	76
	150		164	173	232	84
	160		175	184	249	89
	165		181	190	256	92
	170	172	187	196	267	95
	175	178	193	204	277	98
	180	184	199	212	287	102
30 100	60		65	68	86	34
	70		76	80	103	39
	80		88	93	116	46
	90		100	105	138	55
	100	103	112	119	159	61
	110	114	125	132	178	70
	120	126	138	146	198	77
	130	138	152	160	218	84
	135	144	158	166	228	88
	140	149	164	172	238	93
	145	155	171	179	248	96
	150	162	178	187	259	100

Depth m ft	Min	Meters / Feet 15 / 50	12 / 40	≥ 78% O2 9 / 30	6 / 20	4.5 / 15	% CNS
33 110	50			56	58	74	34
	60			68	71	93	42
	70		74	81	85	110	47
	80		86	94	99	131	57
	90		98	107	114	155	68
	100		110	121	129	176	77
	110		123	136	144	197	86
	115		130	143	151	209	90
	120		136	150	159	220	95
	125		142	157	162	231	100
	130		149	164	172	243	105
36 120	40			46	48	63	31
	50		54	59	62	82	39
	60		66	72	76	102	47
	70		79	87	92	123	57
	80		92	101	108	149	69
	85		98	108	117	161	74
	90	94	105	116	124	173	79
	95	100	112	124	133	185	85
	100	106	119	132	140	196	90
	105	111	126	140	149	209	95
	110	117	132	147	155	221	100

Depth m ft	Min	Meters / Feet 18 / 60	15 / 50	12 / 40	> 78% O2 9 / 30	6 / 20	4.5 / 15	% CNS
39 130	30				36	38	48	23
	40			44	49	52	67	32
	50			57	64	67	89	41
	60			70	78	83	110	50
	70		75	84	94	100	138	63
	80		87	98	110	118	165	75
	85		94	106	119	127	178	79
	90		100	113	127	135	190	85
	95		105	120	135	143	203	90
	100		112	128	144	152	218	98
	105		118	136	152	161	231	102
	110		125	144	160	172	246	108
42 140	20				25	26	32	19
	30			35	38	40	51	27
	40			48	53	56	73	36
	50		54	62	68	72	97	47
	60		67	76	85	90	123	60
	65		73	84	93	100	139	66
	70		79	91	101	109	153	74
	75		86	99	111	119	167	81
	80	84	92	107	120	128	181	86
	85	89	99	115	129	137	195	92
	90	96	106	123	133	146	211	99

(see other side)

⚠ Warning: DO NOT attempt to use these tables unless you are fully trained & certified in the use of gas mixtures other than air, or are under the supervision of a gas mixtures other than air instructor. Proper use of these tables will reduce the risk of decompression sickness & oxygen toxicity, but no table or computer can eliminate those risks.

IANTD *RUNTIME* TABLES FOR EAN 25% WITH EAN 78% ACCELERATED DECO. (continued)

Depth m ft	Min	Meters/Feet 21/70	18/60	15/50	12/40	≥ 78 % O2 9/30	6/20	4.5/15	% CNS
45 150	20					26	28	35	22
	30				37	40	44	56	31
	40			44	51	56	61	81	43
	50			58	66	73	79	106	55
	55			65	74	82	89	121	64
	60		64	71	81	91	98	137	72
	65		70	78	89	100	109	153	79
	70		76	85	98	110	119	169	87
	75		82	92	106	120	129	183	94
	80		88	99	114	129	138	199	100
48 160	15					21	22	27	20
	20				25	28	30	37	24
	25				31	35	37	48	31
	30				38	43	46	60	38
	35			41	46	52	55	74	45
	40			47	54	61	65	88	52
	45			55	62	70	75	101	60
	50		58	61	70	79	85	116	69
	55		62	68	78	89	95	134	78
	60		68	76	87	98	106	151	87
	65		74	83	96	109	117	168	94
	70	74	81	90	105	120	128	184	103

Depth m ft	Min	Meters/Feet 21/70	18/60	15/50	12/40	≥ 78 % O2 9/30	6/20	4.5/15	% CNS
51 170	15					22	23	28	22
	20				27	29	31	39	24
	25			30	34	37	40	52	32
	30			36	41	46	49	65	40
	35			43	50	55	59	80	46
	40		45	50	58	65	69	94	54
	45		52	58	67	75	80	109	63
	50		58	64	75	84	90	128	73
	55	60	65	73	85	95	103	148	84
	60	66	71	80	94	106	114	165	91
	65	72	78	88	104	118	126	182	99

Run Times are computed as the departure time from each stop, using Cybortronics DPA Software.

Decompression Run Times in Green Columns must be completed using EAN 78%.

Increased FiO2 will increase CNS O2 figures.

To obtain repetitive group, Please see IANTD Accelerated Decompression Tables for EAN 26%, or convert to EAD and use repetitive group from IANTD Accelerated Decompression Tables for Air.

IANTD *RUNTIME* TABLES FOR EAN 29% WITH EAN 78% ACCELERATED DECO.

Depth m	Depth ft	Min	Meters/Feet ≥78% O2 9 / 30	6 / 20	4.5 / 15	% CNS
24	80	70			84	29
		80			98	35
		90			112	39
		100		103	126	45
		110		113	139	50
		120		125	156	56
		130		136	172	61
		140		147	189	69
		150		158	204	73
		160	163	170	219	79
		170	173	181	234	86
		180	184	192	250	92
		190	195	203	266	98
		200	206	214	281	105
27	90	70		74	92	39
		80		86	107	45
		90		97	121	52
		100	103	109	136	59
		110	114	120	155	67
		120	125	132	173	75
		130	137	145	190	83
		140	148	157	206	90
		150	159	168	222	99
30	100	60	64	66	82	40
		70	74	78	99	47
		80	86	90	114	54
		90	97	102	130	63
		100	109	114	150	73
		110	121	127	169	83
		120	132	140	187	91
		130	145	153	205	101

Depth m	Depth ft	Min	Meters/Feet ≥78% O2 15 / 50	12 / 40	9 / 30	6 / 20	4.5 / 15	% CNS
33	110	40				45	55	29
		50			55	57	72	39
		60			66	69	89	48
		70			78	82	106	57
		80			90	95	122	66
		90		95	103	108	145	76
		100		106	116	123	166	88
		110		118	129	137	186	96
		120		130	148	151	206	107
36	120	30				35	43	22
		40			45	48	60	32
		50			57	61	77	43
		60		64	69	74	97	50
		70		76	83	89	115	60
		80		88	96	103	138	71
		90		100	110	118	161	82
		95		106	117	126	172	87
		100		113	125	134	184	94
		105		120	132	141	195	98
		110		126	139	148	205	103

(see other side)

⚠ Warning: DO NOT attempt to use these tables unless you are fully trained & certified in the use of gas mixtures other than air, or are under the supervision of a gas mixtures other than air instructor. Proper use of these tables will reduce the risk of decompression sickness & oxygen toxicity, but no table or computer can eliminate those risks.

IANTD *RUNTIME* TABLES FOR EAN 29% WITH EAN 78% ACCELERATED DECO.

(continued)

Depth m ft	Min	Meters Feet 15 50	12 40	≥78% O2 9 30	6 20	4.5 15	% CNS
39 130	20				25	29	18
	30			35	37	46	29
	40			48	50	64	40
	50		53	61	65	84	48
	60		67	75	79	104	59
	70		80	89	95	127	72
	75		87	97	103	141	80
	80	84	93	104	111	153	86
	85	90	100	111	119	165	92
	90	96	107	120	128	178	99
42 140	20				25	31	23
	30			37	39	49	36
	40		46	50	53	69	47
	50		59	65	69	91	59
	60	64	72	79	85	112	73
	65	70	79	88	93	127	81
	70	76	86	96	102	141	89
	75	82	93	103	111	155	97
	80	89	101	112	120	169	105

Run Times are computed as the departure time from each stop, using Cybortronics DPA software.

Decompression Run Times in Green Columns must be completed using EAN 78%.

Increased FiO2 will increase CNS O2 figures.

To obtain Repetitive group, Please see IANTD Accelerated Decompression Tables for EAN 28%, or convert to EAD and use repetitive group from IANTD Accelerated Decompression Tables for Air.

⚠ **Warning:** DO NOT attempt to use these tables unless you are fully trained & certified in the use of gas mixtures other than air, or are under the supervision of a gas mixtures other than air instructor. Proper use of these tables will reduce the risk of decompression sickness & oxygen toxicity, but no table or computer can eliminate those risks.

IANTD *RUNTIME* TABLES FOR EAN 31% WITH EAN 78% ACCELERATED DECO.

Depth m	Depth ft	Min	≥78% O2 Meters 9 / Feet 30	6 / 20	4.5 / 15	% CNS
24	80	90			110	46
		100			124	52
		110			137	57
		120		123	152	64
		130		134	168	70
		140		145	185	78
		150		156	200	84
		160		168	215	91
		170		179	230	97
		180		190	244	104
27	90	70		74	90	42
		80		85	105	48
		90		96	119	56
		100		107	133	63
		110	113	119	151	71
		120	124	130	169	79
		130	135	142	186	88
		140	146	154	202	96
		150	157	166	218	104
30	100	60		65	81	39
		70	74	77	97	46
		80	85	89	112	54
		90	96	101	127	61
		100	107	113	146	71
		110	119	125	165	80
		120	131	138	183	89
		130	142	150	200	97
		140	158	162	217	106

Depth m	Depth ft	Min	Meters 15 / Feet 50	12 / 40	≥78% O2 9 / 30	6 / 20	4.5 / 15	% CNS
33	110	50			54	56	70	38
		60			65	68	87	47
		70			77	81	104	57
		80			89	93	119	64
		90			101	106	139	76
		100		104	113	119	160	86
		110		116	126	134	181	96
		120		128	140	148	200	105
36	120	40			44	47	59	36
		50			56	60	76	47
		60			68	73	94	58
		70		74	81	86	112	67
		80		86	94	100	133	78
		90		98	107	115	156	90
		100		110	121	130	178	103
39	130	30			35	36	45	34
		40			47	49	63	45
		50		54	60	63	82	57
		60		66	73	77	102	68
		70		79	87	93	123	83
		80		91	101	108	147	97
		90	94	104	116	124	171	112

Run Times are computed as the departure time from each stop, using Cybortronics DPA Software. Decompression Run Times in Green Columns must be completed using EAN 78%. Increased FiO2 will increase CNS O2 figures. To obtain repetitive group, Please see IANTD Accelerated Decompression Tables for EAN 30%, or convert to EAD and use repetitive group from IANTD Accelerated Decompression Tables for Air.

⚠ Warning: DO NOT attempt to use these tables unless you are fully trained & certified in the use of gas mixtures other than air, or are under the supervision of a gas mixtures other than air instructor. Proper use of these tables will reduce the risk of decompression sickness & oxygen toxicity, but no table or computer can eliminate those risks.

IANTD *RUNTIME* TABLES FOR EAN 33% WITH EAN 78% ACCELERATED DECO.

Depth m ft	Min	Meters/Feet ≥78% O2 9 / 30	6 / 20	4.5 / 15	% CNS
24 80	100			122	51
	110			135	56
	120			148	62
	130		133	164	69
	140		143	180	75
	150		154	196	83
	160		166	211	89
	170		177	225	95
	180		188	240	101
27 90	80		84	103	48
	90		95	117	54
	100		106	131	61
	110		117	147	69
	120		129	164	77
	130	133	140	181	86
	140	144	152	198	93
	150	155	164	213	100
30 100	70		76	95	50
	80	84	88	110	58
	90	95	99	125	67
	100	106	111	142	76
	110	118	123	161	86
	120	129	136	179	96
	130	140	148	196	105

Depth m ft	Min	Meters/Feet ≥78% O2 12 / 40	9 / 30	6 / 20	4.5 / 15	% CNS
33 110	60		65	67	85	53
	70		76	80	102	63
	80		88	92	117	71
	90		99	104	136	83
	100		111	117	156	96
	110	114	123	131	175	105
36 120	50		55	59	74	54
	60		67	72	92	66
	70		79	84	109	78
	80	84	92	98	128	91
	90	97	105	112	151	103

Run Times are computed as the departure time from each stop, using Cybortronics DPA Software

Decompression Run Times in Green Columns must be completed using EAN 78%.

Increased FiO2 will increase CNS O2 figures.

To obtain repetitive group, please see IANTD Accelerated Decompression Tables for EAN 32%, or convert to EAD and use repetitive group from IANTD Accelerated Decompression Tables for Air.

⚠ Warning: DO NOT attempt to use these tables unless you are fully trained & certified in the use of gas mixtures other than air, or are under the supervision of a gas mixtures other than air instructor. Proper use of these tables will reduce the risk of decompression sickness & oxygen toxicity, but no table or computer can eliminate those risks.

IANTD Trimix Decompression Runtime Tables For 160 to 180 Feet (48 to 54 m)

Bottom mix range: O_2 16% - 22%

He 10% - 18%

Depth	B/T Min	To 1st Stop	EAN 35% 90 f 27 m	80 f 24 m	70 f 21 m	60 f 18 m	50 f 15 m	40 f 12 m	EAN 75% 30 f 9 m	20 f 6 m	15 f 4.5 m	% CNS	OTU
160 f 48 m	10	13							14	15	19	6	23
	15	18						19	22	24	32	11	38
	20	23					24	26	30	32	45	17	53
	25	28					29	33	38	41	58	24	69
	30	33				34	37	41	47	51	72	30	85
	35	38				39	42	47	55	59	84	36	103
	40	42			43	46	50	57	65	71	101	42	119
	45	47			49	52	57	65	75	81	116	49	136
	50	52			54	58	64	73	84	91	132	56	156
	55	57		58	61	65	72	82	94	102	149	63	175
	60	62		63	67	72	80	92	105	114	168	70	194
	65	67		68	73	79	87	100	115	124	184	77	214
	70	72		73	79	86	95	109	125	135	203	84	233
	75	77		78	84	91	102	117	134	146	223	92	255
	80	82		84	91	98	110	127	145	157	242	100	278
170 f 51 m	10	13							14	15	20	7	26
	15	18						20	22	24	33	13	42
	20	23					24	28	31	33	47	21	59
	25	28				29	32	37	41	45	63	27	75
	30	33				34	37	42	48	52	75	34	94
	35	38			39	42	46	53	60	65	92	41	112
	40	42			44	47	52	61	69	75	108	47	131
	45	47		48	50	54	60	70	80	86	126	55	150
	50	52		53	56	60	67	78	89	97	142	62	171
	55	57		59	63	68	76	89	101	110	163	70	191
	60	62		64	68	74	82	96	110	119	178	78	213
	65	67	68	71	76	83	93	108	123	133	200	86	234
	70	72	73	77	83	90	101	117	133	145	222	94	257
	75	77	78	83	89	97	109	127	144	157	243	103	282
180 f 54 m	10	14						15	16	17	23	8	28
	15	18					19	22	25	27	38	15	46
	20	23				24	25	29	32	35	52	24	64
	25	28				29	32	37	42	46	67	31	82
	30	32			33	36	39	45	52	56	82	39	102
	35	37			39	42	46	54	62	68	99	46	121
	40	42		43	46	49	54	64	73	79	116	54	142
	45	47		49	52	56	63	73	84	91	135	63	164
	50	52	53	55	58	63	71	83	95	104	155	71	186
	55	57	58	60	64	70	78	92	105	114	173	80	210
	60	62	63	66	71	78	87	102	117	127	194	89	232
	65	67	69	73	79	86	97	113	129	141	217	98	257

⚠ **Warning: DO NOT attempt to use these tables unless you are fully trained & certified in the use of gas mixtures other than air, or are under the supervision of a gas mixtures other than air instructor. Proper use of these tables will reduce the risk of decompression sickness & oxygen toxicity, but no table or computer can eliminate those risks.**

IANTD Trimix Repetitive Dive Runtime Tables For 160 to 180 Feet (48 to 54m)
Bottom mix range: O_2 16% - 22%
He 10% - 18%

	B/T	To	EAN 35%						EAN 75%			%	tot.
	Min	1st Stop	90 f 27 m	80 f 24 m	70 f 21 m	60 f 18 m	50 f 15 m	40 f 12 m	30 f 9 m	20 f 6 m	15 f 4.5 m	CNS	OTU
REP. 160 f 48 m	10	13							14	15	21	7	49
	15	18						19	23	25	37	13	80
	20	23					24	27	31	34	52	19	93
	25	28					30	34	40	44	67	27	148
	30	33				34	37	42	50	55	86	35	183
	35	38				39	43	50	59	65	107	43	224
	40	42			43	46	50	58	68	75	127	52	264
	45	47			49	52	58	67	79	87	154	61	307
	50	52			54	58	65	75	88	96	178	72	356
	55	57		58	61	66	74	86	101	111	204	82	403
	60	62		63	67	73	81	94	110	122	226	92	448
	65	67		68	73	79	88	102	120	134	250	101	493
REP. 170 f 51 m	10	13							15	16	23	8	55
	15	18						20	23	25	38	15	89
	20	23					24	29	33	36	55	23	125
	25	28				29	32	37	43	47	73	31	161
	30	33				34	37	43	50	55	90	39	203
	35	38			39	42	46	54	63	69	116	49	246
	40	42			44	47	52	62	72	80	141	59	292
	45	47		48	50	54	61	72	84	92	169	70	342
	50	52		53	56	61	69	82	95	105	196	81	393
	55	57		59	63	69	77	91	106	118	220	92	442
	60	62		64	68	74	83	98	115	129	243	102	491
	65												
	70												
	75												
REP. 180 f 54 m	10	13						14	16	17	26	10	61
	15	18					19	22	25	27	43	19	98
	20	23				24	26	31	35	39	61	27	136
	25	28				29	32	37	43	47	77	41	191
	30	32			33	36	39	47	55	61	102	45	222
	35	37			39	42	47	56	65	72	126	56	270
	40	42		43	46	50	56	66	77	85	156	68	321
	45	47		49	52	56	63	75	88	97	184	80	377
	50	52	53	55	58	64	72	86	100	111	211	92	431
	55	57	58	60	64	70	79	94	110	124	236	104	484
	60												
	65												

⚠ Warning: DO NOT attempt to use these tables unless you are fully trained & certified in the use of gas mixtures other than air, or are under the supervision of a gas mixtures other than air instructor. Proper use of these tables will reduce the risk of decompression sickness & oxygen toxicity, but no table or computer can eliminate those risks.

IANTD Trimix Decompression Runtime Tables For 190 to 220 Feet (57 to 66m)
Bottom mix range: O_2 14% - 18%
He 17% - 36%

	B/T Min	To 1st Stop	Bottom 120 f 36 m	110 f 33 m	EAN 35% 100 f 30 m	90 f 27 m	80 f 24 m	70 f 21 m	60 f 18 m	50 f 15 m	40 f 12 m	EAN 75% 30 f 9 m	20 f 6 m	15 f 4.5m	% CNS	OTU
190 f 57 m	10	13								14	15	17	19	27	9	31
	15	18							19	22	25	28	31	45	15	49
	20	22						23	25	28	32	37	41	60	24	69
	25	27					28	29	31	35	40	46	52	77	31	88
	30	32					34	36	39	44	50	58	64	96	39	110
	35	37				38	40	43	47	53	61	70	78	118	47	133
	40	42				43	45	48	53	60	69	80	88	136	56	157
	45	47			48	49	51	55	60	69	79	91	101	159	65	182
	50	52			53	55	58	62	68	77	89	103	114	183	75	209
	55	57			58	61	65	70	77	87	101	117	129	208	85	236
	60	62			64	67	71	76	83	94	109	126	140	227	95	278
	65	67		68	71	75	79	85	93	106	122	142	157	253	104	288
200 f 60 m	10	13								14	16	18	20	29	10	33
	15	17						18	20	21	24	27	31	45	18	53
	20	22					23	24	26	28	32	37	41	61	26	74
	25	27					28	30	33	37	43	50	56	82	34	96
	30	32				33	35	37	41	46	53	61	68	103	43	120
	35	37			38	39	40	43	48	54	63	73	81	124	52	145
	40	42			43	44	47	51	57	64	74	86	95	148	62	170
	45	47			48	50	53	57	63	71	82	95	106	170	72	199
	50	52		53	54	57	61	66	74	83	97	112	124	200	83	228
	55	57		58	60	63	67	72	80	90	105	122	136	221	94	256
	60	62		63	66	70	74	80	89	101	117	136	151	244	104	284
210 f 63 m	10	14							15	16	17	20	21	31	11	36
	15	18						19	20	22	25	30	33	48	20	58
	20	23					24	26	28	31	35	42	46	67	29	80
	25	28				29	30	33	36	40	46	54	59	88	37	103
	30	33			34	35	36	40	44	49	57	67	74	111	47	129
	35	38			39	41	43	47	52	58	68	80	87	134	57	156
	40	43		44	45	47	50	55	60	68	78	92	101	159	68	185
	45	48		49	51	54	58	64	70	79	92	107	117	188	79	216
	50	53		54	56	59	63	69	76	85	100	117	129	211	91	246
	55	58		60	63	67	71	78	86	97	112	132	146	237	102	277
220 f 66 m	10	14							15	16	18	21	23	34	12	39
	15	18						19	21	23	26	31	34	51	22	62
	20	23				24	25	27	29	32	37	44	48	71	31	85
	25	28				29	31	34	37	42	48	57	62	94	41	112
	30	33			34	36	38	42	46	52	60	70	77	118	51	139
	35	38		39	40	42	45	50	55	62	72	85	92	144	62	168
	40	43		44	46	48	51	57	62	70	82	96	106	170	74	199
	45	48	49	51	53	56	60	66	73	82	96	112	123	201	87	234
	50	53	54	57	59	63	67	74	82	93	108	127	141	229	99	266
	55	58	59	63	66	70	75	83	91	104	121	143	157	255	110	298

⚠ **Warning:** DO NOT attempt to use these tables unless you are fully trained & certified in the use of gas mixtures other than air, or are under the supervision of a gas mixtures other than air instructor. Proper use of these tables will reduce the risk of decompression sickness & oxygen toxicity, but no table or computer can eliminate those risks.

IANTD Trimix Repetitive Dive Runtime Tables For 190 to 220 Feet (57 to 66m)

Bottom mix range: O_2 14% - 18%

He 17% - 36%

		To	Bottom		EAN 35%							EAN 75%				
	B/T Min	1st Stop	120 f 36 m	110 f 33 m	100 f 30 m	90 f 27 m	80 f 24 m	70 f 21 m	60 f 18 m	50 f 15 m	40 f 12 m	30 f 9 m	20 f 6 m	15 f 4.5m	% CNS	tot. OTU
REP. 190 f 57 m	10	13								14	15	17	20	32	10	66
	15	18							19	22	25	29	33	51	18	106
	20	22						23	25	28	32	38	43	71	28	150
	25	27					28	29	31	36	42	50	56	96	38	196
	30	32					34	36	39	45	52	61	69	127	50	252
	35	37				38	40	43	47	54	63	74	83	157	63	308
	40	42				43	45	48	53	61	71	84	95	183	74	364
	45	47			48	49	51	55	60	69	81	96	109	215	87	424
	50	52			53	55	58	62	68	77	91	108	123	245	100	487
	55															
	60															
	65															
REP. 200 f 60 m	10	13								14	16	18	21	33	11	72
	15	17						18	20	22	25	30	34	54	21	114
	20	22					23	24	27	30	35	41	47	78	31	162
	25	27					28	30	33	37	43	51	58	103	43	214
	30	32				33	35	37	41	46	54	64	72	137	56	275
	35	37			38	39	40	43	49	55	65	77	87	167	69	336
	40	42			43	44	47	51	57	65	76	90	102	198	82	395
	45	47			48	50	53	57	64	72	85	101	116	231	97	464
	50															
	55															
	60															
REP. 210 f 63 m	10	14							15	16	19	22	24	37	13	78
	15	18						19	20	22	25	31	34	56	23	124
	20	23					24	27	29	32	37	45	50	84	34	176
	25	28				29	30	33	36	41	48	57	64	115	47	233
	30	33			34	35	36	40	44	50	59	71	79	150	62	300
	35	38			39	41	43	47	52	59	69	83	93	179	75	363
	40	43		44	45	47	50	55	60	68	81	97	110	217	90	430
	45	48		49	51	54	58	64	70	79	93	112	127	252	105	502
	50															
	55															
REP. 220 f 66 m	10	14							15	16	18	22	24	38	14	84
	15	18					19	21	22	24	28	34	38	61	25	134
	20	23				24	25	27	29	32	38	46	51	89	38	190
	25	28				29	31	34	37	42	49	59	66	123	52	255
	30	33			34	36	38	42	46	52	62	74	83	159	68	323
	35	38		39	40	42	45	50	55	63	74	89	100	194	82	391
	40	43		44	46	48	51	57	63	71	85	102	116	232	98	465
	45															
	50															
	55															

⚠ Warning: DO NOT attempt to use these tables unless you are fully trained & certified in the use of gas mixtures other than air, or are under the supervision of a gas mixtures other than air instructor. Proper use of these tables will reduce the risk of decompression sickness & oxygen toxicity, but no table or computer can eliminate those risks.

IANTD Trimix Decompression Runtime Tables For 230 to 260 Feet (69 to 78m)

Bottom mix range: O_2 12% - 16%
He 24% - 45%

Depth	B/T Min	To 1st Stop	Bottom Mix 140 f 42 m	Bottom Mix 130 f 39 m	Bottom Mix 120 f 36 m	Bottom Mix 110 f 33 m	EAN 35% 100 f 30 m	EAN 35% 90 f 27 m	EAN 35% 80 f 24 m	EAN 35% 70 f 21 m	EAN 35% 60 f 18 m	EAN 35% 50 f 15 m	EAN 35% 40 f 12 m	EAN 75% 30 f 9 m	EAN 75% 20 f 6 m	EAN 75% 15 f 4.5 m	% CNS	OTU
230 f 69 m	10	13								14	15	16	19	22	24	37	13	43
	15	18						19	21	22	23	25	30	35	38	57	23	67
	20	23					24	25	27	29	32	36	43	50	54	82	33	93
	25	28				29	30	31	34	37	41	46	55	64	70	109	44	122
	30	33				34	36	38	41	45	49	56	66	77	84	135	56	154
	35	38			39	42	44	46	51	55	61	69	82	95	104	171	69	189
	40	43			44	47	49	52	57	62	69	78	92	108	120	200	82	225
	45	47		48	50	54	57	60	65	71	78	89	106	125	138	230	95	259
	50	52		53	57	62	65	69	75	81	90	101	121	143	159	265	108	295
240 f 72 m	10	13								14	15	18	20	23	25	39	16	45
	15	18						19	20	21	23	27	31	36	40	61	25	72
	20	23					24	26	28	30	33	38	44	52	57	88	37	101
	25	28				29	31	34	36	39	43	49	57	67	73	116	48	133
	30	33			34	36	38	41	44	48	53	61	71	83	92	149	61	166
	35	37		38	40	43	45	49	53	57	64	73	86	100	110	184	75	205
	40	42		43	46	50	53	57	61	67	74	86	100	118	131	218	89	242
	45	47		49	53	58	61	65	70	76	85	97	114	135	150	250	103	279
250 f 75 m	10	13							14	15	16	18	20	23	27	41	17	48
	15	18					19	20	21	22	24	28	33	38	43	65	28	76
	20	23				23	25	26	28	30	33	39	45	53	60	93	39	108
	25	28			29	31	34	36	38	41	45	52	61	71	79	125	52	141
	30	32		33	34	37	40	42	45	49	54	63	74	86	96	159	66	180
	35	37		38	41	44	47	50	54	59	66	76	89	105	118	196	82	221
	40	42	43	45	48	52	56	59	64	70	78	90	106	125	140	232	96	260
260 f 78 m	10	14							15	16	18	20	23	27	31	46	19	53
	15	19					20	21	22	23	26	29	34	40	45	68	30	82
	20	24				25	27	29	31	34	38	43	50	58	65	100	43	115
	25	29			30	34	36	38	41	45	50	57	66	77	85	135	57	152
	30	33		34	37	41	43	46	50	54	61	69	81	94	104	173	73	194
	35	38	39	41	44	49	52	55	59	65	73	83	96	113	127	211	89	237

⚠ Warning: DO NOT attempt to use these tables unless you are fully trained & certified in the use of gas mixtures other than air, or are under the supervision of a gas mixtures other than air instructor. Proper use of these tables will reduce the risk of decompression sickness & oxygen toxicity, but no table or computer can eliminate those risks.

IANTD Trimix Repetitive Dive Runtime Tables For 230 to 260 Feet (69 to 78m)

Bottom mix range: O_2 12% - 16%
He 24% - 45%

	B/T Min	To 1st Stop	Bottom Mix 140 f 42 m	130 f 39 m	120 f 36 m	110 f 33 m	EAN 35% 100 f 30 m	90 f 27 m	80 f 24 m	70 f 21 m	60 f 18 m	50 f 15 m	40 f 12 m	EAN 75% 30 f 9 m	20 f 6 m	15 f 4.5 m	% CNS	tot. OTU
REP. 230 f 69 m	10	13								14	15	17	20	24	27	44	15	93
	15	18						19	21	22	23	26	32	38	42	71	28	147
	20	23					24	25	27	29	32	36	43	51	57	105	42	211
	25	28				29	30	31	34	37	41	46	56	67	75	146	59	285
	30	33				34	36	38	41	45	49	56	68	81	92	183	75	359
	35	38			39	42	44	46	51	55	61	69	83	100	113	229	92	441
	40																	
	45																	
	50																	
REP. 240 f 72 m	10	13								14	15	18	21	25	28	47	18	99
	15	18						19	20	21	23	27	32	38	42	75	31	159
	20	23					24	26	28	30	33	39	46	55	61	115	47	230
	25	28				29	31	34	36	39	43	50	59	70	79	156	64	309
	30	33			34	36	38	41	44	48	53	61	73	87	99	201	81	387
	35	37		38	40	43	45	49	53	57	64	74	87	106	121	251	101	479
	40																	
	45																	
REP. 250 f 75 m	10	13							14	15	16	19	22	26	30	49	20	105
	15	18					19	20	21	22	24	28	34	41	47	82	34	170
	20	23				24	26	27	29	31	34	40	48	57	64	124	51	247
	25	28			29	31	34	36	38	42	46	54	64	76	87	170	69	329
	30	32		33	34	37	40	42	45	49	55	64	77	93	107	218	89	421
	35																	
	40																	
REP. 260 f 78 m	10	14							15	16	18	20	23	28	32	52	22	114
	15	19					20	21	22	24	27	31	37	44	50	88	37	184
	20	24				25	27	29	31	34	39	44	52	62	70	135	57	268
	25	29			30	34	36	38	41	45	51	58	69	82	94	184	75	354
	30	33		34	37	41	43	46	50	54	61	69	82	99	114	234	97	453
	35																	

⚠ Warning: DO NOT attempt to use these tables unless you are fully trained & certified in the use of gas mixtures other than air, or are under the supervision of a gas mixtures other than air instructor. Proper use of these tables will reduce the risk of decompression sickness & oxygen toxicity, but no table or computer can eliminate those risks.

IANTD Trimix Decompression Runtime Tables For 270 to 280 Feet (81 to 84m)

Bottom mix range: O_2 12% - 14%

He 38% - 50%

Depth	B/T Min	To 1st Stop	Bottom Mix 150 f 45 m	Bottom Mix 140 f 42 m	Bottom Mix 130 39 m	Bottom Mix 120 f 36 m	Bottom Mix 110 f 33 m	EAN 35% 100 f 30 m	EAN 35% 90 f 27m	EAN 35% 80 f 24 m	EAN 35% 70 f 21 m	EAN 35% 60 f 18 m	EAN 35% 50 f 15 m	EAN 35% 40 f 12 m	EAN 75% 30 f 9 m	EAN 75% 20 f 6 m	EAN 75% 15 f 4.5m	% CNS	OTU
270 f 81 m	10	14							15	16	18	19	21	24	29	32	49	19	56
	15	19					20	21	22	23	26	29	33	38	46	50	77	31	88
	20	24				25	27	28	29	31	35	39	44	52	62	68	109	45	124
	25	28			29	32	34	36	38	41	46	51	58	68	81	90	149	61	167
	30	33		34	36	39	43	45	48	51	57	63	72	84	100	112	189	78	214
	35	38	39	40	43	48	53	56	59	64	71	79	90	106	127	141	235	94	257
280 f 84 m	10	14							15	16	18	19	21	24	30	33	51	21	59
	15	19					20	21	22	24	27	30	34	39	47	51	80	34	93
	20	23			24	25	27	28	30	32	36	40	46	54	65	71	116	49	133
	25	28		29	31	33	36	38	40	43	48	54	61	72	86	95	160	66	180
	30	33	34	35	38	41	45	48	51	55	62	68	78	91	109	121	203	84	228
	35	38	39	41	45	49	55	58	62	67	74	83	94	112	134	150	250	102	276

IANTD Trimix Decompression RuntimeTables For 290 to 300 Feet (87 to 90m)

Bottom mix range: O_2 10% - 13%

He 38% - 50%

Depth	B/T Min	To 1st Stop	Bottom Mix 160 f 48 m	Bottom Mix 150 f 45 m	Bottom Mix 140 f 42 m	Bottom Mix 130 39 m	Bottom Mix 120 f 36 m	Bottom Mix 110 f 33 m	EAN 35% 100 f 30 m	EAN 35% 90 f 27m	EAN 35% 80 f 24 m	EAN 35% 70 f 21 m	EAN 35% 60 f 18 m	EAN 35% 50 f 15 m	EAN 35% 40 f 12 m	EAN 75% 30 f 9 m	EAN 75% 20 f 6 m	EAN 75% 15 f 4.5m	% CNS	OTU
290 f 87 m	10	14							15	16	18	19	20	22	27	32	35	54	22	62
	15	19					20	22	23	24	27	29	32	37	44	52	58	90	35	99
	20	23			24	25	27	30	32	34	38	42	46	53	63	74	82	133	51	141
	25	28		29	31	33	35	39	41	44	48	53	59	67	80	95	106	179	70	192
	30	33	34	35	38	41	45	50	53	56	62	68	76	87	104	123	137	229	88	241
	35	38	39	41	45	49	54	60	63	68	74	81	90	103	124	148	165	282	109	297
300 f 90 m	10	14						15	16	18	19	20	21	25	29	34	38	59	23	66
	15	18				19	20	22	23	25	27	30	34	40	47	55	61	97	38	104
	20	23			24	26	28	31	33	36	39	43	48	56	66	77	86	142	55	151
	25	28		29	31	33	36	40	43	47	51	56	62	72	85	101	113	192	76	206
	30	33	34	37	39	42	46	52	55	60	65	71	80	92	109	130	145	245	95	258

⚠ Warning: DO NOT attempt to use these tables unless you are fully trained & certified in the use of gas mixtures other than air, or are under the supervision of a gas mixtures other than air instructor. Proper use of these tables will reduce the risk of decompression sickness & oxygen toxicity, but no table or computer can eliminate those risks.

IANTD Trimix Repetitive Dive Runtime Tables For 270 to 280 Feet (81 to 84m)

Bottom mix range: O_2 12% - 14%
He 38% - 50%

	B/T Min	To 1st Stop	Bottom Mix 150 f 45 m	140 f 42 m	130 39 m	120 f 36 m	110 f 33 m	EAN 35% 100 f 30 m	90 f 27m	80 f 24 m	70 f 21 m	60 f 18 m	50 f 15 m	40 f 12 m	EAN 75% 30 f 9 m	20 f 6 m	15 f 4.5m	% CNS	tot. OTU
REP 270 f 81 m	10	14							15	16	18	19	21	25	31	35	58	23	122
	15	19					20	21	22	23	26	29	33	39	48	54	99	40	200
	20	24				25	27	28	29	31	35	39	45	53	65	73	146	61	292
	25	28			29	32	34	36	38	41	46	51	58	70	85	97	201	83	394
	30																		
	35																		
REP 280 f 84 m	10	14							15	16	18	20	22	26	32	36	61	25	130
	15	19					20	21	22	24	27	30	35	41	50	56	105	44	214
	20	23			24	25	27	28	30	32	36	40	46	55	68	77	157	65	311
	25	28		29	31	33	36	38	40	43	48	54	62	74	91	104	216	89	422
	30																		
	35																		

IANTD Trimix Repetitive Dive RuntimeTables For 290 to 300 Feet (87 to 90m)

Bottom mix range: O_2 10% - 13%
He 38% - 50%

	B/T Min	To 1st Stop	Bottom Mix 160 f 48 m	150 f 45 m	140 f 42 m	130 39 m	120 f 36 m	110 f 33 m	EAN 35% 100 f 30 m	90 f 27m	80 f 24 m	70 f 21 m	60 f 18 m	50 f 15 m	40 f 12 m	EAN 75% 30 f 9 m	20 f 6 m	15 f 4.5m	% CNS	tot. OTU
REP 290 f 87 m	10	14							15	16	18	19	20	23	29	35	39	67	26	138
	15	19					20	22	23	24	27	29	32	37	45	54	60	119	47	230
	20	23			24	25	27	30	32	34	38	42	47	54	66	79	90	181	70	333
	25	28		29	31	33	35	39	41	44	48	53	59	68	82	101	116	247	96	456
	30																			
	35																			
REP 300 f 90 m	10	14						15	16	18	19	20	21	25	30	36	40	72	29	147
	15	18				19	20	22	23	25	27	30	34	40	48	58	65	131	51	245
	20	23			24	26	28	31	33	36	39	43	48	56	67	81	93	193	76	357
	25	28		29	31	33	36	40	43	47	51	56	62	73	88	108	124	267	105	492
	30																			

⚠ Warning: DO NOT attempt to use these tables unless you are fully trained & certified in the use of gas mixtures other than air, or are under the supervision of a gas mixtures other than air instructor. Proper use of these tables will reduce the risk of decompression sickness & oxygen toxicity, but no table or computer can eliminate those risks.

IANTD Trimix Decompression Runtime Tables For 310 to 330 Feet (93 to 99m)

Bottom mix range: O_2 10% - 12%

He 40% - 60%

	B/T Min	To 1st Stop	Bottom Mix 180 f 54 m	170 f 51 m	160 f 48 m	150 f 45m	140 f 42 m	130 f 39 m	120 f 36 m	110 f 33 m	EAN 35% 100 f 30 m	90 f 27 m	80 f 24 m	70 f 21 m	60 f 18 m	50 f 15 m	40 f 12 m	EAN 75% 30 f 9 m	20 f 6 m	15 f 4.5 m	% CNS	OTU
310 f 93 m	10	14							15	16	18	19	20	21	23	27	32	38	43	67	26	74
	15	18					19	20	22	24	26	28	30	33	37	44	52	62	69	112	44	121
	20	23				24	26	28	30	34	37	40	43	47	53	62	73	87	98	167	65	179
	25	28		29	31	33	35	38	42	48	52	56	61	66	74	85	101	120	135	227	87	237
	30	33	34	35	37	40	43	48	54	61	66	70	76	83	92	107	128	153	172	294	112	303
320 f 96 m	10	15							16	18	19	20	21	23	27	31	36	42	47	73	28	79
	15	19					20	22	24	27	29	31	33	36	41	47	55	65	73	119	47	129
	20	24			25	26	28	30	33	38	40	43	46	51	58	67	78	93	105	179	70	191
	25	29		30	32	34	37	40	45	52	55	59	64	70	79	90	106	127	143	243	93	253
330 99 m	10	14						15	17	18	19	20	21	24	27	31	36	44	49	77	30	84
	15	19				20	21	23	26	28	30	32	35	39	43	49	58	69	77	128	51	137
	20	24			25	27	29	31	36	40	43	46	50	56	62	71	83	100	112	190	75	203
	25	29	30	31	33	35	38	41	47	53	56	60	65	73	81	93	111	134	149	258	100	270

⚠ Warning: DO NOT attempt to use these tables unless you are fully trained & certified in the use of gas mixtures other than air, or are under the supervision of a gas mixtures other than air instructor. Proper use of these tables will reduce the risk of decompression sickness & oxygen toxicity, but no table or computer can eliminate those risks.

IANTD TRIMIX *RUNTIME*

DIVE DECOMPRESSION TABLES

BOTTOM MIX : 23 % O2 and 17% to 21 % HE

TRIMIX RUNTIME TABLES

DEPTH	BT	STOP 90 ft 27 m	EAN 36% 70 ft 21m	EAN 36% 60 ft 18 m	EAN 36% 50 ft 15 m	EAN 36% 40 ft 12 m	EAN 75% 30 ft 9 m	EAN 75% 20 ft 6 m	EAN 75% 15 ft 4.5m	CNS
130 ft 39 m	15	18						22	28	8
	20	23					26	28	38	12
	25	28					33	35	48	17
	30	33				36	39	41	57	22
	35	38				43	47	50	69	28
	40	43			46	49	54	58	81	33
	45	48			51	55	61	65	90	38
	50	53			57	63	70	75	104	43
140 ft 42 m	15	18					21	23	29	9
	20	23					27	30	39	15
	25	28				31	34	37	51	20
	30	33				38	42	46	62	26
	35	38			41	44	49	54	74	32
	40	43			47	51	57	62	84	37
	45	48			53	59	66	72	99	42
	50	53		55	58	65	73	79	111	49
150 ft 45 m	15	18					21	24	31	11
	20	23				26	29	32	43	17
	25	28				33	36	39	54	23
	30	33			36	39	43	47	65	29
	35	38			42	46	52	57	79	35
	40	43		45	47	52	59	65	91	42
	45	48		49	53	59	66	72	102	48
	50	53		56	61	68	77	83	119	55
160 ft 48 m	15	19				22	24	26	34	13
	20	24				27	31	33	45	20
	25	29			32	35	39	42	58	26
	30	34			39	43	49	53	73	33
	35	39		41	44	48	55	59	83	40
	40	44		47	51	57	65	70	99	47
	45	49	51	52	57	64	73	78	112	54
	50	54	56	59	64	72	83	89	129	62
170 ft 51 m	15	19				22	24	26	35	16
	20	24			27	30	33	35	49	23
	25	29			33	37	41	44	61	30
	30	34		36	39	44	50	54	76	37
	35	39		42	45	52	59	64	90	45
	40	44	46	48	52	60	68	73	104	52
	45	49	51	54	59	68	77	83	121	61
	50	54	57	61	67	77	87	95	139	69

TRIMIX RUNTIME TABLES

⚠ Warning: DO NOT attempt to use these tables unless you are fully trained & certified in the use of gas mixtures other than air, or are under the supervision of a gas mixtures other than air instructor. Proper use of these tables will reduce the risk of decompression sickness & oxygen toxicity, but no table or computer can eliminate those risks.

TRIMIX RUNTIME TABLES

TRIMIX RUNTIME TABLES

IANTD TRIMIX *RUNTIME*

REPETITIVE DIVE DECOMPRESSION TABLES

BOTTOM MIX : 23 % O2 and 17% to 21 % HE

DEPTH	BT	STOP 90 ft 27 m	EAN 36% 70 ft 21m	EAN 36% 60 ft 18 m	EAN 36% 50 ft 15 m	EAN 36% 40 ft 12 m	EAN 75% 30 ft 9 m	EAN 75% 20 ft 6 m	EAN 75% 15 ft 4.5m	CNS
REP 130 ft 39 m	15	18					21	22	30	9
	20	23					27	29	42	15
	25	28				31	33	35	53	20
	30	33				37	41	44	66	26
	35	38				43	49	52	80	33
	40	43			46	49	55	60	96	40
	45	48			51	56	63	68	112	47
	50	53			57	64	72	78	132	55
REP 140 ft 42 m	15	18					21	24	33	11
	20	23				26	28	31	44	16
	25	28				32	35	39	58	23
	30	33			36	38	43	47	72	31
	35	38			41	45	51	57	89	38
	40	43			47	52	59	65	106	46
	45	48			53	60	68	75	125	54
	50	53		55	58	65	74	82	145	64
REP 150 ft 45 m	15	18					22	25	35	13
	20	23				25	29	32	48	19
	25	28			31	33	37	41	62	27
	30	33			36	40	46	51	79	35
	35	38			43	48	55	61	98	43
	40	43		45	48	54	62	69	116	52
	45	48		50	54	61	70	78	138	63
	50	53		55	60	68	79	88	161	73
REP 160 ft 48 m	15	19				22	25	27	39	15
	20	24				29	33	36	54	23
	25	29			32	35	41	45	69	31
	30	34			39	43	50	55	87	40
	35	39		41	44	50	58	63	106	49
	40	44		47	51	58	68	75	129	60
	45	49	51	53	58	66	77	85	154	71
	50	54	56	59	65	74	87	95	177	82
REP 170 ft 51 m	15	19				22	25	27	40	18
	20	24			26	30	33	36	55	26
	25	29			33	38	43	47	73	35
	30	34		36	39	45	52	57	93	45
	35	39		42	46	54	62	68	116	56
	40	44	46	48	53	62	72	80	143	68
	45	49	51	54	60	70	81	89	167	80
	50	54	57	61	68	79	92	102	192	92

⚠ Warning: DO NOT attempt to use these tables unless you are fully trained & certified in the use of gas mixtures other than air, or are under the supervision of a gas mixtures other than air instructor. Proper use of these tables will reduce the risk of decompression sickness & oxygen toxicity, but no table or computer can eliminate those risks.

TRIMIX RUNTIME TABLES

IANTD TRIMIX *RUNTIME*

DIVE DECOMPRESSION TABLES

BOTTOM MIX : 19 % O2 and 25 % to 35 % HE

DEPTH	BT	STOP 130ft 39m	EAN 36% 100ft 30m	90 ft 27 m	80 ft 24 m	70 ft 21 m	60 ft 18 m	50 ft 15 m	40 ft 12 m	EAN 75% 30 ft 9 m	20 ft 6 m	15 ft 4.5m	CNS
150 ft 45 m	15	17							21	24	26	34	11
	20	22						26	28	31	34	47	16
	25	27						32	35	39	43	61	22
	30	32					36	38	42	47	52	73	28
	35	37					42	45	50	56	61	87	34
	40	42				45	47	51	57	65	71	104	41
	45	47				50	53	58	65	73	81	119	47
	50	52				55	60	65	73	83	91	136	54
160 ft 48 m	15	17							22	26	27	37	12
	20	22						27	30	34	37	51	18
	25	27					31	33	36	42	45	64	25
	30	32					37	40	45	52	56	80	31
	35	37				40	42	46	52	60	65	95	38
	40	42				45	48	53	60	70	75	111	45
	45	47				51	55	60	68	78	85	128	52
	50	52			55	58	62	68	77	89	96	146	60
170 ft 51 m	15	18						22	25	27	29	41	13
	20	23					27	29	33	37	40	56	21
	25	28					33	35	40	45	49	69	27
	30	33				36	38	40	47	53	58	84	34
	35	38				42	45	49	56	64	69	102	42
	40	43			46	47	50	55	64	73	80	120	50
	45	48			51	53	57	62	72	82	89	136	58
	50	53			55	58	63	70	80	92	100	155	66
180 ft 54 m	15	18						22	26	29	31	45	15
	20	23					27	29	33	37	40	58	23
	25	28				31	33	36	41	47	51	74	30
	30	33				37	39	43	50	57	62	92	38
	35	38			41	43	46	51	59	67	73	110	46
	40	43			46	49	53	58	67	77	84	129	55
	45	48		51	52	55	60	66	76	87	94	147	64
	50	53		56	58	62	67	75	86	98	107	170	73
190 ft 57 m	15	18					22	24	26	29	32	45	18
	20	23				26	27	30	33	38	42	61	26
	25	28				32	34	38	43	49	55	79	33
	30	33			36	38	41	46	52	60	66	98	42
	35	38		41	42	44	47	53	61	70	78	117	51
	40	43		46	47	50	55	62	71	82	90	138	60
	45	48		51	54	58	63	71	81	93	102	158	70
	50	53		57	60	64	69	78	90	103	114	182	81
200 ft 60 m	15	19					23	25	28	31	35	49	20
	20	24				27	30	32	36	41	45	65	42
	25	29			32	34	37	40	46	53	59	85	37
	30	34		37	38	40	44	49	55	63	70	104	47
	35	39		42	44	47	52	57	65	75	83	126	57
	40	44		48	50	55	59	65	75	87	95	147	67
	45	49	51	52	55	59	64	73	84	97	107	170	78
	50	54	56	58	61	65	72	80	93	107	118	193	90
210 ft 63 m	15	19				21	22	24	27	32	35	50	22
	20	24			27	29	31	33	37	44	48	69	31
	25	29			33	36	38	42	48	56	61	89	41
	30	34		37	39	42	45	50	57	67	73	110	51
	35	39	41	42	44	48	53	59	68	79	86	132	63
	40	44	46	48	51	56	61	68	78	91	99	155	74
	45	49	51	53	55	61	67	75	87	101	111	180	87

TRIMIX RUNTIME TABLES

⚠ Warning: DO NOT attempt to use these tables unless you are fully trained & certified in the use of gas mixtures other than air, or are under the supervision of a gas mixtures other than air instructor. Proper use of these tables will reduce the risk of decompression sickness & oxygen toxicity, but no table or computer can eliminate those risks.

IANTD TRIMIX *RUNTIME*

REPETITIVE DIVE DECOMPRESSION TABLES

BOTTOM MIX : 19 % O2 and 25% to 35 % HE

TRIMIX RUNTIME TABLES

DEPTH	BT	STOP 130ft 39m	100ft 30m	90 ft 27 m	80 ft 24 m	70 ft 21 m	60 ft 18 m	50 ft 15 m	40 ft 12 m	30 ft 9 m	20 ft 6 m	15 ft 4.5m	CNS
			EAN 36%							EAN 75%			
REP 150 ft 45 m	15	17							21	24	27	40	13
	20	22						26	28	32	36	54	19
	25	27						32	35	40	45	71	26
	30	32					36	38	43	49	54	90	36
	35	37					42	46	52	60	67	116	45
	40	42				45	48	52	59	68	76	139	55
	45	47				50	54	60	67	77	86	161	65
	50	52				55	60	66	75	87	97	183	74
REP 160 ft 48 m	15	17						22	23	27	29	43	14
	20	22						27	30	35	38	59	21
	25	27					32	34	38	45	49	79	31
	30	32					37	40	46	54	59	100	40
	35	37				40	42	46	52	61	68	125	51
	40	42				45	48	53	61	72	79	150	62
	45	47				51	55	60	69	81	90	172	72
	50	52			55	58	62	68	78	92	103	198	83
REP 170 ft 51 m	15	18						22	25	28	31	47	16
	20	23					27	29	33	38	41	64	25
	25	28					33	36	42	48	53	87	35
	30	33				36	38	42	49	57	63	111	45
	35	38				42	45	50	58	67	74	138	58
	40	43			46	47	51	56	66	77	85	163	69
	45	48			51	53	57	63	74	87	97	187	80
	50	53			56	59	64	71	83	97	109	215	92
REP 180 ft 54 m	15	18						23	27	30	33	51	18
	20	23					27	29	33	38	42	69	28
	25	28				31	33	36	42	49	54	93	38
	30	33				37	40	44	51	59	66	122	51
	35	38			41	43	46	51	60	70	77	149	64
	40	43			46	49	53	59	69	81	90	175	75
	45	48		51	52	55	60	67	79	93	105	206	88
	50	53		56	58	62	67	75	88	103	116	234	101
REP 190 ft 57 m	15	18					22	25	28	32	36	55	21
	20	23				26	27	30	34	40	45	74	31
	25	28				32	34	38	44	51	57	99	43
	30	33			36	38	41	47	54	63	71	133	57
	35	38		41	42	44	48	54	63	74	83	161	70
	40	43		46	47	50	54	63	73	86	98	190	83
	45	48		51	54	58	63	72	84	99	113	223	98
	50	53	*no repetitive dive available !!*										
REP 200 ft 60 m	15	19					23	25	28	32	36	56	23
	20	24				27	30	33	38	44	50	82	35
	25	29			32	34	37	41	47	55	62	110	48
	30	34		37	38	40	44	49	57	67	75	143	64
	35	39		42	44	47	52	58	67	79	89	172	77
	40	44		48	50	53	59	66	77	91	104	204	92
	45		*no repetitive dive available !!*										
	50		*no repetitive dive available !!*										
REP 210 ft 63 m	15	19				22	23	25	28	34	37	59	26
	20	24			27	29	31	34	39	47	52	88	39
	25	29			33	36	39	43	50	59	66	120	54
	30	34		37	39	42	46	51	60	72	80	154	70
	35	39	41	42	44	48	53	60	70	84	94	184	85

TRIMIX RUNTIME TABLES

⚠ Warning: DO NOT attempt to use these tables unless you are fully trained & certified in the use of gas mixtures other than air, or are under the supervision of a gas mixtures other than air instructor. Proper use of these tables will reduce the risk of decompression sickness & oxygen toxicity, but no table or computer can eliminate those risks.

TRIMIX RUNTIME TABLES

IANDT TRIMIX *RUNTIME*

DIVE DECOMPRESSION TABLES

BOTTOM MIX : 20 % O2 and 25 % HE

DEPTH	BT	STOP 90ft 27m	TRIMIX 80ft 24m	70 ft 21 m	60 ft 18 m	50 ft 15 m	EAN 70% 40 ft 12 m	30 ft 9 m	20 ft 6 m	15 ft 4.5m	CNS
130 ft 39 m	10	12							14	18	3
	15	17						19	20	27	7
	20	22						25	27	38	11
	25	27					29	31	33	48	16
	30	32					35	39	42	59	20
	35	37					40	45	48	69	25
	40	42				44	47	53	57	81	29
140 ft 42 m	10	12							15	18	5
	15	17						19	21	28	9
	20	22					24	26	29	40	14
	25	27					30	33	36	51	19
	30	32				34	36	40	44	63	24
	35	37				40	43	49	54	76	30
	40	42				46	50	56	62	88	36
150 ft 45 m	10	12							15	19	5
	15	17						20	23	31	10
	20	22					24	27	30	43	16
	25	27				29	31	34	38	54	21
	30	32				35	38	43	47	68	27
	35	37				42	46	52	57	81	33
	40	42			44	49	54	61	67	96	39
160 ft 48 m	10	13						16	17	21	6
	15	18					20	23	25	34	12
	20	23					26	30	32	46	18
	25	28				31	34	39	42	60	24
	30	33			35	38	41	48	52	75	31
	35	38			41	46	51	58	63	90	37
	40	43			47	53	58	67	72	106	44
170 ft 51 m	10	13						16	17	22	7
	15	18					21	21	25	35	14
	20	23				25	28	31	33	48	21
	25	28				33	37	42	45	65	27
	30	33			36	40	45	51	55	79	34
	35	38		40	43	49	55	62	67	98	41
	40	43		45	50	58	64	73	79	117	48
180 ft 54 m	10	14						16	17	24	8
	15	19					22	25	27	39	16
	20	24				26	30	33	36	53	23
	25	29			30	34	38	43	46	69	30
	30	34		35	38	43	49	55	60	88	38
	35	39		41	45	52	58	66	71	107	46
	40	44		47	52	61	68	77	84	128	54
190 ft 57 m	10	14						17	19	26	10
	15	19				21	23	26	29	42	18
	20	24			25	29	32	36	40	58	25
	25	29			32	37	41	47	52	75	33
	30	34		36	40	47	52	59	65	95	42
	35	39	40	42	47	56	62	71	78	117	50
	40	44	45	49	55	66	73	83	91	139	60
200 ft 60 m	10	14					16	17	19	27	12
	15	19				22	24	27	30	44	20
	20	24			27	31	34	39	43	63	28
	25	29		30	35	40	44	50	56	81	37
	30	34		37	42	49	54	62	68	102	46
	35	39	41	45	52	61	68	77	85	128	56
	40	44	47	52	61	71	79	90	98	151	66

TRIMIX RUNTIME TABLES

⚠ Warning: DO NOT attempt to use these tables unless you are fully trained & certified in the use of gas mixtures other than air, or are under the supervision of a gas mixtures other than air instructor. Proper use of these tables will reduce the risk of decompression sickness & oxygen toxicity, but no table or computer can eliminate those risks.

TRIMIX RUNTIME TABLES

IANTD TRIMIX *RUNTIME*

REPETITIVE DIVE DECOMPRESSION TABLES 180 MIN SURFACE INTERVAL

BOTTOM MIX : 20 % O2 and 25 % HE

DEPTH	BT	STOP 90ft 27m	TRIMIX 80ft 24m	70 ft 21 m	60 ft 18 m	50 ft 15 m	EAN 70% 40 ft 12 m	30 ft 9 m	20 ft 6 m	15 ft 4.5m	CNS
REP 130 ft 39 m	10	12							14	19	4
	15	17						19	20	30	8
	20	22						25	27	42	13
	25	27					29	32	35	55	18
	30	32					35	40	43	68	24
	35	37				39	42	48	52	85	30
	40	42				44	48	55	60	101	37
REP 140 ft 42 m	10	12							15	21	5
	15	17						20	23	34	10
	20	22					24	26	29	45	16
	25	27					30	34	38	59	22
	30	32				34	37	42	47	75	29
	35	37				40	44	50	56	93	37
	40	42				47	52	60	67	114	45
REP 150 ft 45 m	10	12						14	16	22	7
	15	17						20	23	35	12
	20	22					25	28	32	50	19
	25	27				29	31	36	40	64	25
	30	32				36	39	45	51	83	33
	35	37			39	42	47	54	60	104	42
	40	42			44	50	55	64	72	129	52
REP 160 ft 48 m	10	13						16	17	25	8
	15	18					20	23	25	39	14
	20	23				25	27	31	34	53	21
	25	28				31	34	40	44	71	29
	30	33			35	38	42	50	55	93	38
	35	38			41	46	51	60	66	117	48
	40	43			47	55	61	72	79	147	58
REP 170 ft 51 m	10	13						16	18	26	9
	15	18					21	24	26	41	16
	20	23				26	30	34	37	58	24
	25	28			30	33	37	43	48	79	33
	30	33			36	41	47	54	59	103	43
	35	38		40	43	50	56	65	72	133	54
	40	43		45	50	59	67	78	86	164	65
REP 180 ft 54 m	10	14						17	19	29	10
	15	19					22	25	27	44	19
	20	24				27	31	36	39	64	27
	25	29			31	35	40	46	51	87	37
	30	34		35	38	43	49	57	63	114	48
	35	39		41	45	53	60	70	77	149	61
	40	44		47	52	62	70	82	91	178	73
REP 190 ft 57 m	10	14					16	18	21	31	12
	15	19				21	23	26	30	48	21
	20	24			25	29	32	37	42	69	30
	25	29			32	38	43	50	56	97	41
	30	34		36	40	48	53	62	70	129	54
	35	39	40	42	47	57	64	75	84	164	68
	40	44	45	49	56	67	75	88	100	195	80
REP 200 ft 60 m	10	14					16	18	21	33	14
	15	19				22	25	28	32	51	24
	20	24			27	31	34	40	45	76	34
	25	29		30	35	40	45	53	60	106	46
	30	34		37	42	50	56	66	74	142	61
	35	39	41	45	52	62	69	81	91	178	75
	40	44	47	52	61	73	82	96	109	214	89

TRIMIX RUNTIME TABLES

⚠ Warning: DO NOT attempt to use these tables unless you are fully trained & certified in the use of gas mixtures other than air, or are under the supervision of a gas mixtures other than air instructor. Proper use of these tables will reduce the risk of decompression sickness & oxygen toxicity, but no table or computer can eliminate those risks.

IANTD TRIMIX *RUNTIME*

DIVE DECOMPRESSION TABLES BOTTOM MIX : 16 % O_2 and 40 % HE

TRIMIX RUNTIME TABLES

DEPTH	BT	STOP	TRIMIX			EAN 36%							EAN 75%			CNS
		150ft 45m	130ft 39m	120ft 36m	110ft 33m	100ft 30m	90 ft 27m	80 ft 24m	70 ft 21 m	60 ft 18 m	50 ft 15 m	40 ft 12 m	30 ft 9 m	20 ft 6 m	15 ft 4.5m	
200 ft 60 m	10	12									15	17	19	22	32	11
	15	17							19	21	23	26	30	34	50	19
	20	22							25	28	31	35	40	45	66	27
	25	27						29	31	35	39	45	52	57	86	36
	30	32					34	35	37	41	46	53	61	68	105	45
	35	37					39	41	44	49	55	64	74	82	128	54
	40	42				44	45	47	51	57	64	74	86	96	153	65
	45	47				49	51	54	58	65	73	85	98	109	178	76
210 ft 63 m	10	12								15	16	18	21	23	34	12
	15	17							20	21	23	26	31	34	51	20
	20	22						24	26	28	31	36	43	47	70	29
	25	27					29	30	33	36	40	46	55	60	92	39
	30	32					34	36	40	44	49	57	67	74	115	48
	35	37				39	40	42	46	51	57	66	78	85	135	59
	40	42				44	46	49	54	59	67	78	91	101	164	70
	45	47			49	50	52	56	61	68	76	89	105	116	191	82
220 ft 66 m	10	12								15	16	18	21	23	35	13
	15	17							20	22	24	27	33	36	54	23
	20	22						24	27	29	32	37	44	48	73	31
	25	27					29	31	34	37	42	48	57	63	97	42
	30	32				34	35	37	41	45	50	59	70	77	121	53
	35	37				39	41	44	49	54	61	70	83	91	145	64
	40	42			44	46	48	51	56	62	70	82	96	106	175	77
	45	47			50	52	55	59	65	72	81	95	112	124	204	89
230 ft 69 m	10	12								15	17	20	23	25	38	14
	15	17						20	21	23	25	30	35	38	57	25
	20	22					24	26	28	30	34	41	48	52	79	34
	25	27				29	30	32	35	38	43	51	59	65	101	46
	30	32				34	36	39	42	47	53	63	74	81	128	57
	35	37			39	41	43	47	51	56	64	76	88	97	157	70
	40	42			45	47	50	55	59	66	74	88	103	114	189	84
	45	47		49	52	54	57	62	68	75	85	100	117	130	216	97
240 ft 72 m	10	13							15	16	18	20	23	25	39	16
	15	18						20	21	23	26	30	35	39	60	27
	20	23					25	27	29	32	37	43	50	55	85	38
	25	28				29	32	34	37	41	47	55	64	71	111	49
	30	33			34	36	39	42	46	51	59	68	80	87	139	62
	35	38		39	41	43	46	49	53	59	68	80	93	103	171	77
	40	43		44	47	49	53	57	62	69	79	93	109	121	202	91
250 ft 75 m	10	13							15	16	19	21	24	28	42	18
	15	18					20	21	22	24	28	32	37	42	63	29
	20	23				25	26	27	29	32	37	43	51	57	88	41
	25	28			29	31	33	35	38	42	48	57	67	75	118	54
	30	33		34	35	38	40	43	47	52	60	70	82	91	147	68
	35	38		39	42	45	48	52	56	62	71	84	98	109	182	83
	40	43	44	45	49	53	56	60	66	73	84	98	115	129	215	99
260 ft 78 m	10	13							15	17	19	22	26	30	45	20
	15	18					20	21	23	26	29	34	40	45	68	31
	20	23				25	26	28	30	34	39	45	53	59	92	44
	25	28			31	33	35	37	40	46	52	61	71	79	125	58
	30	33		34	37	39	41	44	48	54	62	73	85	95	157	74
	35	38	39	40	44	46	49	53	58	66	75	89	104	116	194	91
270 ft 81 m	10	13						15	17	18	20	23	28	31	47	22
	15	18					20	22	25	27	30	35	42	46	70	34
	20	23			25	26	27	29	33	36	41	48	57	63	99	48
	25	28		30	32	34	36	39	44	49	55	64	76	83	133	63
	30	33	34	36	38	40	42	46	51	57	65	77	91	101	169	81
	35	38	39	43	47	49	52	56	62	69	79	93	111	124	207	98

TRIMIX RUNTIME TABLES

⚠ Warning: DO NOT attempt to use these tables unless you are fully trained & certified in the use of gas mixtures other than air, or are under the supervision of a gas mixtures other than air instructor. Proper use of these tables will reduce the risk of decompression sickness & oxygen toxicity, but no table or computer can eliminate those risks.

IANTD TRIMIX *RUNTIME*

REPETITIVE DIVE DECOMPRESSION TABLES 240 MIN SURFACE INTERVAL

BOTTOM MIX : 16 % O2 and 40 % HE

TRIMIX RUNTIME TABLES

DEPTH	BT	STOP Trimix 150ft 45m	130ft 39m	120ft 36m	110ft 33m	EAN 36% 100ft 30m	90 ft 27m	80 ft 24m	70 ft 21 m	60 ft 18 m	50 ft 15 m	40 ft 12 m	EAN 75% 30 ft 9 m	20 ft 6 m	15 ft 4.5m	CNS
REP 200 ft 60 m	10	12									15	17	20	23	37	13
	15	17							19	21	23	26	31	35	57	22
	20	22						24	25	28	31	36	43	48	82	34
	25	27						29	31	35	39	45	53	60	111	47
	30	32					34	35	37	42	47	55	65	73	142	60
	35	37					39	41	44	49	55	64	76	87	171	73
	40	42				44	45	47	51	57	65	77	91	104	207	88
	45	!!!!REPETITIVE DIVE NOT AVAILABLE!!!!														
REP 210 ft 63 m	10	12								15	16	18	22	25	40	14
	15	17							20	22	24	27	33	37	60	24
	20	22						24	27	29	32	38	46	51	88	37
	25	27					29	30	33	36	41	48	58	65	122	51
	30	32					34	36	40	44	49	58	70	78	152	65
	35	37				39	40	42	47	52	59	69	83	94	185	79
	40	42				44	46	49	54	59	67	79	95	108	219	95
	45	!!!!REPETITIVE DIVE NOT AVAILABLE!!!!														
REP 220 ft 66 m	10	12								15	16	18	22	25	41	16
	15	17							20	22	24	28	34	38	64	27
	20	22						24	27	29	33	39	48	54	94	40
	25	27					29	31	34	37	42	50	61	68	131	56
	30	32				34	35	37	41	46	52	61	74	83	163	71
	35	37				39	41	44	49	54	62	73	88	100	199	86
	40	!!!!REPETITIVE DIVE NOT AVAILABLE!!!!														
	45	!!!!REPETITIVE DIVE NOT AVAILABLE!!!!														
REP 230 ft 69 m	10	12								15	17	20	24	27	44	17
	15	17						20	21	23	26	32	38	42	70	30
	20	22					24	26	28	31	35	42	50	56	101	44
	25	27				29	30	32	35	39	44	53	63	70	138	61
	30	32				34	36	39	42	47	54	65	77	87	173	77
	35	37			39	41	43	47	51	56	64	77	92	105	214	95
	40	!!!!REPETITIVE DIVE NOT AVAILABLE!!!!														
	45	!!!!REPETITIVE DIVE NOT AVAILABLE!!!!														
REP 240 ft 72 m	10	13							15	16	18	21	25	28	47	19
	15	18						20	22	24	28	33	39	43	75	32
	20	23					25	27	29	32	38	45	53	60	112	49
	25	28				29	32	34	37	41	47	56	67	75	149	66
	30	33			34	36	39	42	46	51	59	70	83	94	188	84
	35	!!!!REPETITIVE DIVE NOT AVAILABLE!!!!														
	40	!!!!REPETITIVE DIVE NOT AVAILABLE!!!!														
REP 250 ft 75 m	10	13							15	16	19	22	26	30	49	21
	15	18					20	21	22	24	28	33	40	45	79	36
	20	23				25	26	27	29	32	38	45	54	62	118	53
	25	28			29	31	33	35	38	43	50	59	71	81	159	72
	30	33		34	35	38	40	43	47	52	61	73	87	100	203	91
	35	!!!!REPETITIVE DIVE NOT AVAILABLE!!!!														
	40	!!!!REPETITIVE DIVE NOT AVAILABLE!!!!														
REP 260 ft 78 m	10	13							15	18	20	23	28	32	52	23
	15	18					20	21	23	26	29	35	42	48	85	39
	20	23				25	26	28	30	34	39	47	57	65	126	58
	25	28			31	33	35	37	40	46	53	63	75	86	169	77
	30	!!!!REPETITIVE DIVE NOT AVAILABLE!!!!														
	35	!!!!REPETITIVE DIVE NOT AVAILABLE!!!!														
REP 270 ft 81 m	10	13						15	17	18	20	23	29	32	54	25
	15	18					20	22	25	27	31	37	45	50	89	42
	20	23			25	26	27	29	33	37	42	50	61	68	135	64
	25	28		30	32	34	36	39	44	49	56	67	81	92	182	84
	30	33		34	37	39	41	44	48	55	63	76	91	105	216	99
	35	!!!!REPETITIVE DIVE NOT AVAILABLE!!!!														

TRIMIX RUNTIME TABLES

⚠ Warning: DO NOT attempt to use these tables unless you are fully trained & certified in the use of gas mixtures other than air, or are under the supervision of a gas mixtures other than air instructor. Proper use of these tables will reduce the risk of decompression sickness & oxygen toxicity, but no table or computer can eliminate those risks.

IANTD TRIMIX *RUNTIME*

TRIMIX RUNTIME TABLES

DIVE DECOMPRESSION TABLES. BOTTOM MIX : 14 % O_2 and 50 % HE

DEPTH	BT	STOP 170ft 51m	Trimix 150ft 45m	140ft 42 m	130ft 39 m	120ft 36 m	110ft 33 m	EAN 36% 100ft 30 m	90 ft 27 m	80ft 24m	70 ft 21 m	60 ft 18 m	50 ft 15 m	40 ft 12 m	EAN 75% 30 ft 9 m	20 ft 6 m	15 ft 4.5m	CNS
230 ft 69 m	10	12									15	16	18	21	24	27	41	15
	15	17							19	21	22	23	26	31	36	40	61	25
	20	22						24	25	27	29	32	36	43	50	55	86	36
	25	27					29	30	31	34	37	41	46	55	65	71	114	47
	30	32					35	37	39	43	47	52	59	70	81	90	146	60
	35	37				39	41	43	46	50	54	60	68	81	95	105	177	74
	40	42				45	49	52	55	60	65	71	81	95	112	124	208	87
240 ft 72 m	10	12								15	16	17	19	21	25	28	44	16
	15	17							20	21	22	24	28	33	39	43	67	27
	20	22						24	26	28	30	33	39	45	53	59	93	38
	25	27					30	32	35	37	40	44	51	59	69	75	122	50
	30	32				34	36	38	41	44	48	53	61	72	84	93	156	65
	35	37				40	43	45	49	52	57	63	73	85	100	112	190	80
	40	42			44	47	51	54	58	62	68	75	86	101	120	133	224	94
250 ft 75 m	10	12								15	16	17	20	23	27	31	47	18
	15	17						20	21	22	23	25	29	34	40	45	69	29
	20	22					24	26	27	29	32	36	42	49	57	64	100	42
	25	27				29	31	33	35	37	41	45	52	60	71	79	129	56
	30	32				35	38	41	44	47	51	57	65	77	90	100	168	71
	35	37			39	41	45	49	52	56	61	67	78	91	108	121	203	87
260 ft 78 m	10	13								15	16	18	20	23	27	31	48	19
	15	18						20	21	22	23	26	29	34	41	46	72	31
	20	23					25	26	27	29	32	37	42	50	59	66	105	44
	25	28				29	33	35	37	40	44	49	56	65	76	85	140	59
	30	33			34	36	40	42	45	48	52	59	67	79	93	105	178	77
	35	38		39	40	43	48	51	54	58	64	72	82	96	114	128	216	92
270 ft 81 m	10	13							15	16	18	19	21	24	30	33	51	21
	15	18						20	21	22	25	28	32	37	45	49	77	33
	20	23				25	27	28	30	32	36	40	45	53	64	70	112	48
	25	28			29	32	34	36	38	41	46	51	58	68	81	90	150	65
	30	33		34	35	38	42	44	47	50	56	62	71	83	100	112	190	83
280 ft 84 m	10	13							15	16	18	19	21	25	31	34	52	23
	15	18					20	21	22	23	26	29	33	39	47	52	82	36
	20	23				25	27	28	30	32	36	40	46	54	65	71	116	52
	25	28			30	32	35	37	39	42	47	53	60	71	85	94	160	70
	30	33		34	37	40	44	47	50	54	60	66	76	89	107	119	202	89
290 ft 87 m	10	13							15	17	18	20	22	27	32	35	54	24
	15	18					20	21	22	25	27	30	35	42	50	55	87	39
	20	23			25	26	28	29	31	34	38	42	48	57	68	75	124	56
	25	28		30	31	33	36	38	41	45	49	55	63	76	90	100	171	76
	30	33	34	36	38	41	45	48	51	56	62	69	79	95	113	126	214	95
300 ft 90 m	10	13						15	17	18	19	20	24	28	33	37	58	26
	15	18				20	21	22	24	26	29	32	38	45	53	59	94	41
	20	23			25	27	29	31	34	37	41	45	53	62	73	81	135	60
	25	28		30	32	34	38	40	44	47	52	58	68	80	95	106	182	81
310 ft 93 m	10	13						16	17	18	19	21	25	30	35	40	61	28
	15	18				20	22	24	25	27	30	34	40	47	55	62	99	45
	20	23		25	26	28	30	33	35	38	42	47	55	65	76	86	144	65
	25	28	30	31	33	36	40	44	47	50	55	61	71	83	99	112	192	87

TRIMIX RUNTIME TABLES

⚠ Warning: DO NOT attempt to use these tables unless you are fully trained & certified in the use of gas mixtures other than air, or are under the supervision of a gas mixtures other than air instructor. Proper use of these tables will reduce the risk of decompression sickness & oxygen toxicity, but no table or computer can eliminate those risks.

IANTD TRIMIX *RUNTIME*

REPETITIVE DIVE DECOMPRESSION TABLES. 240 MIN SURFACE INTERVAL

BOTTOM MIX : 14 % O2 and 50 % HE

TRIMIX RUNTIME TABLES

DEPTH	BT	STOP 170ft 51m	Trimix 150ft 45m	140ft 42m	130ft 39m	120ft 36m	110ft 33m	EAN 36% 100ft 30m	90 ft 27 m	80ft 24m	70 ft 21 m	60 ft 18 m	50 ft 15 m	40 ft 12 m	EAN 75% 30 ft 9 m	20 ft 6 m	15 ft 4.5m	CNS
REP 230 ft 69 m	10	12									15	16	18	22	26	29	48	18
	15	17							19	21	22	24	27	33	39	43	76	31
	20	22						24	25	27	29	32	37	45	54	60	115	47
	25	27					29	30	31	34	37	41	47	56	67	76	151	63
	30	32					35	37	39	43	47	52	59	71	85	96	195	81
	35	!!!!REPETITIVE DIVE NOT AVAILABLE!!!!																
	40	!!!!REPETITIVE DIVE NOT AVAILABLE!!!!																
REP 240 ft 72 m	10	12								15	16	17	19	22	27	30	51	19
	15	17							20	21	23	25	29	34	41	46	83	34
	20	22						24	26	28	30	33	39	46	55	61	122	51
	25	27					30	32	35	37	40	44	51	60	72	81	163	68
	30	32				34	36	38	41	44	48	53	61	73	88	100	209	88
	35	!!!!REPETITIVE DIVE NOT AVAILABLE!!!!																
	40	!!!!REPETITIVE DIVE NOT AVAILABLE!!!!																
REP 250 ft 75 m	10	12								15	16	17	20	23	28	32	53	21
	15	17						20	21	22	23	25	30	35	42	48	87	37
	20	22					24	26	27	29	32	36	42	50	60	68	133	56
	25	27				29	31	33	35	37	41	45	53	63	76	87	176	75
	30	32				35	38	41	44	47	51	57	66	78	95	109	227	97
	35	!!!!REPETITIVE DIVE NOT AVAILABLE!!!!																
REP 260 ft 78 m	10	13								15	16	19	21	25	30	35	58	22
	15	18						20	21	22	23	27	31	37	44	51	93	40
	20	23					25	26	27	29	32	37	42	50	60	69	139	60
	25	28				29	33	35	37	40	44	50	57	68	82	94	192	81
	30	!!!!REPETITIVE DIVE NOT AVAILABLE!!!!																
	35	!!!!REPETITIVE DIVE NOT AVAILABLE!!!!																
REP 270 ft 81 m	10	13							15	16	18	19	21	25	31	35	60	26
	15	18						20	21	22	25	28	32	38	47	53	100	43
	20	23				25	27	28	30	32	36	40	46	54	66	75	150	65
	25	28			29	32	34	36	38	41	46	51	58	70	85	97	203	88
	30	!!!!REPETITIVE DIVE NOT AVAILABLE!!!!																
REP 280 ft 84 m	10	13							15	16	18	20	23	27	34	38	65	28
	15	18					20	21	22	23	26	29	34	41	50	56	109	48
	20	23				25	27	28	30	32	36	40	46	55	68	77	158	70
	25	28			30	32	35	37	39	42	47	53	61	73	90	103	217	95
	30	!!!!REPETITIVE DIVE NOT AVAILABLE!!!!																
REP 290 ft 87 m	10	13							15	17	18	20	23	29	35	39	68	29
	15	18					20	21	22	25	27	30	35	43	52	58	116	51
	20	23			25	26	28	29	31	34	38	42	49	60	73	83	171	75
	25	!!!!REPETITIVE DIVE NOT AVAILABLE!!!!																
	30	!!!!REPETITIVE DIVE NOT AVAILABLE!!!!																
REP 300 ft 90 m	10	13						15	17	18	19	20	24	29	35	39	72	32
	15	18				20	21	22	24	26	29	33	39	47	57	64	128	56
	20	23			25	27	29	31	34	37	41	46	54	65	78	89	185	81
	25	!!!!REPETITIVE DIVE NOT AVAILABLE!!!!																
REP 310 ft 93 m	10	13						16	17	18	19	21	25	30	37	42	76	35
	15	18				20	22	24	25	27	30	34	40	48	58	66	134	60
	20	23		25	26	28	30	33	35	38	42	47	55	67	81	94	197	88
	25	!!!!REPETITIVE DIVE NOT AVAILABLE!!!!																

TRIMIX RUNTIME TABLES

⚠ Warning: DO NOT attempt to use these tables unless you are fully trained & certified in the use of gas mixtures other than air, or are under the supervision of a gas mixtures other than air instructor. Proper use of these tables will reduce the risk of decompression sickness & oxygen toxicity, but no table or computer can eliminate those risks.